Applied
Superconductivity

WILEY SERIES ON THE SCIENCE AND TECHNOLOGY OF MATERIALS

Advisory Editors: J. H. Hollomon, J. E. Burke, B. Chalmers, R. L. Sproull, A. V. Tobolsky

---

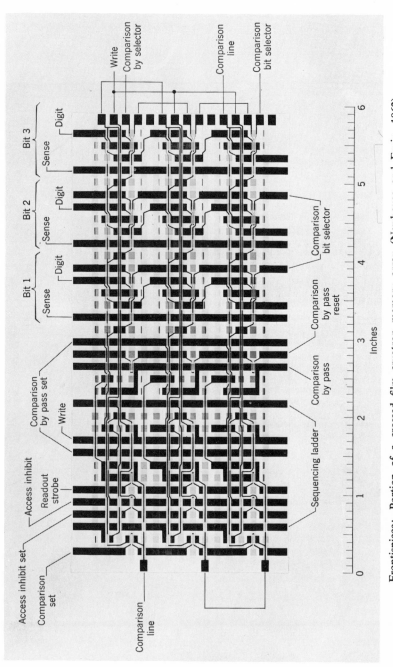

Frontispiece: Portion of a crossed film cryotron memory array (Newhouse and Fruin, 1962).

Applied

Superconductivity

by Vernon L. Newhouse, Ph.D.
General Electric Research Laboratory
Schenectady, New York

John Wiley & Sons, Inc., New York · London · Sydney

Preface

For the past seven years, the author has been engaged in research on applications of superconductivity. At the outset, the need for a text that treats superconductivity from the device standpoint became apparent. This book, which is believed to be the first of its kind, is designed to fill that need.

The book is divided into two approximately equal sections, one on the physics of superconductivity, the other on superconductive devices. The discussion of superconductivity includes the latest concepts and consequences of modern theory but does not presuppose a knowledge of advanced quantum mechanics. To make such a discussion possible, material that bridges the gap between the Schrödinger equation introduced in elementary quantum mechanics and the band theory of metals has been included. The section of the book devoted to applications describes most of the superconductive devices which have been developed, or proposed for development.

The book is intended as an introduction and reference for physicists and engineers engaged in the development and exploitation of superconductivity, and as background material for cryogenic engineers and other users of superconductive devices. Since it does not require a knowledge of advanced quantum mechanics, it should also be useful to senior undergraduate and post-graduate students of physics and engineering.

Since this type of book is more often dipped into than read from cover to cover, the chapters have been designed to be relatively independent of one another. The repetition which this type of treatment imposes is felt to be a small price to pay for the freedom of being able to read most chapters out of context.

Owing to the wealth of material available, it has only been possible to reference selected publications on the physics of superconductivity. An effort has been made not to highlight work done in the General Electric Company at the expense of work done elsewhere, and to give adequate representation to the very considerable Russian literature in this field. A virtually complete coverage of references on superconductive devices has been attempted. However, the treatment of these is in order of increasing complexity rather than historical and is not intended to assign priority in time.

The author has drawn heavily on the knowledge of his associates at the General Electric Research Laboratory. He is particularly indebted to H. H. Edwards; I. Giaever; H. R. Hart, Jr.; B. W. Roberts and S. Roberts; K. Rose; M. D. Sherrill; and P. S. Swartz, who each consented to read and criticize one or more chapters of the book in manuscript; and to W. DeSorbo and C. P. Bean for several helpful discussions. Grateful thanks are extended to the authors and publishers who gave permission to use previously published figures and tables, and supplied photographic originals. The sources of all this material are given in the text. Finally, the author would like to thank the management of the General Electric Research Laboratory for providing the environment in which this book could be written.

V. L. N.

February, 1964

Contents

ix

chapter 1

Introduction

This chapter is intended to provide an introductory link between Chapters 2, 3, and 4, which describe the physics of superconductivity, and Chapters 5 to 8, which describe and analyze superconductive devices. Section 1, which follows, describes some of the remarkable phenomena of superconductivity and the history of their discovery. Section 2 discusses a selection of superconductive devices, chosen to illustrate how the different manifestations of the superconductive state have found application. Section 3 summarizes the contents of the remaining chapters and explains their organization.

1. BASIC PHENOMENA OF SUPERCONDUCTIVITY

1.1 Discovery and Origin

To cool a specimen to the temperature range below 20°K where superconductive phenomena make their appearance it may be immersed in liquid hydrogen or helium. The specimen is thus brought to the liquid boiling temperature, evaporating some of it in the process (see Table 1.1.). Temperatures below those shown can be obtained by pumping on the vapor above the liquid, thus reducing the pressure (see Fig. 1.1.).

A number of gases of successively lower boiling point were first liquefied in the closing years of the last century. After considerable effort, the liquefaction of helium was accomplished in 1908 by Kamerlingh Onnes, who then became able to reach hitherto unattainably low temperatures. He decided to investigate the temperature dependence of metallic resistivity in this new temperature region.

According to the account by Shoenberg,[1] Onnes was inclined to expect

---

[1] D. Shoenberg, *Superconductivity*. New York: Cambridge University Press, 1952, Ch. 1.

a gradual approach of the resistivity towards zero with decreasing temperature. However, in his first experiments, which were on platinum, he found that the resistivity approached a "residual" value strongly dependent on the impurity content. He chose mercury as the next metal to investigate because it could readily be purified by vacuum distillation. In this case

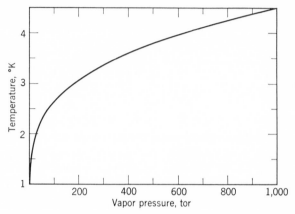

Fig. 1.1 Boiling temperature of liquid helium as a function of vapor pressure.

the resistivity did indeed fall to zero[2] not in the asymptotic manner which had been expected, but instead extremely sharply, somewhat as shown in Figure 1.2. (It was later discovered that impure mercury would exhibit the same behavior.) Onnes recognized that he had found a new state of matter characterized by zero ohmic resistance, for which he coined the name "superconductivity."

TABLE 1.1

**Boiling Points of Some Common Low Temperature
Refrigerants at One Atmosphere Pressure***

Gas	b.p. °K
Nitrogen	77.32
Hydrogen	20.37
Helium 4	4.216
Helium 3	3.195

* He^4 is the common isotope of helium. It undergoes a transition to the superfluid He II phase below 2.17°K. For refrigeration below about 1.2°K, the rarer isotope He^3, which does not become a superfluid, is preferred. He^3 forms about one part per million of naturally occurring helium, and is produced by certain nuclear reactions.

---

[2] Onnes (1911a-d).

The explanation of the origin of superconductivity was not achieved until long after all other known phenomena of the solid state had been accounted for. Following a series of inadequate but successively improved theoretical models developed by Fröhlich and others, Bardeen, Cooper, and Schrieffer (1957), followed by Bogoliubov et al. (1958), were at last able to show that a model involving the condensation of pairs of conduction electrons into a lower energy phase was able to account for most of the known phenomena of the superconductive state. This condensation process is found to be associated with the interaction between the conduction electrons and the crystal lattice, a process that is also responsible

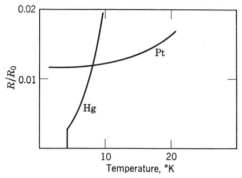

Fig. 1.2 Variation of R/R_0 versus temperature for platinum and mercury (Onnes, 1913a). (R_0 is the resistance at $0°C$.)

for the electrical resistance of metals in the normal (non-superconductive) state. For this reason, superconductivity occurs in the poorer metallic conductors such as tin, lead, and tantalum rather than in the better conductors such as copper, silver, and gold. The temperature below which a superconductor becomes superconducting is known as the *critical temperature*. Critical temperatures for a number of elements are shown in Table 1.2.

TABLE 1.2

Critical Temperatures of some Important Superconductors

Element	$°K$
Niobium	9.4 $\pm$ 0.2
Lead	7.19
Tantalum	4.45 $\pm$ 0.05
Mercury (α form)	4.15
Tin	3.72
Indium	3.40
Aluminum	1.20

In an attempt to set an upper limit to the resistance of a metal in the superconducting state, Onnes (1914b) devised an experiment in which a persistent circulating current was induced in a superconducting ring by cooling it below its critical temperature in a magnetic field that was then removed. The magnitude of the persistent current could be determined by measuring its magnetic field, and the resistance of the superconducting ring could be deduced from the rate of decay of this field. Onnes found the rate of decay to be immeasurably small. In the latest experiment of

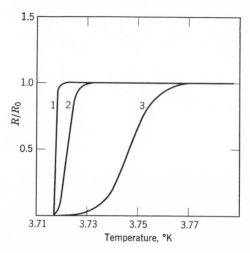

Fig. 1.3 Magnetic field induced phase transition, showing influence of specimen purity (de Haas and Voogd, 1931). Temperature corrected to 1949 scale by Shoenberg (1952). (1) Pure tin single crystal, (2) pure tin polycrystal, (3) less pure tin polycrystal.

this type Quinn and Ittner (1962) showed that the resistivity of super-conducting lead is less than 4×10^{-23} ohm cm. In a graphic demonstration, Professor S. Collins of M.I.T. has kept a persistent current "alive" in a superconducting lead ring for several years with no apparent change in magnitude!

1.2 Magnetoresistance

While attempting to construct a superconducting electromagnet, Onnes (1913a, c) discovered that a current-carrying wire of superconducting lead would return to the normal state if a *critical current* were exceeded. A later discovery[3] showed that a superconductor will become normal in the presence of a magnetic field above a critical value but returns to the superconducting state when the field is removed. As shown in Figure 1.3

---

[3] Onnes (1914a).

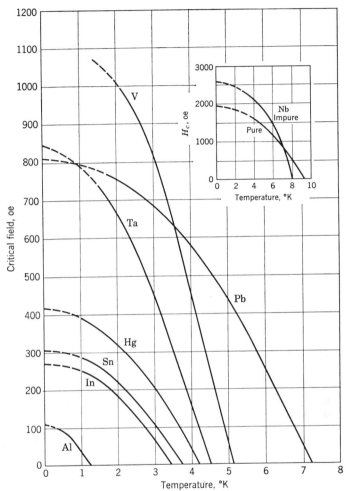

Fig. 1.4 Critical field curves of some superconductors. The curve for tantalum is from data by Budnick (1960); curve for pure niobium is from data by Stromberg and Swenson (1962). The other curves are taken from Shoenberg, *op. cit.* p. 225.

the field induced transition can be very sharp for a carefully purified and annealed superconducting specimen of suitable shape.

With only small deviations, the critical field H_c varies with temperature according to the parabolic law

$$H_c = H_0\left[1 - \left(\frac{T}{T_c}\right)^2\right]$$

Here H_0 is the critical field at absolute zero and T_c is the critical temperature. Critical field curves for a number of superconductors are given in Figure 1.4.

After the discovery of the magnetic-field induced transition it was suggested by Silsbee (1916) that the current-induced transition might be a special case of the field-induced transition that occurs when the surface field of a current-carrying wire exceeds H_c. This has been confirmed by experiment and will be referred to as the "Silsbee condition."

1.3 Diamagnetism

If a normal non-ferromagnetic metal is exposed to a magnetic field, eddy currents are induced in the surface in such a direction as to "shield" the interior. When these currents have decayed, the internal field rises to the external value. In a perfect conductor exposed to a magnetic field, these induced eddy currents would not be able to decay. Hence the external field would be excluded permanently and the internal field would remain zero except in a thin surface layer. It is in fact found by experiment that a magnetic field applied to a superconducting body can only penetrate a minute distance into the surface, provided that the surface field nowhere exceeds H_c.[4]

However, the analogy between a superconductor and a perfect conductor breaks down completely for the case in which a superconductor is brought from the normal to the superconducting state in the presence of a magnetic field. In the normal state the internal field in a superconductor is equal to the applied external field. If the temperature is lowered so that the superconductor becomes superconducting, experience with conventional materials suggests that the internal field should remain unchanged. Furthermore if the external field were removed, one would expect permanent surface eddy currents to be generated, so as to keep the internal field constant. In other words, the superconductor might be expected to "trap" the internal field present during the normal-to-superconducting transition.

The actual behavior of a superconductor is strikingly different. This was discovered by Meissner and Ochsenfeld (1933), who found that the field distribution around a homogeneous superconducting body of low demagnetizing factor *always corresponds to a zero internal field*, whatever its magnetic and thermal history. If such a body is brought from the normal into the superconducting state by lowering the temperature in the presence of a magnetic field, it is found that all the flux penetrating the superconductor is abruptly expelled as the normal-to-superconducting transition takes place. At the same time the external field rises to a value that indicates that the internal field is zero.

Proof that all or virtually all of the flux passing through a superconductor in the normal state is expelled during the normal-to-superconducting

---

[4] This statement must be modified for the so-called class II superconductors (see Sec. 1.4).

transition, is provided by an experiment described by Shoenberg.[5] A long cylindrical superconductor is wound with a coil connected to a ballistic galvanometer. If a field is applied parallel to the axis of the cylinder at a temperature above T_c, the field will penetrate the coil causing the galvanometer to execute a deflection. If the temperature is now reduced so that the cylinder becomes superconducting, the galvanometer will execute an equal and opposite deflection, indicating that all the flux penetrating the cylinder has been expelled.

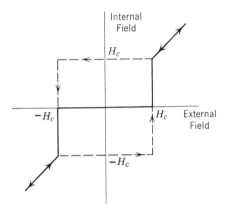

Fig. 1.5 Internal field as a function of external field in a real superconductor (solid line), and a hypothetical perfect conductor (broken line).

The discovery of the Meissner effect made it possible to explain the experimental fact that the magnetically induced transition between the superconducting and normal states of a solid superconductor exhibits very little or no hysteresis and is reversible in the thermodynamic sense. If, for instance, the magnetic field applied parallel to a long thin superconducting cylinder is cycled through values above H_c, the internal field varies according to the solid line of Figure 1.5. In contrast, the internal field variation of a hypothetical perfect conductor would be like that shown by the broken curve which exhibits hysteresis. (It is shown in Chapter 2 that such hysteresis curves are observed for hollow superconducting cylinders or rings.)

1.4 Distribution of Superconductivity Among the Elements

Superconductivity occurs in over twenty of those metallic non-ferromagnetic elements having between two and eight valence electrons, and also in many alloys and compounds of both superconductive and

---

[5] Shoenberg, *op. cit.* p. 19.

non-superconductive elements.[6] The list of elements exhibiting super-conductivity is still being enlarged. For instance it is found that bismuth and beryllium are superconductive when evaporated at low temperatures,[7] and that molybdenum exhibits superconductivity when trace impurities of iron are removed. A list of all the elements that are presently known to exhibit superconductivity is given in Section 8.

The properties of the high-melting-point superconductive elements, such as tantalum and niobium, are strongly dependent on the presence of impurities. Even when carefully purified, these elements, as well as most superconducting alloys and compounds, are not perfectly diamagnetic, trap flux, and have extremely broad magnetic transitions. These materials are known as "hard" or "class II" superconductors. The superconducting characteristics of the mechanically soft superconductors such as tin, lead, and indium are much less sensitive to strains and impurities, because these low melting-point metals can anneal at room temperature. Even in a relatively impure state they have sharp transitions and exhibit the Meissner effect. They are known as "soft" or "class I" superconductors.

2. SELECTED APPLICATIONS

This section introduces a variety of devices chosen to illustrate the large range of superconductive phenomena that have applications. We begin with devices that depend on the unique electromagnetic properties of superconductors.

2.1 Electromagnets

Since a superconducting wire has no ohmic resistance it is possible to construct superconducting solenoids that produce no joule heat during operation. The design of a superconducting solenoid must assure that the combined effect of the field due to the solenoid as a whole and that due to the current in any particular wire segment is insufficient to render that segment normal. By designing the solenoid to carry a current that is only a small fraction of the critical current at zero field for the wire used, it is possible to generate a magnetic field that approaches the critical field of the coil material.

---

[6] The adjective "superconduct*ive*" will be taken to mean "capable of exhibiting superconductivity"; the adjective "superconduct*ing*" will be used to mean "in the superconducting state," e.g., a superconduct*ive* element is superconduct*ing* below its critical temperature.

[7] These films anneal irreversibly to a non-superconducting form when brought to higher temperatures.

The convenience of being able to produce a magnetic field in a low-temperature environment without joule heating has led to the wide employment of superconductive solenoids in laboratory apparatus, and in connection with low-temperature devices, such as the maser.

If a room temperature electromagnet is used to generate steady magnetic fields in the kilo-oersted range, elaborate liquid cooling is required to dissipate the joule heat produced in the windings. Furthermore, hundreds of kilowatts of electrical generating capacity are required for fields of the order of 10 kilo-oersteds or higher. Magnetic fields in the 100 kilo-oersted range are required for research and development in fields such as nuclear fusion processes, and plasma propulsion. The maximum critical field of elemental superconductors is below 10 kilo-oersteds. However, various hard superconducting alloys including niobium-tin, niobium-zirconium, and vanadium-gallium exhibit critical field values above 100 kilo-oersteds at liquid helium temperatures. These permit the construction of virtually dissipationless 100 kilo-oersted coils. The conditions under which such alloys can be used for magnet construction and the reason for their extraordinarily high critical fields are discussed in Chapter 5.

2.2 Suspension Systems

A striking application of superconductors, which depends upon near perfect diamagnetism, is as low viscosity suspension systems. The principle of these systems is demonstrated by an experiment of Arkadiev (1945, 1947) illustrated in Figure 1.6a. This figure shows a permanent magnet floating in equilibrium above a superconducting lead cup welded to copper legs standing in liquid helium. At the outset of this experiment, the magnet rests in the lead cup that is standing in an empty dewar and is in the normal state. Liquid helium is transferred into the dewar until the copper legs supporting the lead cup are partially immersed. As this happens, the lead cup becomes superconducting, and expels the magnetic flux of the magnet. This causes the magnet to rise into an equilibrium position above the cup as shown in the figure.

The inverse of this effect, namely the ability of suitably shaped magnetic fields to support a superconducting sphere, has been demonstrated by Simon (1953) using the arrangement illustrated in Figure 1.6b. This figure shows a lead-coated hollow glass sphere supported by the combined effect of oppositely directed magnetic flux trapped in two lead rings. By means of techniques described in Chapter 5 it is possible to impart high-speed rotation to a body that is superconductively suspended in vacuum. These principles have been applied to the construction of superconducting gyroscopes.[8]

---

[8] Buchhold (1961).

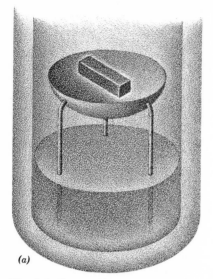 

(a)   (b)

Fig. 1.6 Superconducting suspension devices. (*a*) Magnet floating above super-conducting lead cup (Arkadiev, 1945, 1947). (*b*) Lead-coated glass sphere supported by magnetic field trapped in two superconducting lead rings (Simon, 1953).

2.3   Electrical Switching Elements

Because of the infinite ratio between the resistance of a metal in the normal and the superconducting state, a superconductor can be used to switch electrical current between different possible paths. Either temperature or magnetic field can be used to control the change of state of such a switch. A temperature controlled switch that uses a film of lead as the switching element was described by Pippard and Pullan (1952). The current-carrying film was operated below the critical temperature, so as to be superconducting. When it was desired to interrupt current flow through the switch, the lead film was raised above its critical temperature by means of a heating coil made of a non-superconducting metal. As the lead film became resistive, the current flowing through it was diverted through a parallel path of lower resistance.

A magnetically operated current switch is shown in Figure 1.7. It is operated slightly below the critical temperature (4.4°K), of the tantalum "gate" wire. This acts as the current-diverting element and can be switched to the normal resistive state by the magnetic field generated by passing current through the niobium "control" coil. Niobium has a critical temperature above 8°K, so that the control remains superconducting in operation. The choice of tantalum for the gate wire allows the switch to be operated at 4.2°K, that is, in liquid helium boiling at atmospheric pressure.

This switch appears to have been first described by Casimir-Jonkers and de Haas (1935), who used a lead control wrapped around a gate made of lead-tellurium (Pb-Tl) alloy. A similar device was used by Templeton (1955a, b) as a low temperature modulator and switch, and by Schmitt and Fiske as a low temperature amplifier.[9] The late Dudley A. Buck of M.I.T. demonstrated[10] that the device of Figure 1.7, which he named the "cryotron," could be used as a digital switching element in computer circuits. Buck's work led to widespread interest in the application of superconductivity to digital computers. In recognition of his

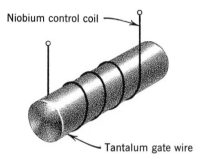

Niobium control coil

Tantalum gate wire

Fig. 1.7 The wire-wound cryotron.

contributions, the term cryotron has been generally adopted to represent any superconductive four-terminal device in which the impedance between the two output terminals is controlled magnetically by means of a current passed through the two input terminals. The structure shown in Figure 1.7 is sometimes called the "Wire Wound Cryotron" (WWC), to distinguish it from metal-film cryotrons.

It is shown in the next chapter that the current in a superconducting wire is carried in a thin surface layer. The critical current of such a wire is therefore unimpaired if the core of the wire is replaced by an insulator. At the same time the switching time of a cryotron employing such a cylinder as the gate conductor is strongly reduced. Considerations such as this led to the development of the so-called Crossed Film Cryotron (CFC) shown in Figure 1.8 in which both the gate and control are composed of metallic films separated by an insulating layer.[11]

For use as computer switching elements, film cryotrons appear to possess several advantages over the transistors presently used. In the

[9] R. W. Schmitt and W. D. Fiske, U.S. Patent 2,935,694.
[10] D. A. Buck (1956a).
[11] Newhouse and Bremer (1959).

first place film cryotrons can be vacuum deposited simultaneously in large circuit arrays in a small number of steps. This feature makes the cost of an individual cryotron in such an array virtually negligible. Another advantage of film cryotrons is their low heat dissipation, which is of the order of microwatts, three orders of magnitude smaller than that of other high-speed amplifiers. Consequently it should be possible to construct cryotron computer systems of unrivaled compactness, since the

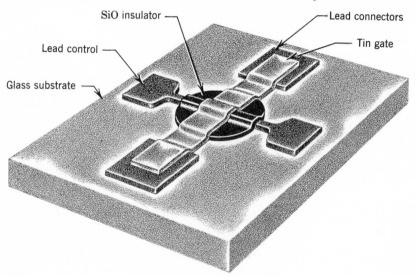

SiO insulator

Lead connectors

Tin gate

Lead control

Glass substrate

Fig. 1.8   The crossed-film cryotron.

lower limit on systems size is at present limited not by the size of available elements but by the difficulty of dissipating their waste heat. Various wire-wound and film cryotrons and their use as amplifying and switching elements are described in Chapter 6.

2.4   Persistent Current Storage

Most digital computers contain a high-speed random-access memory of 10^5 or more binary storage elements, each of which is individually accessible. In most memories of this type each binary storage element consists of a ring or "core" of ferrite possessing a rectangular magnetic hysteresis loop. Positive and negative remanence are used to represent binary *one* and *zero* respectively. Each core is threaded by a number of selection or "drive" lines. By passing current through these lines, the core can be set to positive or negative remanence. This process constitutes the entry of information into a particular binary digit storage position.

In an effort to reduce the cost and size of random access memories and to increase their speed, considerable effort has been expended on the development of persistent current storage devices using superconductive films. One of these[12] is shown in Figure 1.9. The storage portion of this cell consists of a thin superconductive "crossbar" of lead or tin, crossing a hole in a sheet of thicker superconductor. To store binary information,

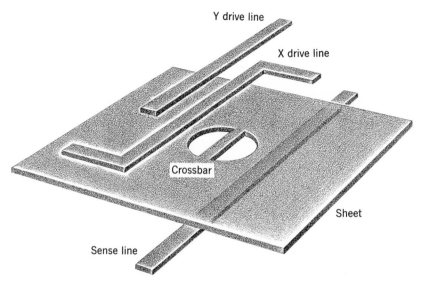

Y drive line

X drive line

Crossbar

Sheet

Sense line

Fig. 1.9 The "Crowe" persistent current cell for digital storage. (The substrate on which the cell is deposited, and the insulating layers which separate the sense line, crossbar, and selection lines, are not shown.)

permanent circulating currents are induced in the crossbar structure in either of the two modes illustrated in Figure 1.10. Switching from one mode to the other is accomplished by passing suitable current pulses in the same direction through the two drive lines.[13] These pulses tend to induce an opposing current equal to their sum in the crossbar, as shown in Figure 1.11. As long as this current is below its critical value, it varies so as to counteract any change in the sum of the drive currents, thus maintaining the net magnetic flux linking the crossbar constant. In that case the crossbar circulating current suffers no permanent change due to the

---

[12] Crowe (1957).
[13] A brief description of a random access memory selection system which explains the need for more than one drive line is given in Sec. 34.

application of the drive pulse or pulses. If the polarity and amplitude of the applied drive pulses is sufficient to raise the circulating current above its critical value, it will return to a new equilibrium value when these drive pulses are turned off. This is illustrated in pulse γ of Figure 1.11. Before this pulse is applied, the value of the circulating current is $+0.3I_c$. During pulse γ the crossbar current is driven towards $1.6I_c$ from which value it decays back towards I_c, while pulse γ is still on. This decay process changes the flux linking the crossbar, producing a voltage pulse on the sense line. As the drive pulse is turned off, the crossbar current is again

"One"   "Zero"

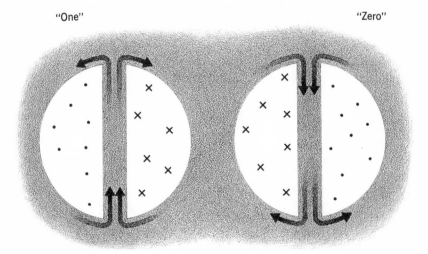

Fig. 1.10   Two modes of persistent current storage.

able to maintain the flux constant, by falling below I_c. It can be seen in Figure 1.11 that after pulse γ, the final crossbar current falls as far below I_c as the sum of the drive currents exceeded it, that is, to $-0.3I_c$.

In its original form the Crowe cell used a lead-film crossbar and was operated at 4.2°K. This is so far below the critical temperature of lead that runaway heating effects occur. These produce a mode of operation that is somewhat more complex than that shown in Figure 1.11. The mode is described in the more detailed analysis of the Crowe cell given in Chapter 7.

The Crowe cell, and some of its later developments, which are described in that chapter, appear to have great advantages over existing magnetic storage cores, with respect to compactness, speed, and economy. It appears likely therefore that superconducting memories will play an important role in digital computers of the near future.

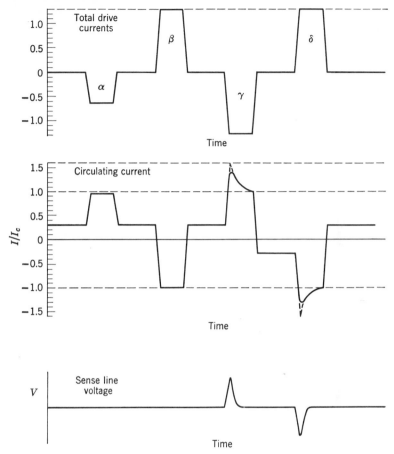

Fig. 1.11   Idealized operating waveforms for a persistent current "Crowe" cell operating in the isothermal mode.

2.5   Bolometers

A bolometer may be defined as a radiation detector whose operation depends on the change of resistance with temperature of a conductor exposed to the heating effect of incident radiation. Bolometers are used in spectrometers and imaging devices for the detection of microwaves and infrared radiation. They derive an advantage from low-temperature operation, because the sensitivity of all room-temperature thermal detectors is limited by thermal fluctuation noise. Furthermore, the specific heat of all materials decreases at low temperatures so that a given amount of radiation will produce a greater temperature rise the lower the temperature of the detector.

Superconductive bolometers,[14] which are described at greater length in Chapter 8, employ a small film or foil of a superconductor as the detecting element. This is held at a temperature in the transition region. The superconductor carries a constant current so that changes in resistance caused by changes in the incident radiation can be detected. The input radiation is often interrupted by a "chopper" disk, so that the bolometer signal can be amplified by a-c methods. The temperature of the bolometer sensing element must be held extremely constant, usually at the steepest part of the dR/dT curve. When operated in this way, superconductive bolometers possessing a time constant of 1.25 sec have been able to detect a radiation power of approximately 10^{-12} watt. For reasons explained in Chapter 8, operation of these devices in conjunction with cryotron output amplifiers should result in even greater sensitivities. Furthermore the use of arrays of film cryotron switches as bolometers may lead to advances in infrared imagining techniques.

2.6   The Heat Valve

A widely used superconductive device is the heat valve in which a superconductor controls the flow of *heat*. This is based on the fact that at temperatures below 1°K, the thermal conductivity of some of the common superconductors such as tantalum and lead increases by two orders of magnitude if the superconductor is made normal by the application of a magnetic field. The drop in thermal conductivity associated with the superconducting state is due to the fact that the conduction electrons, which, in the normal metal, carry most of the heat energy at low temperatures, can no longer interact with the lattice in the superconducting state. Hence the thermal coupling between them and the region outside the superconductor is lost.

The use of superconductors as heat valves appears to have been first demonstrated successfully by Heer and Daunt (1949) of the University of Illinois. Their valve consisted of a tantalum wire 0.017 cm in diameter and 56 cm long. At 0.7°K the heat leak through this device could be varied from 7 to 7500 ergs per minute by applying a magnetic field above the critical value.

Superconductive heat valves are preferred in most of the laboratory refrigeration systems designed to obtain temperatures below 0.3°K[15] because the use of mechanical valves with moving parts in the low-temperature region of such a refrigerator would result in vibrations that would be converted to heat, severely limiting the lowest attainable temperature.

---

[14] Developed by Andrews et al. (1942) at Johns Hopkins University.
[15] Two of these systems are described in some detail in Section 35.2.

3. BOOK ORGANIZATION

This section describes the arrangement of the following chapters in sufficient detail to bring out the extent to which any particular chapter is dependent on earlier material. Used in conjunction with the table of contents this arrangement should help the reader with a single specific interest to avoid irrelevant material, and enable the student to read the chapters in an order different from that in which they are presented. More detailed summaries are given in the introduction to each chapter.

As mentioned earlier, Chapters 2, 3, and 4 describe the phenomena of superconductivity and their theoretical interpretation, whereas Chapters 5, 6, 7, and 8 analyze the various classes of superconductive devices. Chapter 2 begins with a survey of the properties of bulk superconductors from the experimental standpoint. This is followed by sections on electromagnetic behavior, thermodynamic properties, interphase boundary effects, and superconductive alloys. This chapter constitutes sufficient introduction for at least a preliminary reading of the material on bulk superconductive devices. Chapter 3 describes the phenomenological and microscopic theories of superconductivity and their application to various quantum mechanical effects. These theories are particularly important for the description and analysis of the properties of superconductive films. The chapter also develops analytical methods for calculating current flow in bulk superconductors. Chapter 4 describes and analyzes superconductive films with emphasis on those properties important to device operation. Also discussed are joule heating phenomena that apply to bulk superconductors as well as to films.

The device chapters 5 to 8 are almost completely independent of one another and may be read in any order. Chapter 5, which discusses superconductive solenoids, flux pumps, bearings, and motors, includes a discussion of the physics of filamentary superconductors, which has been incorporated here rather than in Chapter 2, because the results apply mainly to superconducting solenoids.

Chapters 6 and 7 describe superconductive amplifiers as well as digital switching and storage devices. In addition Chapter 6 reviews microwave mixers and demodulators, and Chapter 7 describes superconductive resonant cavities. Chapter 8 describes devices such as superconductive bolometers that are controlled by changes in temperature, as well as superconductive thermal valves that control the flow of heat. Each chapter is followed by a bibliography.

chapter 2

Superconductivity
in Bulk Materials

4. GENERAL SURVEY

4.1 Theoretical Concepts

This section introduces the theoretical concepts that are used in the remainder of this chapter. A more detailed account of the various theories of superconductivity is given in Chapter 3.

Although the development of quantum mechanics in the 1920's led to the understanding of the "normal" process of electrical conduction in metals, the origins of superconductivity were to remain obscure until 1956. This situation encouraged the development of phenomenological theories. These theories, although not attempting to account for the origin of superconductivity, have established that most superconducting phenomena can be derived from a small number of empirical postulates. The task of a microscopic theory of superconductivity is thus reduced to that of explaining these postulates.

An early step towards a phenomenological theory of superconductivity was made by Gorter and Casimir (1934), who showed that the thermodynamic properties of superconductors could be accounted for by assuming that their conduction electrons were divided into two "fluids" or phases. The electrons in one phase are considered to retain their normal properties, but a proportion β is assumed to be condensed into a lower free energy phase in which it can carry current without interacting, that is, without ohmic dissipation. The precise variation of β with temperature can be calculated from the specific heat on the basis of the assumption that β is unity at absolute zero and decreases towards zero as the critical temperature is approached.

Following the discovery of the Meissner effect, it became clear that the electromagnetic properties of a superconductor could not be predicted by simply writing down Maxwell's equations for a metal, and assuming zero resistivity. The brothers F. and H. London (1935) were able to show however that most of the electromagnetic properties of superconductors, including the Meissner effect, could be accounted for by Maxwell's equations with the addition of the expression

$$\frac{ne^2}{mc}\mathbf{H} + \text{curl } \mathbf{J} = 0 \qquad (2.1)$$

where $\mathbf{J}$ is the current density, $\mathbf{H}$ the field, and n, e, and m are respectively the density, charge, and mass of the conduction electrons.

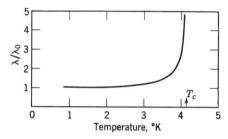

Fig. 2.1 Variation of the reduced penetration depth with temperature for mercury (Shoenberg, 1940).

It is shown in Section 10.2 that when combined with Maxwell's equations, Equation 2.1 leads to the expression

$$\mathbf{H} = \mathbf{H}_0 e^{-x/\lambda} \qquad (2.2)$$

where

$$\lambda^2 = \left(\frac{mc^2}{4\pi ne^2}\right) \qquad (2.3)$$

for the field $\mathbf{H}$ at a depth inside a semi-infinite superconductor whose surface field is $\mathbf{H}_0$. λ is known as the penetration depth. Equation 2.1 predicts that the field should fall to zero inside a superconductor in agreement with the Meissner effect, and that it should do so exponentially with a decrement λ. This prediction is found to be approximately correct. The penetration depth can be measured experimentally and is found to vary with temperature, increasing from a value $\lambda(0)$ at absolute zero towards infinity at T_c. Experimentally, the temperature dependence of λ is found to be given by the relation.

$$\frac{\lambda(T)}{\lambda(0)} = \left[1 - \left(\frac{T}{T_c}\right)^4\right]^{-1/2} \qquad (2.4)$$

Fxperimental data for mercury plotted in Figure 2.1 follows this curve. Eor lead, mercury, tin, and indium $\lambda(0)$ lies between 4 and 6 $\times$ 10^{-6} cm. It is found that Equation 2.4 can be deduced from the London theory by thermodynamic arguments[1] if n in Equation 2.3 is regarded as the density of the "superconducting" portion of the conduction electrons as calculated from the two-fluid model. Although later work (see Section 10) has shown that the concepts of the two-fluid model and the equations of

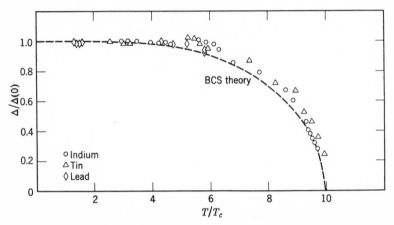

Fig. 2.2 Experimental temperature dependence of the energy gap for lead, tin, and indium, compared with that calculated from the BCS theory (Giaever and Megerle, 1961).

the London theory are only exact under certain limiting conditions, these concepts and equations still provide a most convenient framework for describing many of the phenomena of superconductivity discussed in the succeeding sections.

The London theory and the two-fluid model do not, of course, attempt to explain the origin of superconductivity. This achievement was vouchsafed to J. Bardeen and his students, who derived the first successful microscopic theory of superconductivity.[2] According to this theory (known as the "BCS theory"), the electrons responsible for superconductivity (roughly corresponding to the condensed phase of the two-fluid model) are coupled together in pairs due to lattice deformations, with a binding energy -2Δ. It is calculated that the attractive force between the electrons of a pair extends over a relatively long distance of the order of 10^{-4}, called the *distance of correlation*, ξ. To decouple such an electron

---

[1] See for instance D. Shoenberg *Superconductivity* 2nd ed. New York: Cambridge University Press 1952 Sec. 6.3.2.
[2] Bardeen, Cooper, and Schrieffer (1957).

pair into two "normal" electrons that can interact with the lattice, a minimum energy Δ has to be supplied to the system. We may therefore say that the condensed phase is separated from the normal phase by an "energy gap" 2Δ. At absolute zero the BCS theory predicts that

$$2\Delta = 3.52kT_c \qquad (2.5)$$

a result that is in good agreement with experiment. The energy gap decreases with increasing temperature and vanishes at T_c (see Fig. 2.2).

The BCS "model" has been successful in quantitatively accounting for most of the phenomena of the superconducting state in terms of param- eters of the normal state. The theory reduces to the London equation near T_c.

4.2 Characteristics of the Superconducting State

SUPERCONDUCTIVITY. The experimental evidence for the diamagnetism exhibited by superconductors has already been described in Chapter 1 and need not reviewed here. Some comments on the zero electrical resistance are however in order, since this can be interpreted in a partic- ularly straightforward manner, in terms of the BCS model. A flowing current is associated with the movement of electrons through the lattice. Ohmic resistance is due to the scattering of these moving electrons to lower velocities by lattice impurities and thermal vibrations of the lattice ions. The kinetic energy lost by the electrons on being scattered is given up to the lattice. In a BCS superconductor the current is carried by the electron pairs of the condensed phase. If one of these electrons were to be scattered to a lower velocity it would suffer an *increase* in potential energy due to being "depaired." For low currents and correspondingly low electron velocities, this increase in potential energy is more than sufficient to counterbalance any loss in kinetic energy due to the loss in velocity. Electron scattering to lower velocities with a net transfer of energy to the lattice can therefore only take place for electron velocities above a certain minimum. For currents corresponding to electron velocities less than this, the conduction electrons involved can give no energy to the lattice, so that the ohmic resistance must be zero. The critical electron velocity and the corresponding critical current density are derived in Chapter 3.

LATENT HEAT OF TRANSITION AND SPECIFIC HEAT.[3] Since the super- conducting phase is associated with pairs of coupled electrons it has a higher degree of order and therefore lower entropy than the normal phase. It is found that there is a finite latent heat of transition, except at absolute

---

[3] For most of the concepts in this section the author is indebted to M. D. Sherrill.

zero, and at T_c where the transition occurs in the absence of a magnetic field.

The reason that the latent heat of transition is finite in the presence of a magnetic field, that is, at temperatures below T_c, is due to the fact that in such a transition a large number of electron pairs must be split, which requires a finite energy. However as the temperature of a superconductor is raised through T_c, both the number of electron pairs and the coupling

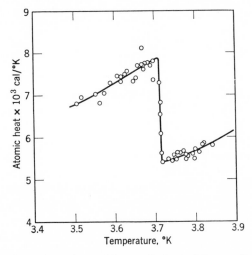

Fig. 2.3 Temperature dependence of the specific heat of tin near T_c (Keesom and Kok, 1932).

energy per pair vanish smoothly, so that the phase transition takes place without a latent heat of transition. This type of transition is typical of one involving a change in an order parameter and is known as a "transition of the second kind," or a "second order transition."[4]

The specific heat of any conductor can be assigned partly to contributions due to the lattice ions, and partly to those due to the conduction electrons. The lattice contribution to the specific heat is believed to be virtually unchanged in the superconducting state. However the electronic contribution to the specific heat of a superconductor rises sharply and discontinuously as the temperature is lowered through T_c (see Fig. 2.3). This may be ascribed to the fact that the size of the energy gap and thus the number of paired superelectrons varies very rapidly with temperature in this region. At temperatures close to absolute zero, on the other hand, the superconducting electron pairs can only be excited to higher energy

---

[4] The derivation of these terms is explained in Sec. 6.3.

states by receiving an amount of energy that exceeds $2\Delta(0)$. Hence at these temperatures we would expect the electronic specific heat in the superconducting state to be *less* than that in the normal state. This is confirmed by experiment.

Since the phase transition of a superconductor is reversible, it can be treated by the techniques of classical thermodynamics. This is done in Section 6, where it is shown that the characteristic latent and specific heat behavior of a superconductor, which we have here interpreted in terms of the microscopic theory, can be derived thermodynamically from the experimental relation between temperature and critical field.

THERMAL CONDUCTIVITY. Heat conduction in the normal state is due to both lattice vibrations and conduction electrons. The condensed portion of the conduction electrons in the superconducting state cannot interact with the lattice, and cannot therefore contribute to heat conduction. Hence the thermal conductivity in the superconducting state is alway less than that of the normal metal. The utilization of this difference in a magnetic field-controlled heat switch has already been mentioned in the Introduction, and is further discussed in Chapter 8.

It is found that a magnetic field applied to a superconductor of suitable geometry will drive it into the so-called intermediate state, in which it consists of alternate domains of superconducting and normal phases. It was discovered by Mendelsohn and Olsen (1950a,b) that the thermal conductivity in a direction at right angles to the interphase boundaries reaches a minimum, even lower than the thermal conductivity in the superconducting state. The effect has been analyzed by Cornish and Olsen (1953) and Laredo and Pippard (1955) and shown to be due to scattering of the lattice waves or *phonons* in normal regions present in the intermediate state.

ULTRASONIC ATTENUATION. At room temperatures a large part of the attenuation of sound waves in metals is due to phonon scattering by lattice vibrations. As the temperature is reduced these lattice vibrations decrease, as does the acoustic attenuation. At very low temperatures, the lattice contribution to the attenuation becomes small, and the attenuation actually begins to increase again due to the effect of the conduction electrons. It can be shown that this increase occurs because the electron mean free path[5] becomes comparable to or larger than the acoustic wavelength. In the superconducting state a large proportion of these conduction electrons can no longer interact with the lattice (whose vibrations carry the sound wave), so that the acoustic attenuation is reduced. The minimum in the attenuation of the normal metal at low temperatures

---

[5] See Sec. 11 for an explanation of this term.

and the difference between the normal and superconducting attenuation
are shown in Figure 2.4. As the temperature approaches absolute zero, a
large proportion of the conduction electrons become superconducting (in
the terminology of the two-fluid model), and the ratio of the superconducting to the normal attenuation becomes small.

The above considerations apply to longitudinal acoustic waves for
which the lattice is alternately compressed and stretched. For further
details including the behavior of shear waves, the reader is referred to the
review by Morse (1959).

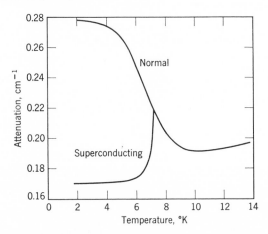

Fig. 2.4   Ultrasonic attenuation in normal and superconducting lead (Bömmel, 1954).

ABSORPTION OF ELECTROMAGNETIC RADIATION.   For very low frequencies
a superconductor behaves as a perfect conductor with zero surface
resistance, and completely reflects all incident radiation. As the frequency
is increased, absorption begins to occur due to acceleration of the "normal"
electrons of the superconductor by the a-c electric field from the incident
radiation which can penetrate into the superconductor. As the frequency
is increased further, so that the photon energy $h\nu$ becomes comparable
to the electron binding energy, the EM absorption sharply increases to the
normal value. From 2.5 we expect that for temperatures much smaller
than T_c, the critical frequency is given by the relation

$$h\nu \sim 3.5kT_c \qquad\qquad (2.6)$$

For superconductors with a very low T_c such as aluminum, this critical
frequency lies in the microwave region.[6] For metals such as tin, lead,

<hr />

[6] Biondi and Garfunkel (1959).

tantalum, and niobium the critical frequencies lie in the infrared. Equation 2.6 has been confirmed for infrared absorption in both superconducting films,[7] and bulk superconductors.[8]

TUNNELING. If two metals are separated by an insulator of the same order of thickness (10–100 Å) as the interatomic distance in a crystal, there is a finite probability that an electron approaching the barrier will pass from one metal to the other. This process is called "tunneling" and occurs because an electron has some of the properties of a wave. A

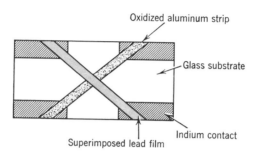

Fig. 2.5 A tunnelling junction.

convenient way of producing the very narrow separation between two metals required for tunneling is to use the oxide film which readily forms on metals such as aluminum at room temperature in air. For instance, to form a junction of $Al-Al_2O_3-Pb$, an Al strip is first vacuum-deposited on a glass substrate. The strip is allowed to form an oxide layer by exposure to air for a few minutes, and a film of lead is then vacuum-deposited across it.[9] The resultant junction appears as in Figure 2.5. The current voltage relation of such a junction is ohmic (see Fig. 2.6a), but in contrast to the resistance of a metal that falls with decreasing temperature, and the resistance of a semiconductor which rises with decreasing temperature, the resistance of a tunnel junction of this type is almost independent of temperature. Giaever (1960a) discovered that if one of the metals of a tunneling junction becomes superconducting, the current-voltage characteristic changes from a line to a curve as shown in Figure 2.6b. At temperatures below T_c the tunneling current remains small until the junction voltage exceeds a critical voltage V_c and then rises sharply to the value for the "normal" junction. The inhibition of current at low voltage levels occurs because the electrons from the normal aluminum

[7] Glover and Tinkham (1957).
[8] Richards and Tinkham (1960).
[9] I. Giaever (1960a).

cannot tunnel into the forbidden energy gap region of the superconducting lead unless they are given sufficient energy to surmount the gap.

As is to be expected, $eV_c = 2\Delta$, where e is the electronic charge and 2Δ the energy gap of lead at the temperature of operation. The junction characteristic is restored to the normal linear type in the presence of a field larger than the critical value.

If the temperature is reduced far enough for the aluminum to become superconducting also, the current-voltage curve develops a negative

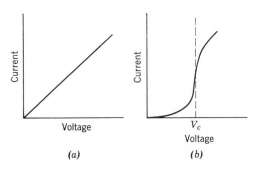

Fig. 2.6 Tunnelling characteristics. (*a*) Both metals normal. (*b*) One metal normal and one superconducting.

resistance region.[10] This phenomenon is analyzed in Section 11.5 of the next chapter.

A double superconductor junction with a negative impedance portion in its characteristic can be employed as an amplifier or oscillator, similarly to a tunnel diode. This has been demonstrated by Miles et al. (1963) who have operated an Al—Al$_2$O$_3$—Sn junction as an oscillator at 72.5 Mc/s and as an amplifier at somewhat lower frequencies.

Josephson (1962) has predicted that a double superconductor junction should be able to sustain a steady current without exhibiting voltage drop, due to tunneling by Cooper pairs. This has been confirmed experimentally by Anderson and Rowell (1963). In the presence of microwaves of frequency ν, Josephson predicts that tunneling current will flow at voltages $nh\nu/2e$ where n is an integer and the other symbols carry their usual meaning. This effect has been confirmed experimentally by Shapiro (1963).

MISCELLANEOUS EFFECTS. It is found both experimentally and theoretically that the *Hall effect* and the *thermo-electric effect* disappear in the superconducting state.

---

[10] Giaever (1960b); Nicol, Shapiro, and Smith (1960).

Experiments by Condon and Maxwell (1949) have shown that a suspended superconducting sphere executing torsional oscillations suffers no additional damping in the presence of a magnetic field. This indicates that the screening currents generated in the presence of the field can move freely within the sphere. If the sphere contains non-superconducting regions however, strong damping effects occur in the presence of a field.

A well-known method of measuring the ratio of the magnetic moment to the angular momentum of the electrons responsible for the magnetization of a ferromagnetic, depends on the fact that a slight rotation is communicated to a suspended body if a magnetic field parallel to the axis of suspension is suddenly switched on (Einstein-de Haas effect). Kikoin and Goobar (1940) have measured this *gyromagnetic ratio* for a superconductor and have found it to be equal to that for free electrons, which indicates that the diamagnetism of a superconductor is caused by a free electron current, and not by the rotation of electron spins.

4.3 Factors that Influence the Phase Transition

A number of factors other than magnetic field and electric current influence the phase transition between the superconducting and normal states.

STRESS. The superconducting-to-normal transition is associated with a very small change in volume. Correspondingly, pressure produces a small change in T_c, which in the case of tin is approximately -5×10^{-5}°K/atm. Tension usually produces an increase in T_c.

IMPURITIES. The effect of impurities on the superconducting properties and the critical temperature is small in soft superconductors, though appreciable in hard superconductors. These effects are discussed in Section 8.

THE ISOTOPE EFFECT. In the course of an early attempt to explain superconductivity on the basis of an interaction between a single electron and the lattice,[11] Fröhlish (1950) was led to predict that the critical temperatures of the different isotopes of an element should be related by the expression

$$T_c \propto M^{-\frac{1}{2}}$$

where M is the atomic weight. This prediction was confirmed experimentally for mercury by Maxwell (1950) and independently by Reynolds et al. (1950), confirming that superconductivity is due to some type of electron-lattice interaction. All superconductors that have been tested exhibit the isotope effect. However the exponent of M differs from $-\frac{1}{2}$ for the transition elements.

---

[11] The interaction is now known to involve electron *pairs*.

INTERPHASE BOUNDARY ENERGY. In the presence of a sufficiently strong surface magnetic field that varies from point to point, a soft superconductor enters the so-called intermediate state (see Sec. 5.3 for further details), in which superconducting and normal regions coexist. These domains of superconducting and normal material are separated by narrow regions of "mixed" phase called interphase boundaries. The free energy per unit volume of this mixed phase region is larger than that of either the superconducting or the normal regions on either side. The boundary can thus be said to have a positive surface energy, analogous to that of the domain boundaries in ferromagnetics that separate regions having different directions of magnetization. The fact that both superconductors and ferromagnets exhibit domain behavior leads to many analogies between them. For instance, both ferromagnetic and superconducting materials exhibit magnetic hysteresis. The domain boundaries in both materials can be observed visually by the attractive effect exerted by their stray fields on fine magnetic powder.

SPECIMEN DIMENSIONS. As one or more dimensions of a superconductor are reduced to a value comparable to the size of a superconducting domain, certain hysteresis effects appear that are associated with the interphase boundary energy (see Sec. 7.3 below). If one or more of the dimensions is reduced further and approaches or falls below the penetration depth, these hysteresis effects disappear. This is probably due to changes in the interphase boundary energy that is believed to vanish for very small specimens (see Sec. 7.1). The most striking characteristic of superconductors of small dimensions is that their critical field is much higher than the value for bulk material. On the other hand, the critical current per unit surface area decreases, owing to a scarcity of paired conduction electrons. Hence for a thin superconducting film or wire Silsbee's relation no longer holds. Dimensional effects on the critical field and current are exhaustively analyzed in Chapters 3 and 4.

5. FIELD AND CURRENT INDUCED TRANSITIONS

A sharp magnetic field induced transition independent of specimen geometry occurs only when the superconductor is in the shape of a long thin wire or strip, whose longest axis is parallel to the field. This section contains analyses of the magnetic field induced transition of a superconducting ellipsoid, and the current induced transition of a wire, two cases where these conditions are not fulfilled. It is shown that these transitions take place over a range of field values, during which the specimen is in the intermediate state in which normal and superconducting regions coexist.

To calculate the field distribution around the superconducting ellipsoid, we introduce the "diamagnetic approximation" in which the super-conductor is treated as a perfectly diamagnetic material, using magnetic potential theory. This method has applications to many problems in superconductivity.

5.1 The Diamagnetic Approximation

To describe ferromagnetic and superconducting bodies it is useful to define the *magnetic moment per unit volume* M usually referred to as the "magnetization." We define the *magnetic susceptibility* as

$$\kappa = \frac{M}{H} \tag{2.7}$$

It can be shown that the magnetic flux density is given by

$$\mathbf{B} = \mathbf{H} + 4\pi\mathbf{M} \tag{2.8}$$

Dividing throughout by $\mathbf{H}$ and using Equation 2.7, we obtain

$$\frac{B}{H} = \mu = 4\pi\kappa + 1 \tag{2.9}$$

where μ is the magnetic permeability.

If a body of finite permeability is brought into a uniform field H_0 it will become magnetized. The field close to it will change to a new value but will remain undisturbed at infinity. The magnetic polarization M of the body produces an internal field opposed to the external one. If the shape of the body is that of an ellipsoid of rotation and if an axis of symmetry is parallel to H_0 (which is now regarded as the field at infinity), then it can be proved that the internal magnetization M and field H_i are everywhere uniform[12] and that

$$\mathbf{H}_i = \mathbf{H}_0 - 4\pi N \mathbf{M} \tag{2.10}$$

where N is the demagnetizing factor along the axis of the ellipsoid parallel to $\mathbf{H}_0$ and is a function of its ellipticity only. In the case of the general ellipsoid, N is different along each major axis.[13] Values of N along an infinite cylinder and at right angles to an infinite thin plate are derived by considering these bodies as limiting cases of prolate and oblate ellipsoids respectively. Values of N for these and some other important cases are given in Table 2.1.

---

[12] For this reason the internal magnetization per unit volume equals the magnetization of the ellipsoid measured externally, divided by the volume.

[13] See R. M. Bozorth, *Ferromagnetism*, New York: Van Nostrand, 1951.

TABLE 2.1

**Demagnetizing Factors and Equatorial Fields for
Superconductors of Common Geometries**

Field Direction	Demagnetizing Factor, N	Equatorial Field $H_0/(1 - N)$
Sphere	$\frac{1}{3}$	$\frac{3}{2}H_0$
Normal to cylinder axis	$\frac{1}{2}$	$2H_0$
Parallel to cylinder axis	0	H_0
Normal to flat, infinitely thin, plate	1	$H_0/0\ (= \infty)$
Parallel to flat, infinitely thin, plate	0	H_0

The field distribution around a superconductor subjected to an external field can be calculated by assuming the presence of surface screening currents. These are determined by the requirement that the field inside the superconductor be zero. With this procedure it is assumed that inside the superconductor $\mu = 1$ and that $B_i = H_i = 0$. An alternative method, which allows us to use the results of magnetic potential theory, treats the superconductor as a diamagnet with $\mu = 0$. Since $B_i = \mu H_i$, this ensures

TABLE 2.2

Surface Current Treatment	Diamagnetic Treatment
Outside superconductor	
$\mathbf{B} = \mathbf{H}_e$	$\mathbf{B} = \mathbf{H}_e$
Inside superconductor,	
$\mu = 1, \mathbf{B} = \mathbf{H} = 0$	$\mu = 0, \mathbf{B} = 0, \mathbf{H}_i = -4\pi\mathbf{M}$
Surface current density*	
$g = 1/4\pi\, H_e$	$g = 0$

* The surface current **g** is normal to the surface field $\mathbf{H}_e$.

that $B_i = 0$ inside the superconductor as required by experiment, even though the internal field H_i is not. So as to maintain B_i zero, this internal field is assumed to be everywhere opposed by the hypothetical internal magnetization M. From Equation 2.8 we find

$$\mathbf{M} = -\frac{\mathbf{H}_i}{4\pi} \tag{2.11}$$

From the definition of magnetic susceptibility $\kappa = -1/4\pi$. The surface screening currents are assumed zero. Their role is taken over by hypothetical circulating currents throughout the material, which generate the magnetization. The terminology of these two mathematically equivalent methods is compared in Table 2.2.

5.2 The Superconducting Ellipsoid in a Magnetic Field

In this section we derive expressions for the surface field of a superconducting ellipsoid brought into a previously uniform field H_0. The ellipsoid dimensions are assumed large compared to λ. By treating the superconductor as a diamagnetic material of zero permeability we can use Equations 2.10 and 2.11 for the internal field and magnetization respectively. Eliminating **M** between these two equations gives

$$\mathbf{H}_i = \frac{H_0}{(1 - N)} \tag{2.12}$$

while eliminating $\mathbf{H}_i$ gives

$$\mathbf{M} = -\frac{H_0}{4\pi(1 - N)}. \tag{2.13}$$

As required by the diamagnetic approximation, the magnetization and field inside the ellipsoid are everywhere uniform and parallel to H_0 at infinity. The field H_e just outside the superconductor is everywhere parallel to its surface.

That this holds for any superconducting body can be seen by considering B on both sides of the surface. It is known that the normal component of B is continuous across any surface. Since $B = 0$ inside the superconductor, the normal component of B just outside it must likewise be zero. Hence just outside any superconductor, B (and therefore H_e) must be parallel to the surface.

The flux lines around an ellipsoidal superconductor are shown schematically in Figure 2.7a. H_e can be calculated by using the fact that the field component parallel to a surface is continuous across it. Hence for an element of the superconducting surface whose tangent makes an angle θ with the direction of H_0 (see Fig. 2.7b), we have

$$H_e = H_i \cos \theta$$

Substituting for H_i from Equation 2.12, gives

$$H_e = H_0 \cos \theta / (1 - N) \tag{2.14}$$

This equation shows that H_e is zero at the poles of the ellipsoid where $\theta = 90°$, and reaches a maximum $H_m = H_0/(1 - N)$ at the equator. N always lies between zero and unity, hence the equatorial field H_m is always

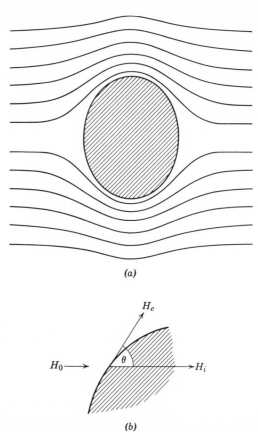

(a)

(b)

Fig. 2.7 (*a*) Magnetic field lines around an ellipsoidal superconductor. (*b*) Field directions near the surface.

equal or larger than the applied field H_0. Values of the equatorial field in terms of H_0 for some common geometries are shown in Table 2.1. Note that in the limiting case of H_0 normal to an infinitely thin flat plate, the field at the edges approaches infinity.

5.3   The Ellipsoid in the Intermediate State

Equation 2.14 shows that when the applied field H_0 is increased to the value

$$H_0 = H_c(1 - N) \tag{2.15}$$

the equatorial field reaches H_c. The ellipsoid can now no longer remain completely superconducting. However, since $H_0 < H_c$ only a portion of the ellipsoid can become normal. The ellipsoid now enters the *intermediate state* that is characterized by the simultaneous presence of both normal and superconducting regions. It might be supposed that the normal phase would be confined to the equatorial regions somewhat as shown in Figure 2.8a, with boundaries at which the field equals H_c. Closer consideration shows that this structure is impossible because the field outside any super-conducting convex boundary must be *less* than the field on it. However the structure shown assumes that the equatorial region is normal, which implies that the field in it is *larger* than that on the boundary.

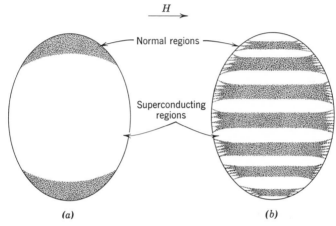

(a)   *(b)*

Fig. 2.8 (*a*) Hypothetical intermediate state structure for the ellipsoid. (*b*) Actual intermediate state structure (schematic).

In fact, it is found experimentally that the ellipsoid in the intermediate state splits up into an arrangement of alternately normal and super-conducting laminae somewhat as shown in Figure 2.8b. The width of the laminae is typically less than 10^{-2} cm and depends on specimen dimensions and on the interphase boundary energy (see Sec. 7.2).

It has been shown theoretically by Peierls (1936) and H. London (1936), and confirmed experimentally by numerous investigators,[14] that the average magnetization per unit volume of the superconductor in the intermediate state adjusts itself so that the internal field equals H_c. This condition is sufficient to determine the magnetization curve for a super-conductor of specific shape. Magnetization curves for fields applied to a sphere, parallel to a cylinder, and transverse to a cylinder are shown in Figure 2.9. To derive these curves we proceed as follows.

---

[14] See the review by Serin (1956).

As the field applied to a superconductor is increased from zero, M increases linearly in accordance with Equation 2.13. From Equations 2.13 and 2.15 we find that M at the onset of the intermediate state is independent of N, that is,

$$M = -\frac{H_c}{4\pi} \quad \text{for} \quad H_0 = H_c(1 - N)$$

As the applied field is increased further, M can be determined from the

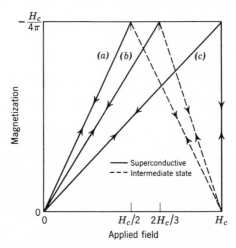

Fig. 2.9 Variation of the average magnetization with field for several geometries. (a) Transverse cylinder, (b) sphere, (c) longitudinal cylinder.

Peierls-London criterion that $H_i = H_c$, using Equation 2.10. We find accordingly that for $H_c(1 - N) < H_0 < H_c$.

$$M = -\frac{(H_c - H_0)}{4\pi N} \tag{2.16}$$

Hence M decreases linearly from its maximum value as H_0 is increased, reaching zero at H_c. It should be noted that the flux density, which is a measure of the flux penetrating the superconductor, rises linearly from zero at the onset of the intermediate state to its full value when $H = H_c$. This can be shown from Equations 2.8 and 2.16, which give B_i in the intermediate state as

$$B_i = \left(H_c - \frac{H_c - H_0}{N}\right)$$

The fields just outside the pole and equator of the ellipsoid are plotted in Figure 2.10. The polar field equals B_i, since the normal component of B is continuous across the boundary. The equatorial field equals H_i, since the component of H parallel to the surface is continuous across it.

The expressions which have been derived for field and magnetization in the intermediate state, are for average values taken over a region large compared to the scale (approximately 10^{-2} cm) of the domain pattern.

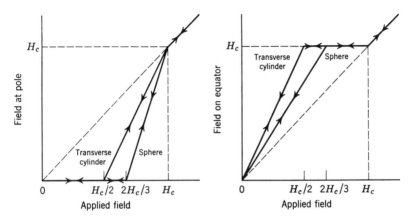

Fig. 2.10   Magnetic field at the pole and on the equator of a sphere and a transverse cylinder.

The way in which the behavior described above is modified for small specimens is described in Section 7.3.

5.4   Current Induced Transition in a Wire

As predicted by Silsbee (1916), resistance appears in a carefully annealed current-carrying wire when the surface field due to the current exceeds H_c. The transition process is complex. The simplest initial assumption is that when the surface field exceeds H_c the current retreats to a superconducting core of slightly smaller radius than that of the wire, leaving a normal outer shell. Closer consideration shows that this simple picture is impossible, because if the field at the boundary between the superconducting and normal regions were equal to H_c, the field in the external region would have to be less than this, in which case this region could not be normal.

The actual domain structure during the transition is believed to consist of a core in the intermediate state, surrounded by a normal region. The core structure, shown schematically in Figure 2.11, was postulated by F. London (1937) and has been confirmed experimentally by Makei

(1958), who inserted a bismuth magnetoresistive probe into a slot cut into a current-carrying wire.

Using the expression $H = 2C/r$ for the field due to a current C, in a cylinder of radius r, we can calculate the current distribution inside the intermediate core where the field is uniform and equal to H_c.

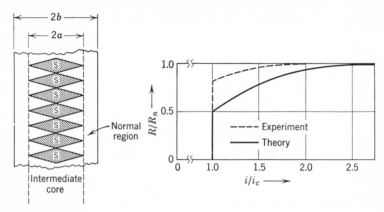

Fig. 2.11   Intermediate state structure of a current-carrying wire. (After F. London, 1937.)

Fig. 2.12   Resistance change associated with the current induced transition of a tin wire (Shubnikow and Alekseyevsky, 1936).

Let the total current inside a radius r be $J(r)$. Then,

$$\frac{2J(r)}{r} = H_c \tag{2.17}$$

The current density inside the intermediate core is

$$\sigma = \frac{1}{2\pi r}\frac{dJ(r)}{dr}$$

$$= H_c/4\pi r \tag{2.18}$$

If the outer radius of this core is a, then the current density at the edge of this region is $H_0/4\pi a$. In the outer region, σ remains constant at this value since the potential drop across all parts of any normal region must be the same.

To calculate the outer radius a of the intermediate region, we proceed as follows. The current carried in the region is $J(a)$. From Equation 2.17

$$\frac{2J(a)}{a} = H_c \tag{2.19}$$

Since the current density for $r > a$ is equal to $H_c/4\pi a$ the current carried in this outer region is

$$C - J(a) = \frac{H_c}{4a}(b^2 - a^2) \qquad (2.20)$$

where C is the total current carried by the wire. Substituting for $J(a)$ from Equation 2.19 in Equation 2.20 and solving for a we obtain

$$\frac{a}{b} = \mu - \sqrt{\mu^2 - 1} \qquad (2.21)$$

where

$$\mu = \frac{2C}{bH_c}$$

μ is the ratio of the field at the wire surface to H_c and must therefore be equal to unity or larger.

The potential drop along unit length of the normal region is

$$[C - J(a)]R_0 \frac{b^2}{b^2 - a^2}$$

where R_0 is the resistance in the normal state. If the resistance of the wire for a total current C is R, then

$$CR = R_0[C - J(a)] \frac{b^2}{(b^2 - a^2)} \qquad (2.22)$$

Substituting in Equations 2.22 from 2.20 and 2.21 we obtain

$$\frac{R}{R_0} = \tfrac{1}{2}(1 + \sqrt{1 - 1/\mu^2})$$

Hence as shown in Figure 2.12 the resistance should rise discontinuously to $\tfrac{1}{2}R_0$ as the critical current is reached and increase monotonically towards the maximum value as the current is increased further. The experimental results lie on a curve of this general shape, but the discontinuous jump in resistance for tin is seen to be closer to $0.8R_0$ than to $0.5R_0$. Scott (1948) found that the resistance ratio varies inversely with wire diameter for indium. Kuper (1952) has attributed this divergence to increased resistance introduced by the scattering of conduction electrons at the interphase boundaries.

5.5   The Superconductive Ring

Superconductive cells for digital storage use films for flux quenching that are thinner than the penetration depth. These films do not obey Silsbee's criterion; hence although these cells are strongly dependent on the induced or injected current, they are almost unaffected by the associated magnetic fields.

It is instructive to consider the opposite extreme, exemplified by the flux-trapping behavior of a bulk superconducting ring.[15] This obeys Silsbee's criterion so that its behavior is influenced by the applied field as well as the circulating current. Figure 2.13 shows the magnetic moment of such a ring as a function of applied field, in slightly idealized form. The

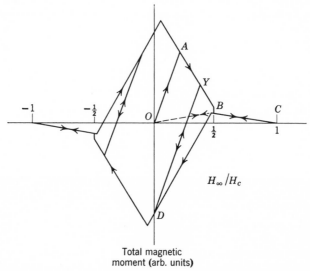

Fig. 2.13   Magnetization curve of a superconducting ring (Shoenberg, *op. cit.*, Fig. 12).

hole inside the ring is taken to have radius a, and the cross-sectional radius of the ring is taken as b. It is assumed that $a \gg b \gg \lambda$.

If a field normal to the plane of the ring is applied, current i is induced in it so as to prevent flux penetration. The ring thus appears to develop a magnetic moment, as indicated by the line OA. The field distribution is shown schematically in Figure 2.14a. It should be noted that fields of both polarities exist inside the ring, although the total flux penetration is zero.

The flux changes in the ring along the line OA are completely reversible, and the induced current is given by the expression

$$Li = \pi b^2 H_\infty \tag{2.23}$$

where H_∞ is the applied field (at infinity), and L is the inductance of the

---

[15] The treatment is based on that of Shoenberg (1960).

ring for surface currents. This can be shown to equal

$$L = 4\pi b \left(\ln \frac{8b}{a} - 2 \right)$$

If the induced currents were uniformly distributed in the ring, the inductance would be slightly greater, given by the expression

$$L' = 4\pi b \left(\ln \frac{8b}{a} - \frac{7}{4} \right)$$

It was shown in Table 2.1 that owing to flux exclusion the maximum surface field of a superconducting cylinder exposed to a uniform magnetic

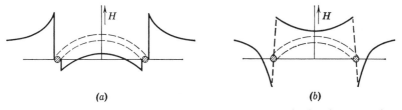

(a)   (b)

Fig. 2.14 Magnetic field distribution in and around a superconducting ring exposed to an external field. (a) No trapped flux—net flux through ring zero. (b) Field in the presence of trapped flux.

field is double the value of the field at infinity. The field H_s at the surface of the closed ring contains an additional component due to the induced current, that is,

$$H_s \sim \frac{2i}{a} + 2H_\infty$$

Substituting for i from Equation 2.23 we obtain

$$H_s \sim \frac{2\pi b^2 H_\infty}{La} + 2H_\infty \qquad (2.24)$$

In region OA of Figure 2.13 the surface field is a maximum along the outer equator of the ring as shown in Figure 2.14a. When this field equals H_c, the induced current is forced to *decrease* with increasing applied field. This corresponds to segment AY of Figure 2.13. It is found that the flux changes along AY are irreversible, since if the applied field is decreased, the ring magnetic moment follows a path such as YD having the same slope as OA.

As the applied field is increased to the vicinity of $\frac{1}{2}H_c$ the induced current falls to zero. For fields between $\frac{1}{2}H_c$ and H_c the ring is in the intermediate state and the magnetic moment follows the path BC. In this region the behavior of the ring is indistinguishable from that of a cut ring and closely approaches that of a straight cylinder.

As the applied field is again reduced below $\frac{1}{2}H_c$ current is induced in the ring, tending to maintain the flux through it at the value at which the ring became superconducting. The field is shown schematically in Figure 2.14b and is seen to be a maximum at the inner surface of the ring. The induced current along the path BD can be calculated by assuming that the field inside the ring is equal to H_c, that is,

$$H_c \sim 2H_\infty - \frac{2i}{a}$$

therefore $$i = -a(\tfrac{1}{2}H_c - H_\infty)$$

A more accurate expression that holds for a/b small compared to unity[16] is

$$i = \frac{\pm a[\tfrac{1}{2}H_c - H_\infty(1 \mp \alpha)]}{1 \pm \beta}$$

where $\alpha = a/4b$ and $\beta = 2\alpha(1 + \ln 2/\alpha)$. This expression shows that the maximum induced current always occurs for zero applied field although Figure 2.13 indicates that the maximum magnetic moment does not. As a/b becomes negligibly small, this difference becomes smaller, and the maximum induced current approaches the critical current of an infinite cylinder.

6. THERMODYNAMICS OF THE PHASE TRANSITION

6.1   Gibbs Thermodynamic Potential for a Superconductor

A number of useful relations can be obtained by applying thermodynamics to the phase transition of superconductors. The various thermodynamic quantities such as the entropy and free energy differences between the normal and superconducting phases are best derived from the Gibbs thermodynamic potential for a superconductor, which is calculated in this section.

The Gibbs thermodynamic potential for a non-magnetic gas is defined by the expression

$$G = U + PV - TS$$

In this expression P, V, and T have their usual meanings of pressure, volume, and temperature, and U is the *internal energy*, which in principle is calculated by summing the kinetic and potential energies of all the particles of a system. S is the entropy which is related to U, P, and V by

---

[16] Schubnikow and Chotkewitsch (1936).

the first law of thermodynamics

$$dU = T\,dS - P\,dV$$

Differentiating G and substituting for dU from the first law, gives

$$dG = V\,dP - S\,dT \tag{2.25}$$

In calculating G for a superconductor, it is convenient to use the diamagnetic formalism described in Section 5.1. The superconductor will therefore be treated as a diamagnetic material, whose magnetization M is always opposed to the internal magnetic field H, so that the magnetic induction B is zero. It is necessary to add a term involving the field and magnetization to the expression for dG to account for the work exchanged between an applied magnetic field and the magnetic material.

It can be shown[17] that the work done in magnetizing a material of magnetization per unit volume $\mathbf{M}$, internal field $\mathbf{H}$, and volume V is

$$dW = V\mathbf{H} \cdot d\mathbf{M}$$

This is equivalent to the term $-P\,dV$ in the first law. Hence to adapt Equation 2.25 to a magnetic system, it is sufficient to supplement the term containing P and V with similar terms containing $\mathbf{H}$ and $-\mathbf{M}V$ respectively. Thus we may define a 'magnetic Gibbs function'

$$dG = V\,dP - S\,dT - V\mathbf{M} \cdot d\mathbf{H}$$

For a superconductor

$$\mathbf{M} = -\mathbf{H}/4\pi$$

It will be assumed that the field is applied parallel to the surface of a long thin plate or cylinder so that the internal and external fields are identical. Hence

$$dG = V\,dP - S\,dT + VH\,dH/4\pi$$

Integrating this equation at constant temperature and pressure we obtain the Gibbs potential for a superconductor in a field H as

$$G_s(H) = G_s(0) + H^2/8\pi \tag{2.26}$$

where for a superconductor in zero field,

$$G_s(0) = U_s - TS_s \tag{2.27}$$

---

[17] See M. W. Zemansky *Heat and Thermodynamics*. New York: McGraw-Hill, 1957, p. 51.

6.2 Free Energy and Entropy in the Superconducting State

For the superconductor in the normal state M is negligible so that G is independent of field and may be written as

$$G_n = U_n - TS_n + PV_n$$

The thermodynamic potential is defined so that it remains constant during a change of phase carried out by an influx of heat at constant temperature and field. Hence

$$G_n = G_s(H_c)$$

Therefore, using Equation 2.26

$$G_n = G_s(0) + \frac{H_c^2}{8\pi} \tag{2.28}$$

The free energy difference between the normal and superconducting phase is

$$F_n - F_s = (U_n - U_s) - T(S_n - S_s) = \frac{H_c^2}{8\pi}$$

The term $(U_n - U_s)$ shows that (magnetic) work must be performed on a superconductor to drive it normal. The term $T(S_n - S_s)$ indicates that in general heat must be supplied also.

At absolute zero Nernst's law indicates that the entropy of a material must be independent of phase. Hence at $T = 0$, $S_n = S_s$ so that

$$U_n(0) - U_s(0) = \frac{H_c^2(0)}{8\pi}$$

where $H_c(0)$ stands for the critical field at absolute zero. According to the BCS model $U_n - U_s$ at $T = 0$ corresponds to the binding energy of the superelectrons that is calculated as being $3.52kT_c$ per electron pair. Hence at $T = 0$,

$$U_n - U_s = \frac{H_c^2(0)}{8\pi} = 3.52kT_c n$$

where n is the number of superelectron pairs per unit volume.

We may calculate the difference in entropy between the normal and superconductive state by differentiating Equation 2.25. This gives

$$\left(\frac{\partial G_n}{\partial T} \right)_P = -S_n \quad \text{and} \quad \left(\frac{\partial G_s(0)}{\partial T} \right)_P = -S_s$$

Applying these Equations to 2.28 we obtain

$$S_n - S_s = -\frac{H_c}{4\pi} \frac{dH_c}{dT} \tag{2.29}$$

Since dH_c/dT is always negative, this relation shows that the entropy of the normal state is always larger than that of the superconducting state, as it must be, since the latter is more highly "condensed" and ordered than the former.

Since $S_n - S_s$ must vanish at absolute zero, and since $H_c(0) \neq 0$, we see from Equation 2.29 that at $T = 0$, dH_c/dT must vanish. It is for this reason that experimental critical-field curves can be extrapolated to absolute zero with confidence.

6.3   Latent Heat of Transition and Specific Heat

Since $dQ = T\,dS$ for a reversible flow of heat we find from Equation 2.29 that the latent heat of transition from the superconducting to the normal state is

$$L = -\frac{TH_c}{4\pi}\frac{dH_c}{dT}$$

This expression is analogous to the Clausius-Clapeyron relation

$$L = T\,\Delta V\frac{dP}{dT}$$

that describes the dependence of the latent heat of a first-order phase transition on change of pressure with temperature and on change of volume with phase.

The latent heat of transition for a superconductor is plotted in Figure 2.15 and is seen to vanish at $T = 0$ because of Nernst's theorem and also at T_c since H_c vanishes there.

The fact that L and thus $S_n - S_s$ is zero at T_c is typical of a phase transition that involves a change of order rather than a change of state. Such transitions are known as transitions of the "second order." In contrast to first-order transitions such as melting or boiling, or that of a super-conductor in a magnetic field, it is dS/dT rather than S that exhibits a discontinuity at a second-order transition. Other ex-

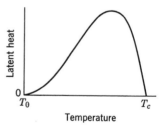

Fig. 2.15 Latent heat of transition for a superconductor versus temperature.

amples of second-order phase transitions are the superfluid transition of liquid helium and the ferromagnetic-paramagnetic transition that occurs at the Curie point.

The change in dS/dT at T_c that is characteristic of second-order transitions leads to a discontinuity in the specific heat. This can be seen by differentiating Equation 2.29, which gives

$$\frac{dS_n}{dT} - \frac{dS_s}{dT} = -\frac{1}{4\pi}\left[H_c\frac{d^2H_c}{dT^2} + \left(\frac{dH_c}{dT}\right)^2\right]$$

Hence the difference between the specific heats C_n and C_s of the normal and superconductive states respectively is

$$C_n - C_s = -\frac{T}{4\pi}\left[H_c\frac{d^2H_c}{dT^2} + \left(\frac{dH_c}{dT}\right)^2\right]$$

Although H_c vanishes at T_c, dH_c/dT does not. Hence the specific heat must exhibit a discontinuity at this temperature as illustrated by Figure 2.3.

6.4   The Magneto-Caloric Effect

The existence of the heat of transition implies that a superconductor that has been adiabatically isolated will drop in temperature when driven

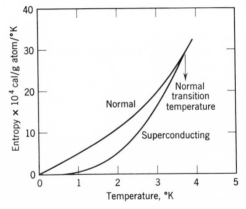

Fig. 2.16   Entropy of a tin sphere in the normal and superconducting state. (Data of Keesom and van Laer (1938), plotted by Shoenberg, *op. cit.*)

normal by a magnetic field. This drop in temperature can be estimated using curves of the type of Figure 2.16 showing the dependence of the entropy of superconducting and normal tin on temperature. If a super-conductor of low demagnetizing factor[18] at 2°K is exposed to a slowly increasing magnetic field, it will start to cool when the critical field at 2°K of approximately 210 oersteds is exceeded. The curves indicate that

---

[18] For a discussion of the magneto-caloric effect in superconductors of high demagnetizing factors see Shoenberg *op. cit.* p. 69.

in this case the superconductor can be cooled to a minimum temperature of approximately 1°K, provided that the applied magnetic field is increased above the critical field at that temperature (approximately 280 oe). An attempt to employ this phenomenon for low temperature refrigeration is discussed in section 35.4.

7. INTERPHASE BOUNDARY ENERGY EFFECTS

7.1 Introduction

Interphase boundaries can exist in superconductors in which the correlation distance ξ exceeds the penetration depth λ. They appear in the intermediate state between normal regions in which the magnetic field strength is H_c, and superconducting regions from which the field is excluded. The variation in field intensity and in the energy gap or density of the superelectrons along a line drawn through a boundary is shown

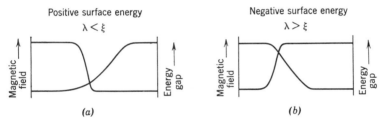

Positive surface energy   Negative surface energy
        $\lambda < \xi$ $\lambda > \xi$

(a)   *(b)*

Fig. 2.17 (*a*) Interphase boundary with positive surface energy. (*b*) Impossible boundary with negative surface energy.

schematically in Figure 2.17a. It is assumed that the magnetic field varies at a rate depending on λ, whereas the energy gap of the super-electrons varies at a rate depending on ξ. It will be shown that the free energy per unit volume of this boundary is higher than that of the region on either side.

The normal region has Helmholtz free energy F_n per unit volume. The superconducting region has the lower free energy F_s, but since it excludes the magnetic field H_c it contributes an amount $H_c^2/8\pi$ magneto-static energy per unit volume to the total system energy. However from Equation 2.28

$$F_n = F_s + \frac{H_c^2}{8\pi}$$

Hence, in the superconducting region, the binding energy due to the superelectrons cancels out the magnetostatic energy due to the excluded magnetic field. This cancellation does not however occur inside the boundary, since along any line drawn through it from the normal to the superconducting region, the magnetostatic energy rises more rapidly than the energy of the superelectrons decreases. The free energy per unit volume of the interphase boundary is therefore higher than that of the regions on either side. The boundary may be considered to possess a positive surface energy α per unit area. Very approximately

$$\alpha = (\xi - \lambda) \frac{H_c^2}{8\pi}$$

The finite interphase boundary energy gives rise to the existence of discrete superconducting and normal domains (see Sec. 7.2), and to various magnetic hysteresis and supercooling effects (see Sec. 7.3).

It has been found that the correlation distance ξ_0 of a pure super-conductor is reduced in the presence of impurities that shorten the electronic mean free path in the normal metal. It is therefore possible to prepare superconducting alloys for which $\lambda > \xi$. A hypothetical boundary for this case is shown in Figure 2.17b. It can be shown that such a boundary would have a free energy *less* than that of either the normal or superconducting phase. For this reason materials with $\lambda > \xi$ are said to possess "negative interphase boundary energy." They are also known as "class II superconductors." Their properties are quite distinct from positive boundary energy superconductors and are described in Section 7.4.

The interphase boundary energy is most conveniently expressed by the equation

$$\alpha = \frac{1}{8\pi} H_c^2 \Delta \tag{2.30}$$

Δ has the dimension of length and is of the same order of magnitude as the boundary thickness. It is found to have the same temperature dependence as the penetration depth (see Eq. 2.4), so that it may be written

$$\Delta(T) = \Delta(0)\left[1 - \left(\frac{T}{T_c}\right)^4\right]^{-\frac{1}{2}}$$

Values of $\Delta(0)$ for pure superconductors assembled from the best available experimental data by Lynton (1962) are shown in Table 2.3.

Theoretical expressions for the boundary energy can be obtained from the Ginzburg-Landau phenomenological theory[19] which is valid at temperatures near T_c. Δ is found to be given by the expression

$$\Delta = \lambda f(\kappa) \tag{2.31}$$

---

[19] This theory is described in Sec. 10.7.

κ is a non-dimensional parameter defined by the equation

$$\kappa = \frac{2\sqrt{2}e}{hc} H_c \lambda^2$$

By substituting for H_c and λ from Equations 1.1 and 2.4 it is found that

$$\kappa = \frac{2\sqrt{2}e}{hc} H(0)\lambda^2(0)\left[1 + \left(\frac{T}{T_c}\right)^2\right]^{-1}$$

This shows that κ is only weakly dependent on temperature since the factor $[1 + (T/T_c)^2]$ only varies by a factor of 2 in the temperature range zero to T_c.

TABLE 2.3

Element	$10^5\Delta(0)$ cm	$10^5\xi_0$ cm	$10^5\lambda(0)$ cm	κ Theory $(0.96\lambda(0)/\xi_0$	Experiment
Aluminum	18	16	0.50	0.03	0.026
Indium	3.4	4.4	0.64	0.14	0.112
Tin	2.3	2.3	0.51	0.21	0.164

For values of κ which are not small, $f(\kappa)$ must be evaluated numerically. The function decreases monotonically with increasing κ and becomes negative for $\kappa > 1/\sqrt{2}$. Negative values of $f(\kappa)$ correspond to the case of class II superconductors.

7.2 Superconducting Domains

Discrete domains occur in the intermediate state of a superconductor with positive surface energy because such a structure has minimum free energy. This can be established by the following argument.

When a superconductor enters the intermediate state, the average internal flux density rises to H_c. The magnetostatic contribution to the free energy is approximately equal to $\frac{1}{8\pi}\int H^2\, dv$ taken over the whole system containing the superconductor. This will be minimized if H is allowed to penetrate the superconductor completely uniformly. However, in a superconductor with positive interphase boundary energy, such a configuration would have higher energy than one of alternating superconducting and normal domains. For a given body, the magnetostatic energy is minimized if the domains are very narrow so that the internal field can become as uniform as possible. On the other hand the total surface energy contribution of the interphase boundary is minimized if the

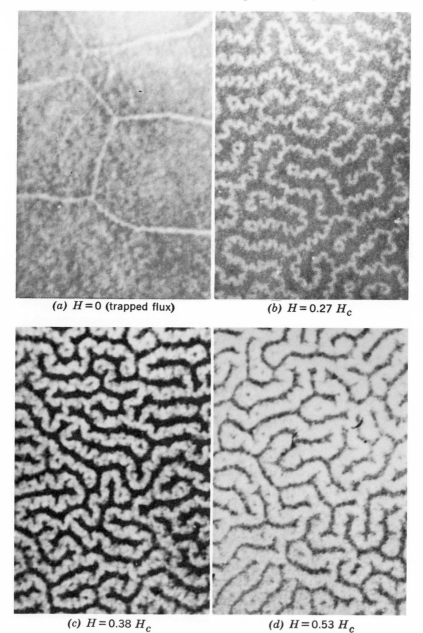

(a) $H = 0$ (trapped flux)   (b) $H = 0.27 \, H_c$

(c) $H = 0.38 \, H_c$ (d) $H = 0.53 \, H_c$

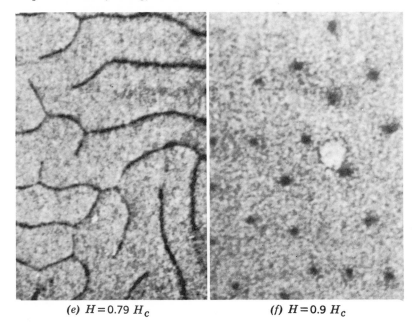

(e) $H = 0.79 \, H_c$ *(f)* $H = 0.9 \, H_c$

0   1   2   3

(g)   cm

Fig. 2.18 Superconducting domain powder patterns. *(a)–(f)* Tin powder on an aluminum plate in an increasing transverse field, approximately 4× enlarged (Faber, 1958). *(g)* Niobium powder revealing flux trapped in a lead sphere (Baloshova and Sharvin, 1957).

domains are wide, thus minimizing the total boundary area. The domain arrangements found in nature must be such as to compromise between these factors.

Landau (1937, 1943) has calculated that in the case of an infinite plate of thickness L, perpendicular to an applied field, the domain structure will consist of alternating laminae of superconducting and normal phases the sum of whose widths is

$$D \sim 10 \sqrt{\frac{L\Delta}{\psi}} \tag{2.32}$$

ψ is a function of H/H_c of order unity, which has been calculated numerically by Lifshitz and Sharvin (1951). Domain structures have also been computed by Kuper (1951) who predicted domain sizes that are several times smaller than in Equation 2.32. Typical experimental results fall between the two estimates.

As H is increased towards H_c the width of the normal laminae will increase at the expense of the superconducting ones. Since ψ in Equation 2.32 varies only weakly with H/H_c, D will remain approximately constant.

The pattern of superconducting domains intersecting a specimen surface can be determined by studying the fine detail of the surface magnetic field. Such observations have been made using tiny magnetoresistive bismuth probes,[20] and by scattering ferromagnetic[21] or superconducting powders such as niobium[22] and tin[23] on the surface to be studied. It is found that ferromagnetic and superconducting powders congregate in regions of high and low surface field respectively. Powders tend to stick to the specimen, so that their use need not be confined to a flat surface. Some outstanding powder-patterns are shown in Figure 2.18.

The probe and powder methods are best suited to the study of static patterns. A method that has been used for studying domains in motion was introduced by Alers (1957) and improved by De Sorbo (1960). This method uses the strong Faraday rotation[24] exhibited at low temperatures by transparent materials containing cerium. In the method as used by De Sorbo, which is shown in Figure 2.19, plane polarized light is reflected from the silvered rear surface of a cerium glass mirror which is laid on top of the superconductor to be examined. Magnetic fringe fields from any

---

[20] Meshkovsky and Shalnikov (1947).

[21] Baloshova and Sharvin (1956).

[22] Schawlow, Matthias, Lewis, and Devlin (1954).

[23] Faber (1958).

[24] Faraday rotation in a material is the property of rotating the plane of polarization of electromagnetic radiation (in this case light) when a steady magnetic field is applied in the direction of propagation. The sense of the rotation is dependent on the magnetic field direction but not on the direction of the light propagation.

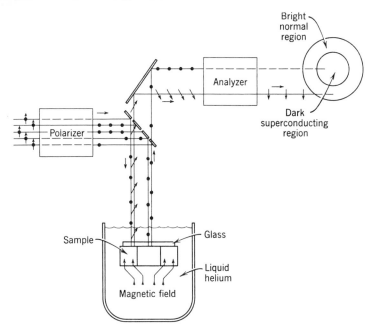

Fig. 2.19   Arrangement for viewing magnetic fields at low temperatures (DeSorbo and Healy, 1961).

domains present rotate the plane of polarization of the reflected light. This rotation is converted into intensity variations by passing the reflected light through an analyzer.

7.3   Macroscopic Domain Effects

This subsection reviews a number of macroscopic effects exhibited by materials with positive interphase boundary energy. For a fuller discussion the reader is referred to Serin, *op. cit.*

MAGNETIC HYSTERESIS.   The magnetization curves for ellipsoids shown in Figure 2.9 hold for specimens large compared to the scale of the domain structure in the intermediate state. For specimen sizes comparable to the domain spacing, the interphase boundary energy predominates over the magnetostatic energy and the superelectron binding energy. Under these circumstances the appearance of the intermediate state tends to be "retarded," because of the extra energy required for the formation of the interphase boundary.

In a wire of diameter L^* a delayed phase transition should become noticeable when

$$L^* \sim D$$

where D is the domain spacing. Substituting for D from Equation 2.32, setting $L^* = L$ and simplifying, gives

$$L \sim 100 \, \Delta$$
$$\sim 10^{-2} \, \text{cm}$$

in the case of tin.

In agreement with this estimate, Andrew (1948a) finds that the transverse field at which a tin wire enters the intermediate state varies from $0.54H_c$ for a 0.105 cm diameter wire to $0.67H_c$ for a 0.0027 cm diameter wire and is independent of temperature. (For an ideal bulk cylinder this field equals $\frac{1}{2}H_c$.) For extremely narrow wires (1.2 × 10^{-4} cm diameter), Lutes and Maxwell (1955) found that the intermediate state does not occur at all and that the wire goes straight from the superconducting to the normal state. At 1.69°K this transition occurred at $H = 0.67H_c$.

SUPERCOOLING. A hysteresis effect that involves abrupt movement of interphase boundaries can be produced in a large superconductor if it is very carefully annealed. It is found that the temperature of such a specimen can be lowered far below T_c before a normal-to-superconducting transition occurs. When the transition does take place, it always starts at certain regions of the specimen, and the superconducting phase then propagates through the remainder in a fraction of a second. The effect is analogous to the supercooling effect in very pure water where the formation of ice crystals is retarded until possible nuclei of crystallization become available. A similarly retarded normal-to-superconducting transition followed by the propagation of the superconducting phase from a "weak spot" can be achieved by holding the specimen normal using an applied field which is then slowly lowered below the critical value. Faber (1952) found that when the applied field was below H_c, the superconducting phase could be initiated from any desired point on his specimen, which was in the form of a rod, by lowering the field at that point with a small auxiliary coil. The propagation of the superconducting phase along the rod leads to flux expulsion, and could be detected by means of small search coils placed around the rod. The superconducting phase initially propagates along the surface of the rod in the form of a thin filament which then expands through the remainder of the rod. Faber (1954, 1955) has calculated the filament velocity as

$$v = A \, \frac{l}{\sigma} \, \Delta^{-2} \left[\frac{H_c - H}{H_c} \right]^3$$

where A is a constant of the specimen, H is the applied field, and H_c is the thermodynamic critical field, defined as the field at which the free energies of the normal and superconducting phases are equal. From measurements of v as a function of temperature, Faber has deduced the temperature dependence of Δ for tin and aluminum.

The nuclei from which the superconducting phase starts to propagate may consist of regions of class-II superconductor having a higher critical field than the remainder of the material. Such regions might be caused by reduction of the electron mean free path due to strain or impurities.

It is instructive to determine the conditions under which a superconducting nucleus embedded in a normal phase region can grow. If the nucleus has volume V and surface area A, growth will only occur in a field H if the attendant increase in surface energy and magnetostatic energy is more than counteracted by the decrease in the Gibbs free energy; that is, if

$$\alpha \, \delta A + \frac{H^2 \, \delta V}{8\pi} < (G_n - G_s) \, \delta V \qquad (2.33)$$

Now $G_n - G_s = \dfrac{1}{8\pi} H_c^2$ and for a spherical nucleus of radius r,

$$\frac{dA}{dV} = \frac{2}{r}$$

By substituting these expressions into Equation 2.33, and substituting for α from Equation 2.30, we find that the critical radius for growth is given by,

$$\frac{\Delta}{r} \leqslant \frac{1}{2}\left[1 - \left(\frac{H}{H_c}\right)^2\right] + n$$

n is a small constant determined by the demagnetizing factor of the nucleus.

Near T_c Δ becomes so large that the flaws in carefully prepared specimens are no longer big enough to initiate phase propagation. Under these 'ideal' conditions the Ginzburg-Landau theory predicts that the lowest supercooling field to which the normal phase can persist in a metastable fashion is

$$H_1 = \sqrt{2}\kappa H_c \qquad (2.34)$$

Values of κ measured by Faber in supercooling experiments are shown in Table 2.3, and compare well with the theoretical estimates.

A condition related to supercooling is "superheating," in which the temperature of magnetic field applied to a superconducting body is raised above the critical value without inducing a superconducting-to-normal transition. Garfunkel and Serin (1952) showed that pronounced superheating of a rod using a field can be achieved by using an arrangement of coils that ensures that the supercritical field is applied to the middle of the rod only. This proves that even when the rods used in their experiments are in the superconducting state, normal regions must persist at their ends. These regions can serve as nuclei for normal phase and thus prevent significant superheating unless they are isolated. This result suggests that pronounced superheating might be obtained with carefully annealed toroidal specimens.

THE PARAMAGNETIC EFFECT. It was found by Steiner and Schoeneck (1943) that when current passed through a superconducting cylinder in a weak longitudinal field exceeds a critical value, the longitudinal flux in the rod instead of being smaller than the flux in the normal state, becomes larger; that is, the rod acts as a "paramagnetic" rather than a diamagnetic material. It appears that the effect is due to spiral current flow on the surface of the rod, which is caused by the presence of domains. It has been studied in a series of papers by Meissner and collaborators[25] and is mentioned here because of its similarity to the so-called Wiedeman effect that forms the basis of the magnetic storage element called the "twistor."[26]

7.4 Class II Superconductors

For these materials the interphase boundary energy is negative. They can be prepared by reducing the electron mean free path of a class I superconductor by alloying, or by other means, such as preparation in the form of a thin film. In the case of tin, for instance, Δ is reduced to zero by a concentration of approximately 2.5 atomic per cent of indium.[27] Niobium appears to be a class II superconductor even in the pure state.

In terms of the Ginzburg-Landau theory, negative boundary energy occurs when $\kappa > 1/\sqrt{2}$ so that $f(\kappa) < 0$, (see Eq. 2.31). The effect on κ of reducing the mean free path has been calculated by Gorkov (1959) who finds that for a pure superconductor,

$$\kappa_0 \sim 0.96 \frac{\lambda(0)}{\xi_0}$$

and that for a strongly alloyed material[28]

$$\kappa = \kappa_0 + 7.5 \times 10^3 \frac{\gamma^{\frac{1}{2}}}{\sigma}$$

In this expression, which is in good agreement with experiment, γ is the temperature coefficient of the electronic specific heat in ergs cm^{-3} deg^{-2}, and σ is the conductivity in ohm^{-1} cm^{-1}.

---

[25] See for instance, Meissner (1958).

[26] Bobeck (1957).

[27] See Davies (1960).

[28] This expression has been derived by Goodman (1962) from an earlier result by Gorkov (1959).

The magnetic properties of negative boundary energy materials differ significantly from those of class I superconductors and have been analyzed by Abrikosov (1952, 1957) on the basis of the Ginzburg-Landau theory. Magnetization curves for various values of κ calculated by Goodman (1962) from the Abrikosov theory are shown in Figure 2.20. Flux is excluded at low fields but penetrates at a field considerably below H_c, as evidenced by the sudden drop in magnetization below the solid line

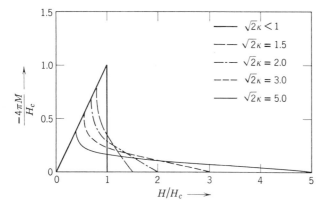

Fig. 2.20 Magnetization curves of ideal class II superconductors (After Goodman, 1962).

corresponding to an ideal diamagnetic. Superconductivity persists to a quenching field H_1, considerably larger than the thermodynamic critical field H_c. The relation between H_1 and H_c is given by Equation 2.34, which also gives the supercooling field for class I superconductors for which $\kappa < 1/\sqrt{2}$.

Abrikosov predicts that the flux penetrating the superconductor does so in filaments parallel to the external field, and arranged in a regular rectangular or triangular pattern. These filaments are believed to consist of individual quanta of flux.[29] The theory predicts no hysteresis in the magnetization curve.

Class II superconductors which correspond to the Abrikosov theory have been prepared by Shubnikow et al. (1936) and Livingston (1963) in the form of lead alloys, by Calverley and Rose-Innes (1960) in the form of mixed crystals of tantalum-niobium, and by Swartz (1962) who studied intermetallics of β-tungsten structure. It is found that the ideal class-II behavior tends to be obscured by hysteresis effects ascribed to the presence of inhomogeneities in the lattice. These effects can be minimized by

---

[29] Flux quantization is discussed in Sec. 10.5.

TABLE 2.4

The Periodic Table. T_c is given for each superconductive element (shown in outline).

H																	He
Li	Be 6-8.4											B	C	N	O	F	Ne
Na	Mg											Al 1.20	Si	P	S	Cl	A
K	Ca	Sc	Ti 0.39	V 5.30	Cr	Mn	Fe	Co	Ni	Cu	Zn 0.88	Ga 1.09	Ge 8.4	As	Se	Br	Kr
Rb	Sr	Y	Zr 0.55	Nb 9.13	Mo 0.92	Tc 8.22	Ru 0.49	Rh	Pd	Ag	Cd 0.56	In 3.40	Sn 3.72	Sb	Te	I	Xe
Cs	Ba	La (α) 5.0 (β) 6.3	→Hf	Ta 4.48	W	Re 1.70	Os 0.66	Ir 0.14	Pt	Au	Hg (α) 4.15 (β) 3.95	Tl 2.39	Pb 7.19	Bi ~6	Po	At	Rn
Fr	Ra	Ac															

← ———— Transition Elements ————— →

Rare Earths	Ce	Pr	Nd	Pm	Sm	Eu	Gd	Tb	Dy	Ho	Er	Tm	Yb	Lu
Actinides	Th 1.37	Pa	U (α) 0.68 (γ) 1.8	Np	Pu	Am	Cm	Bk	Cf	E	Fm	Mv	102	Lw

exceedingly careful preparation and annealing. These types of super-conductor are of importance in connection with superconducting magnets and are described and analyzed in Chapter 5.

8. SUPERCONDUCTIVE ELEMENTS AND ALLOYS

The number of elements known to be superconductors is still increasing, as lower temperatures and improved purification methods become experimentally available. For example, it has recently been shown[30] that molybdenum and iridium exhibit superconductivity provided that ferro-magnetic impurities are reduced to a few parts per million. The distribu-tion of superconductivity in the periodic system is described in Section 8.1, which also includes an account of some empirically determined rules, relating the occurrence of superconductivity to valency and atomic volume.

The list of superconductive alloys and compounds is large and growing. Recent surveys have been complied by Roberts (1963) and by Matthias et al. (1963). The study of superconductive alloys and compounds is motivated by the aim of discovering materials with properties that will improve device performance, and by the hope of increasing the under-standing of fundamental mechanisms. Alloy studies that have contributed to these objectives are discussed in Sections 8.2 and 8.3.

The technologically most important superconductive alloys and com-pounds are the filamentary superconductors used for high field electro-magnets. Because of their specialized field of application, the description of these materials is deferred to Section 20 in the chapter on supercon-ducting electromagnets.

8.1 The Distribution of Superconductivity in the Periodic System

The occurrence of superconductors in the periodic system is shown in Table 2.4, which is compiled from data collected by Roberts (1963). It should be noted that Sn and Bi can exist in non-metallic, non-supercon-ducting forms, and that the metallic superconducting form of Bi is only stable at high pressure. Furthermore Be, Bi, and Ga can exist in a super-conducting form when vacuum deposited at temperatures below $10°K$. Raising the temperature results in an irreversible change to the non-superconducting phase.

Matthias has emphasized a number of empirical regularities in the appearance of superconductivity in the periodic system. These regularities hold for compounds and alloys, as well as elements, and appear to be a

---

[30] See Roberts (1963) for references,

property of only the average number Z of valence electrons, and the electron density in the solid. Some of the most important regularities are:

1. Superconductivity is observed only in metals.

2. Superconductivity is found only in elements for which $2 \leqslant Z \leqslant 8$. Essentially the same rule applies for compounds, though here superconductors with Z slightly less than 2 or slightly greater than 8 can occur.

3. No ferromagnetic or antiferromagnetic elements are superconductors.

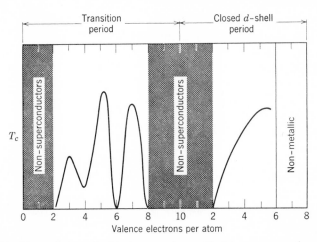

Fig. 2.21 The variation of critical temperature with the average number of valence electrons (Matthias, 1957).

4. For a given Z where $2 > Z > 8$, the transition temperature T_c increases as a high power of the interelectron spacing.

5. For the non-transition element superconductors T_c increases with Z, as shown in Figure 2.21. For the transition element superconductors the dependence of T_c on Z is seen to be periodic.

8.2 Non-Magnetic Alloys

Serin and collaborators have investigated the effect of various solutes on the superconducting properties of tin, indium, and aluminum. It was established that small concentrations decreased the critical temperature linearly with decreasing electronic mean free path, l. Typical results are shown in Figure 2.22. The initial decrease of T_c with impurity to concentration is believed to be due to the smoothing out of slight anisotropies of the energy gap which exist in the pure superconductors, by impurity scattering.[31] This effect should give a decrease of approximately 1 per cent

[31] Anderson (1959).

in T_c and should be complete when $l \sim \xi_0$. The data of Figure 2.22 are seen to be in agreement with this estimate.

For larger concentrations of solute, the curves of critical temperature versus concentration fall into two groups. For solutes that have a higher negative valency than the solvent, T_c starts to increase. For solutes that tend to reduce the average number of valence electrons, T_c continues to decrease with increasing concentration. These results are in agreement

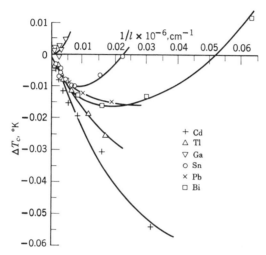

Fig. 2.22 Effect of non-magnetic impurities on the transition temperature of indium (Chanin et al., 1959).

with the Matthias rule for the dependence of critical temperature on valency for non-transition element superconductors.

An interesting consequence of the type of behavior illustrated in Figure 2.22 for electronegative solutes has been pointed out by Reeber (1960). He finds, for In-Hg alloys, that the width of the temperature-induced transition for the composition corresponding to minimum T_c is actually less than that for pure indium. This happens because the width of the temperature transition is at least partly due to inhomogeneities in specimen composition. At a composition corresponding to an extremum in T_c, the effect of composition variations on T_c will be a minimum and the effect of such inhomogeneities will therefore be a minimum also.

8.3 Alloys of Transition Elements and the Rare Earths

Matthias and his collaborators have been able to show that the periodic dependence of T_c on electron density illustrated for the transition elements in Figure 2.21 is also shared by certain of their alloys. For instance, the critical temperatures of any of the elements of column IV, which are at a critical temperature minimum according to Figure 2.21, can be increased by alloying with a non-magnetic element from column VIII, thus increasing the electron concentration. For example the critical temperature of the column IV element, titanium, can be increased an order of magnitude by the addition of the column VIII element, ruthenium. These and other results indicate that T_c in the long transition period is a maximum near three, five, and seven valence electrons per atom, a minimum at four and six valence electrons, and that it vanishes below two and above eight

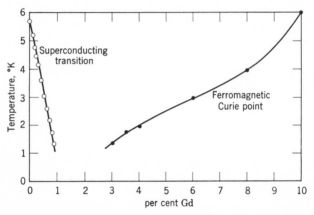

Fig. 2.23   Superconducting and ferromagnetic transition temperatures for solid solutions of gadolinium in lanthanum (Matthias et al., 1959b).

valence electrons. It is found that the addition of iron to titanium increases T_c even more strongly than the addition of ruthenium. Since iron is just above ruthenium in the periodic table, and therefore has the same number of electrons in its outer shell, its extra effect on T_c is presumably due to the magnetic moment of its d shell electrons. For molybdenum and iridium, however, iron has an extremely strong depressant effect on T_c.

Matthias and collaborators have found that the addition to lanthanum of small amounts of the rare earth elements whose magnetic moment is due to an unfilled f shell, lowers T_c. This is illustrated in Figure 2.23 which shows the effect of adding the rare earth gadolinium to lanthanum. Lanthanum occurs just before the rare earths in the periodic table and therefore has the same number of electrons in its outer shell. Hence, the addition of gadolinium to lanthanum should not change Z appreciably, so that the observed change in T_c must be due mostly to the magnetic moment of the gadolinium. In fact, it is found that the depressant effect of the rare earths on T_c is a function of $J(J + 1)$ where J is the atomic spin.

Figure 2.23 shows that lanthanum becomes ferromagnetic for large concentrations of gadolinium. This type of ferromagnetism is called "dilute ferromagnetism." Whereas in ordinary ferromagnetism as exhibited in iron and nickel, the magnetic moments are oriented parallel to each other by a direct nearest neighbors interaction, in dilute ferromagnetism the coupling between the spins is attributed to the effect of the conduction electrons. It is believed that for a concentration of approximately 1 per cent of gadolinium, lanthanum is actually both ferromagnetic and superconductive at temperatures below 0.5°K. The simultaneous occurrence of ferromagnetism and superconductivity at higher temperatures has been demonstrated in several other alloy systems, including $Y_{1-x}Gd_xOs_z$. In such materials remanent magnetization characteristic of ferromagnetism, and diamagnetic screening currents characteristic of superconductors, are observed simultaneously. Whether the two effects actually coexist in the same region, or whether the specimens consist of alternate superconducting and ferromagnetic domains has not been established.

A fuller account of alloying experiments designed to bring out interactions between superconductivity and ferromagnetism is given in a review by Matthias (1962). Discussions of the theoretical implications of the various alloy phenomena are given by Bardeen and Schrieffer (1961) and Lynton (1962).

References

The following books and review articles contain fuller treatments of some of the topics covered in this chapter.

J. Bardeen and J. R. Schrieffer, "Recent Developments in Superconductivity," *Progress in Low Temperature Physics*, Vol. III, ed. C. J. Gorter. Amsterdam: North Holland, 1961.

F. London, *Superfluids*, Vol. 1, 2nd rev. ed. New York: Dover, 1961.

E. A. Lynton, *Superconductivity*, 1962. London: Methuen, New York: Wiley.

B. Matthias, "Superconductivity in the Periodic System," *Progress in Low Temperature Physics*, Vol. II, ed. C. J. Gorter. Amsterdam, North Holland, 1958.

B. Matthias, "Superconductivity and Ferromagnetism," *IBM J. Res. Develop.* **6**, 250 (1962).

R. W. Morse, "Ultrasonic Attenuation in Metals at Low Temperature," *Progress in Cryogenics*, Vol. I, ed. K. Mendelssohn. New York: Academic Press, 1959.

B. Serin, "Superconductivity," *Encyclopedia of Physics*, Vol. XV. Berlin: Springer, 1956.

D. Shoenberg, *Superconductivity*, 1952, 1960, Cambridge University Press, New York.

chapter 3

Theoretical Aspects

This chapter describes the theories of superconductivity, and their application to some important problems.

We begin (Sec. 9) with a description of the classical theory of resistivity, which serves to introduce the concept of the electron mean free path. This concept is used in Section 10, which describes the phenomenological theories of London, Ginzburg-Landau, and Pippard, and applies them to some important examples. Section 11 starts with a review of the free electron version of the theory of metals, followed by a description of the Bardeen-Cooper-Schrieffer model of superconductivity and some of its applications. The treatment does not presuppose a knowledge of advanced quantum mechanics on the part of the reader.

Section 12, which concludes the chapter, shows how the results of classical potential theory can be used to calculate the field distribution around current-carrying superconductors. This topic is important in connection with the design of superconductive devices.

9. CLASSICAL THEORY OF RESISTIVITY

9.1 The Electron Mean Free Path

Although a full treatment of metallic resistivity requires the concepts and terminology of quantum mechanics, it is found that the dependence of metallic resistivity on impurities, temperature, and specimen dimensions can be explained on the basis of a simple semiclassical model due to Drude.[1] According to this picture, a fraction of the electrons in a metal, which is approximately equal to the number of ions, form an electron "cloud" not tied to any individual ion. These electrons, which possess a

---

[1] See Mott and Jones *The Theory of the Properties of Metals and Alloys*. New York: Dover, 1958, p. 240.

random motion v_f due to thermal excitation from the lattice, are responsible for metallic conduction. Ohmic resistance is due to electron scattering by thermal oscillation of the lattice ions and by impurities and strains that constitute lattice irregularities.

To calculate the resistivity, the conduction electrons may be assumed to possess an effective mass m and an effective charge e. Both of these may differ from their values in vacuum. Under the influence of an applied electric field E, the electrons drift in the field direction with an acceleration $\dot{v}$.

$$Ee = m\dot{v}$$

On the average, just after each scattering process the velocity in the direction of E is zero. If the interval between scatterings is τ, the drift velocity just before scattering will be

$$v_d = \dot{v}\tau$$
$$= \frac{Ee}{m}\tau$$

Hence the average drift velocity in the direction of the applied field is

$$\bar{v}_d = \frac{1}{2}\frac{Ee}{m}\tau \tag{3.1}$$

At all temperatures it is found that $\bar{v}_d \ll v_f$. Hence τ is almost independent of E.

The current density is equal to the charge carried by the number of electrons that pass through unit area in unit time in the field direction. This number is equal to the number contained in a cylinder of unit cross-sectional area and height $\bar{v}_d$. If n is the density of conduction electrons, the current density $J = \bar{v}_d en$. Substituting for $\bar{v}_d$ from Equation 3.1,

$$J = \frac{\frac{1}{2}nEe^2}{m}\tau$$

Using the customary definition of resistivity $\rho = E/J$ we find

$$\rho = \frac{m}{\frac{1}{2}ne^2\tau} \tag{3.2}$$

From the mean interval τ between electron collisions that lead to scattering, and the electron velocity v_f, it is possible to define the mean distance l traveled between scattering collisions. This is known as the (electron) *mean free path* (m.f.p.).

$$l = v_f\tau$$

Using this expression to substitute for τ in Equation 3.2 we find the resistivity given by

$$\rho = \frac{mv_f}{\frac{1}{2}ne^2} \frac{1}{l} \tag{3.3}$$

This equation has been found very useful for interpreting the dependence of ρ on impurities and temperature in normal metals because it is found that none of the terms in it except l are sensitive to changes in temperature, to the addition of a small amount of impurities, or to a variation in specimen dimensions. The dependence of ρ on all these factors can therefore be explained in terms of their effect on the m.f.p.

9.2   Mathiessen's Rule

This rule states that the contributions to the metallic resistivity due to different scattering mechanisms add approximately linearly. It is used to derive the effect of specimen dimensions on resistivity in Section 14 and is the basis of a simple method of estimating film thickness described in the same section.

The rule can be derived by writing Equation 3.2 in terms of the mean frequency f between scattering collisions, that is,

$$f = 1/\tau \tag{3.4}$$

If we assume that the scattering frequency due to one mechanism such as thermal oscillations of lattice ions is f_1, whereas that due to another mechanism such as lattice irregularities is f_2, then the total scattering frequency f will be given by

$$f = f_1 + f_2$$

Hence from Equations. 3.3 and 3.4

$$\rho = \frac{m}{\frac{1}{2}ne^2} f$$

$$= \frac{m}{\frac{1}{2}ne^2} f_1 + \frac{m}{\frac{1}{2}ne^2} f_2$$

This can be written as

$$\rho = \rho_1(T) + \rho_r \tag{3.5}$$

where $\rho_1(T) = [(m/\frac{1}{2}ne^2)f_1]$ is the contribution to the resistivity due to thermal lattice oscillations and $\rho_r = (m/\frac{1}{2}ne^2)f_2$ is the contribution due to lattice irregularities. $\rho_1(T)$ varies with temperature and vanishes at absolute zero, whereas ρ_r is independent of temperature. Since the resistivity at absolute zero is equal to ρ_r, this is called the "residual resistivity." Its magnitude is a measure of the strains and impurities present in the conductor. For very pure, single crystals the residual resistivity can be as little as $10^{-3}\%$ of the room temperature value.

Equation 3.5 is Mathiessen's rule and is obeyed very closely by real metals. For ferromagnets there is an additional contribution to the resistivity due to the magnetization, which becomes appreciable at low temperatures.

An important consequence of Mathiessen's rule is obtained by differentiating Equation 3.5. This gives

$$\frac{d\rho}{dT} = \frac{d\rho_1(T)}{dT}$$

showing that the rate of change of resistivity with temperature of a metal is independent of impurities and strains.

10. PHENOMENOLOGICAL THEORIES OF SUPERCONDUCTIVITY

10.1 Historical Introduction

As mentioned in Chapter 2, the brothers London were able to show that the electromagnetic properties of superconductors, in particular the Meissner effect, could be accounted for by Maxwell's equations with the addition of the equation $\Lambda(T) \text{ curl } \mathbf{J}_s = -\mathbf{H}$ where $\mathbf{J}_s$ represents the current carried by superconducting electrons of the two fluid model. In Sections 10.2 to 10.6, we review some of the reasons that suggest this equation, and apply it to a number of important problems. Although the London equations are now known to be exact only if $H \ll H_c$ and $T \sim T_c$, they provide a simple description of the low frequency electromagnetic behavior of superconductors that is accurate to the first approximation.

Since the London theory is only exact at low fields it is neither able to account for the existence of interphase boundaries nor can it be used to analyze field induced phase transitions. To deal with problems of this type Ginzburg and Landau (1950) have developed an extension of the theory, which is valid at $H \sim H_c$ but reduces to the London form in the low field limit. The Ginsburg-Landau theory is described in Section 10.7.

From experiments on the variation of the penetration depth with field, and for other reasons that are reviewed in Section 10.8, A. B. Pippard deduced the existence of a long range coherence effect between superelectrons. This makes it necessary to replace the London relation with a so-called non-local equation which relates the supercurrent density $\mathbf{J}_s$ at a point in space to the *average* value of the vector potential taken over the region around it. This region has dimensions of the order of magnitude of the electron *correlation* or *coherence* distance ξ. Pippard showed experimentally that ξ is reduced by impurities that shorten the electron mean free path in the normal metal. In the limit of $\xi \ll \lambda$ which occurs in pure superconductors just below T_c, in superconducting alloys, and in thin films, the Pippard non-local relation reduces to a "local" form.

The advent of the microscopic BCS theory has confirmed the validity of the concepts introduced by Pippard, but has also made it possible to show that the Ginzburg-Landau and London theories apply under those conditions where the Pippard relation reduces to a local form. These conditions are discussed in Section 10.9, in which the penetration depth and its dependence on the electron mean free path are calculated from the non-local theory.

10.2   The London Theory

Before the discovery of the Meissner effect, Becker, Heller, and Sauter (1933) analyzed the electrodynamic properties of a zero-resistance material. They pointed out that under the influence of an electric field E the conduction electrons of mass m and charge e would be accelerated indefinitely according to the equation

$$m\dot{v} = Ee \tag{3.6}$$

with a resultant current

$$\mathbf{J} = nve \tag{3.7}$$

Here n is the density of the conduction electrons (approximately one per lattice ion). Differentiating Equation 3.7 and eliminating $\dot{v}$ using Equation 3.6, we obtain

$$\mathbf{E} = \frac{m}{ne^2}\,\dot{\mathbf{J}} \tag{3.8}$$

Forming curl $\mathbf{E}$ and using Maxwell's equation for a region where $\mu = 1$

$$\mathrm{curl}\,\mathbf{E} = -\frac{1}{c}\,\dot{\mathbf{H}}$$

we obtain

$$\frac{mc}{ne^2}\,\mathrm{curl}\,\dot{\mathbf{J}} + \dot{\mathbf{H}} = 0 \tag{3.9}$$

To eliminate $\mathbf{J}$ we take Maxwell's other equation

$$\mathrm{curl}\,\mathbf{H} = 4\pi\mathbf{J}/c$$

and form curl curl $\mathbf{H}$. Making use of the vector identity

$$\mathrm{curl}\,\mathrm{curl}\,\mathbf{H} = \mathrm{grad}\,\mathrm{div}\,\mathbf{H} - \mathrm{div}\,\mathrm{grad}\,\mathbf{H}$$

gives

$$\nabla^2\mathbf{H} = -\frac{4\pi}{c}\,\mathrm{curl}\,\mathbf{J} \tag{3.10}$$

since grad div **H** is identically zero. Differentiating both sides with respect to time and substituting for curl $\dot{\mathbf{J}}$ from Equation 3.9 gives

$$\lambda^2 \nabla^2 \dot{\mathbf{H}} = \dot{\mathbf{H}}$$

where

$$\lambda^2 \equiv \frac{mc^2}{4\pi ne^2} \tag{3.11}$$

Integrating with respect to time we obtain

$$\lambda^2 \nabla^2 (\mathbf{H} - \mathbf{H}_0) = (\mathbf{H} - \mathbf{H}_0) \tag{3.12}$$

where H_0 is a constant. By solving Equation 3.12 for a semi-infinite body whose surface is at $x = 0$ it can be shown that the internal field H_i at a distance x from the surface is

$$\mathbf{H}_i = \mathbf{H}_0 + (\mathbf{H}_e - \mathbf{H}_0)e^{-x/\lambda} \tag{3.13}$$

Where $\mathbf{H}_e$ is the external field, and $\mathbf{H}_0$ any field present in the hypothetical body when its resistance fell to zero. Equation 3.13 predicts that the external field falls off exponentially inside a zero-resistivity material to a "trapped" field $\mathbf{H}_0$. This prediction is clearly contradicted by experiment, since (as evinced by the Meissner effect) the internal field in an ideal superconductor is always zero. Using the values of m and e appropriate for free electrons and assuming a density of one electron per atom, Equation 3.11 predicts a value for the decay constant λ of approximately 10^{-6} cm. As shown by Table 2.3, this is of the right order of magnitude at absolute zero.[2]

H. and F. London (1935a) showed that the Meissner effect could be incorporated into the Becker-Heller-Sauter theory if Equation 3.9 were replaced by the equation

$$\frac{mc}{n_s e^2} \operatorname{curl} \mathbf{J}_s + \mathbf{H} = 0 \tag{3.14}$$

where n_s and $\mathbf{J}_s$ are interpreted respectively as the volume density and current density of the 'superconducting' portion of the conduction electrons.

Substituting for curl **J** from Equation 3.10 we now obtain

$$\lambda^2 \nabla^2 \mathbf{H} = \mathbf{H} \tag{3.15}$$

which when solved for a semi-infinite region gives

$$\mathbf{H}_i = \mathbf{H}_e e^{-x/\lambda} \tag{3.16}$$

---

[2] An expression for λ in terms of experimentally measurable parameters is derived in Sec. 11.1.

where $\mathbf{H}_i$ and $\mathbf{H}_e$ have the same meanings as in Equations 3.13. Comparison of these two equations shows that the disagreement between Equation 3.13 and experiment is removed in the case of Equation 3.16, since the latter predicts that the internal field deep inside a bulk superconductor will always be zero. Furthermore the value for λ given by Equation 3.11, which is known to be of the correct order of magnitude at absolute zero, is retained by the London form of the theory, provided that n_s approaches n at absolute zero. This is eminently reasonable since it is equivalent to assuming that *all* the conduction electrons become superconducting as $T \to 0$. At higher temperatures λ is known to approach infinity. In terms of Equation 3.11, this means that at temperatures approaching T_c, the density of the superelectrons n_s becomes vanishingly small.

To account for the zero resistance phenomenon, the London theory retains Equation 3.8 for the superconducting portion n_s of the conduction electrons, that is,

$$\mathbf{E} = \frac{m}{n_s e^2} \frac{d\mathbf{J}_s}{dt} \tag{3.8'}$$

and assumes that the remainder interact with the lattice according to Ohm's law, so that

$$\mathbf{J}_n = \sigma \mathbf{E}$$

where σ is a function of temperature.

Collecting the equations of the London theory, we have

$$\mathbf{J} = \mathbf{J}_s + \mathbf{J}_n \tag{3.17a}$$

$$\mathbf{J}_n = \sigma(T)\mathbf{E} \tag{3.17b}$$

$$\mathbf{E} = \Lambda(T)\dot{\mathbf{J}}_s/c \tag{3.17c}$$

$$\Lambda(T)\,\text{curl}\,\mathbf{J}_s + \mathbf{H} = 0 \tag{3.17d}$$

where we define

$$\Lambda(T) \equiv \frac{mc}{n_s(T)e^2} \equiv \frac{4\pi\lambda^2(T)}{c} \tag{3.17e}$$

By defining a vector potential $\mathbf{A}$ such that div $\mathbf{A} = 0$ and such that the component of $\mathbf{A}$ normal to the boundary of the superconductor is zero, we may write curl $\mathbf{A} = \mathbf{H}$. Equation 3.17d can then be written in the simpler form,

$$\Lambda(T)\mathbf{J}_s = -\mathbf{A} \tag{3.17d'}$$

These equations, when combined with those of Maxwell, successfully formulate the low frequency electromagnetic behavior of superconductors. This is not surprising, of course, since they were chosen to achieve this purpose.

An intimation that the London equations are of more fundamental significance, is provided by the fact[3] that when combined with the thermodynamic treatment of the two-fluid model of Gorter and Casimir, they yield the empirically determined temperature dependence of the penetration depth (Eq. 2.4), that is,

$$\lambda(T) = \lambda(0)\left[1 - \left(\frac{T}{T_c}\right)^4\right]^{-\frac{1}{2}}$$

At its inception the London theory could not be justified on other than phenomonological grounds. Soon afterwards, however, F. London (1935) pointed out that Equation 3.17d of the phenomenological theory implied that the momentum of the superelectrons remained unchanged in the presence of a magnetic field. He suggested that this might be due to the existence of a "long range order" in a superconductor that maintains the electron momentum constant over large distances in space. Experimental evidence for the existence of long range order is presented in Section 10.8.

It is shown in Section 10.7 that the London equations are only exact if $H \ll H_c$ and $\xi \ll \lambda$. This does not strongly limit the usefulness of this theory, whose application to four important problems is described below.

10.3   Kinetic Energy of the Superelectrons

It has been shown that a magnetic field H_e parallel to the surface of a superconductor penetrates according to the expression

$$\mathbf{H}_i = \mathbf{H}_e e^{-x/\lambda} \tag{3.16}$$

where the x axis is taken at right angles to the surface. By combining this with Maxwell's equation

$$\text{curl } \mathbf{H} = \frac{4\pi}{c}\mathbf{J}$$

we can determine the screening current density inside the superconductor. For the simple geometry under consideration,

$$|\text{curl } \mathbf{H}| \equiv \frac{dH}{dx}$$

Hence the screening current density is given by

$$J_s = -\frac{cH_e}{4\pi\lambda}e^{-x/\lambda} \tag{3.18}$$

---

[3] See for instance, D. Shoenberg *Superconductivity* Cambridge University Press, 1960 Sec. 6.3.2.

This screening current may be said to consist of superelectrons and is generated whenever an external magnetic field is applied to a superconductor. Equation 3.18 shows that the screening current density decays exponentially inside the superconductor, from a maximum value of $J_s = -\dfrac{cH_e}{4\pi\lambda}$ at the surface.

The kinetic energy of these superelectrons may be written as $K = \frac{1}{2}n_s mv^2$ per unit volume. Substituting for v in terms of J_s from Equation 3.7 and using Equation 3.11, we have

$$K = \frac{\frac{1}{2}J_s^2 m}{n_s e^2}$$

$$= 2\pi\lambda^2 \frac{J_s^2}{c^2}$$

Equation 3.18 shows that J_s and thus K decreases with distance from the surface of the superconductor.

In addition to the kinetic energy stored in the circulating supercurrent, energy of $H_i^2/8\pi$ per unit volume is stored in the penetration field H_i. The total energy contributed by the external field to unit volume of the superconductor is therefore given by

$$W = \frac{H_i^2}{8\pi} + \frac{2\pi\lambda^2 J_s^2}{c^2} \tag{3.19}$$

The term in H_i may be regarded as the *potential energy* of the superelectrons. If the external field is removed, the energy W is returned to it, since in that case both H_i and J_s vanish. By substituting for H_i and J_s from Equations 3.16 and 3.18, respectively, we find after some simplification that at a depth x below the superconductor surface, the potential and kinetic energy of the superelectrons are both equal to $\dfrac{H_e^2}{8\pi}e^{-2x/\lambda}$. This equality is not true in general.

At the surface where $x = 0$, the superelectron kinetic energy density is $H_e^2/8\pi$. If the external field is increased to the critical value H_c, this kinetic energy is equal to the *difference in free energy of the superconducting and normal phases*. It can be shown[4] that if an interphase boundary is moving through an idealized superconductor, the kinetic energy of the superelectrons is used to increase their free energy so as to convert them to *normal* electrons of zero average velocity, that is, the kinetic energy of the superelectrons is *not* converted into joule heat.

---

[4] F. London *Superfluids* Vol. I 2nd rev. ed. New York: Dover, 1961. p. 137.

In terms of the BCS model, the situation may be described as follows. At the outset, at a point deep inside the superconductor, both the magnetic field and the superelectron current are zero. If a supercritical field is now applied, a normal region will move into the superconductor from the surface. As the interphase boundary approaches the point under consideration, the field and superelectron current density will increase. When the moving boundary reaches this region, the magnetic field rises to H_c and the kinetic energy of the superelectrons rises to $H_c^2/8\pi$. As the boundary moves on, the superelectron pairs 'split' into normal electrons, absorbing the kinetic energy in a reversible non-dissipative fashion. This depairing process is analyzed in greater detail in Section 11.3 in connection with the current induced phase transition.

Interphase boundaries in real superconductors do not move in a smooth and non-dissipative fashion, so that the above results represent a strongly idealized situation. The treatment does, however, explain how it is possible to reconcile the idea of thermodynamically reversible transitions with the concept of screening currents. Furthermore, it is found that when applying the London theory (for instance, to inductance calculations as in Sec. 28.3 of Ch. 6), it is often necessary to take the kinetic energy of the superelectrons into account.

10.4 Field Penetration into a Slab

An important application of the London equations is to the calculation of the magnetic field inside an infinite superconducting slab of thickness $2a$ subjected to a uniform external field H_0, parallel to the surface. The center of coordinates is taken at the midpoint of the slab, with the x axis normal to the slab surfaces, and the y axis parallel to the external field. For this geometry Equation 3.15 reduces to

$$\frac{d^2 H_y}{dx^2} = \frac{H_y}{\lambda^2}$$

with $H_y = H_0$ at $x = \pm a$. The solution of this 2nd order differential equation is known to be of the form

$$H_y = A \exp\left(-\frac{x}{\lambda}\right) + B \exp\left(+\frac{x}{\lambda}\right)$$

where A and B are constants to be derived from the boundary conditions. When this is done it is found that the internal field is

$$H_y = H_0 \frac{\cosh(x/\lambda)}{\cosh(a/\lambda)}$$

10.5   The Quantized Fluxoid

In the analysis of the bulk superconducting ring presented in Section 5.6, it was assumed that any *flux* trapped in a superconducting ring or cylinder was preserved unchanged in the face of changes in the applied field, as long as all parts of the ring remained superconducting. It was shown by F. and H. London (1935) that in a superconducting ring or

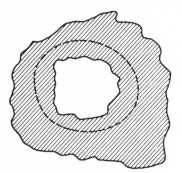

cylinder it is not the *flux*, but a related quantity, which they named the *fluxoid*, that is preserved.

The fluxoid is defined as

$$\phi_f = \iint \mathbf{B} \cdot d\mathbf{S} + \frac{4\pi\lambda^2}{c} \oint \mathbf{J} \cdot d\mathbf{l} \quad (3.20)$$

and equals the sum of the flux passing through the ring or cylinder and the line integral of the persistent current density taken around it.

Fig. 3.1 Cross-section of hollow superconductor.

We will give a non-rigorous proof of this result. It will then be shown that the fluxoid can be identified with the angular momentum of the persistent current associated with it, and, since the angular momentum is *quantized*, that the flux trapped in a cylinder can only assume certain discrete values.

To derive Equation 3.20 consider a hollow superconductor, whose cross-section is shown in Figure 3.1, exposed to a varying magnetic field. Using Maxwell's equation

$$\dot{\mathbf{B}} = -c \operatorname{curl} \mathbf{E}$$

and integrating over the region inside the dotted line, we have

$$\iint \dot{\mathbf{B}} \cdot d\mathbf{S} + c \iint \operatorname{curl} \mathbf{E} \cdot d\mathbf{S} = 0$$

From Stoke's law therefore, $\iint \dot{\mathbf{B}} \cdot d\mathbf{S} + c \oint \mathbf{E} \cdot d\mathbf{l} = 0$ where the line integral for $\mathbf{E}$ is taken around the (arbitrary) broken line inside the super-conducting material. Substituting for $\mathbf{E}$ from Equation 3.17c and integrating with respect to time, we obtain

$$\iint \mathbf{B} \cdot d\mathbf{S} + \frac{4\pi\lambda^2}{c} \oint \mathbf{J} \cdot d\mathbf{l} = \text{const} = \phi_f \quad (3.21)$$

which was to be proved.

To demonstrate that the fluxoid is equal to the angular momentum of each electron of the persistent current, we substitute for $\mathbf{H}$ using the equivalence $\mathbf{H} = \text{curl } \mathbf{A}$, and again apply Stoke's theorem. This gives

$$\mu \oint \mathbf{A} \cdot dl + \frac{4\pi}{c} \lambda^2 \oint \mathbf{J}_s \cdot dl = \phi_f,$$

substituting for λ^2 from Equation 3.17 and for $\mathbf{J}_s$ from Equation 3.7 we obtain

$$\frac{c}{e} \oint \mathbf{p} \cdot dl = \phi_f$$

where

$$\mathbf{p} = m\mathbf{v} + \frac{\mu e}{c} \mathbf{A}$$

It is a well-known result of classical electrodynamics that the quantity $\mathbf{p}$ is the momentum of an electron of charge e and mass m, moving in a magnetic field whose vector potential is $\mathbf{A}$. Furthermore, it is easy to show that a body traveling in a closed path with momentum $\mathbf{p}$, has an angular momentum Ω given by the expression

$$|\Omega| = \oint \mathbf{p} \cdot dl$$

According to the well-known Bohr model of the atom, the angular momentum of the circulating electrons is quantized. This makes it appear reasonable that the angular momentum of the electrons circulating in a superconducting ring or cylinder should be quantized also, that is,

$$|\Omega| = nh$$

hence

$$\frac{e}{c} \phi_f = nh$$

where h is Plank's constant and n is an integer. By combining this result with Equation 3.21, we obtain

$$\phi_f \equiv \iint \mathbf{B} \cdot d\mathbf{S} + \frac{4\pi\lambda^2}{c} \oint \mathbf{J} \cdot dl = \frac{nhc}{e} \tag{3.22}$$

This result was first predicted by London.[5] The appearance of the BCS theory in which superconductivity is associated with electron *pairs*, led to the suggestion by Onsager at a conference held in 1959,[6] that Equation 3.22 should be replaced by the expression

$$\phi_f = \frac{nhc}{2e}$$

---

[5] F. London *op. cit.*, p. 152.
[6] See also Onsager (1961).

For a superconducting cylinder of wall thickness d having an inner wall radius r, this expression becomes

$$\phi_f \equiv \pi r^2 \bar{H} + \frac{4\pi\lambda^2}{c}\frac{i}{d}2\pi r \sim \frac{nhc}{2e} \tag{3.23}$$

where $\bar{H}$ is the average field trapped in the cylinder and i is the current circulating in unit length of the walls. Using Maxwell's equation

$$\frac{4\pi \mathbf{J}}{c} = \text{curl } \mathbf{H}$$

it is easy to show that the circulating current i and the trapped field $\bar{H}$ are related by the equation

$$\frac{4\pi i}{c} \sim \bar{H}$$

provided that the radius r of the cylinder is much larger than its thickness. Using this to substitute for i in Equation 3.23, and rearranging, we find that the flux trapped in a superconducting cylinder is[7]

$$\pi r^2 \bar{H} \sim \frac{nhc}{2e}\left(1 + \frac{2\lambda^2}{rd}\right)^{-1} \tag{3.24}$$

For a "thick-walled" cylinder for which $\lambda^2 \ll rd$ this result reduces to

$$\pi r^2 \bar{H} \sim nhc/2e$$

$$\sim n(2 \times 10^{-7}) \text{ gauss cm}^2$$

Hence, for a cylinder of 10 microns in radius, the trapped field corresponding to one quantum of flux, is approximately 0.063 oersted, a value that is quite large enough to be detectable. This remarkable experiment was first performed almost simultaneously by Deaver and Fairbank (1961), and Doll and Näbauer (1961), using superconducting cylinders made respectively by depositing tin films on copper wires and lead films on quartz fibers. The measurements, which used different methods, showed that the cylinders could only trap integral units of flux. The agreement with Equation 3.24 was sufficiently good to establish the correctness of the factor '2,' indicating, as predicted by the BCS theory, that superconductivity is associated with *pairs* of electrons. A later theoretical study by Byers and Yang (1961) shows that the quantization of the angular momentum of the circulating electrons is associated uniquely with the superconducting state, and does not occur in metals in the normal state.

---

[7] This result was obtained directly from the BCS theory by Bardeen (1961b) and Keller and Zumino (1961).

10.6 Field Penetration into a Thin-walled Cylinder

If a magnetic field is applied parallel to the axis of a thick walled super-conducting cylinder, persistent currents are induced in its wall that prevent the penetration of flux both into the cylinder walls and into the hollow core. If the same experiment is carried out with a thin walled cylinder, that is, with a cylinder whose wall thickness is comparable to the penetration depth, a fraction of the magnetic field will appear inside the cylinder. This is a consequence of the law that the fluxoid rather than

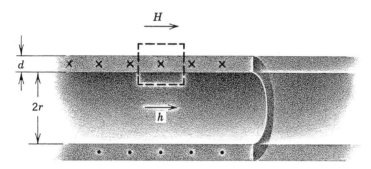

Fig. 3.2   Section through a superconducting cylinder.

the flux is conserved. More directly, it can be regarded as a consequence of the inertia of the superelectrons.

Consider a superconducting cylinder of radius r and wall thickness d subjected to an external field H. Let the resulting internal field be h and let the density of the average screening current be J. Since the fluxoid is conserved, we find, from Equation 3.22 that,

$$0 = h\pi r^2 + \frac{4\pi\lambda^2}{c} 2\pi r J$$

Using Ampere's law $\oint \mathbf{H} \cdot d\mathbf{l} = 4\pi/c \int\int \mathbf{J} \cdot d\mathbf{S}$ and integrating around the broken curve shown in Figure 3.2, we find that

$$H - h = \frac{4\pi J d}{c}$$

It is assumed that $d \ll r$ and that $d \lesssim \lambda$ so that we can ignore the variation of the screening current density in different portions of the cylinder wall. Eliminating J between these two equations, and rearranging, we obtain

$$\frac{h}{H} = \frac{2\lambda^2}{2\lambda^2 - rd}$$

If $r \gg \lambda^2/d$, h/H vanishes. In the other limit, corresponding to the case of the infinitely "thin" film, h/H approaches unity.

10.7   The Ginzburg-Landau Theory

It was shown in Section 6.1 that for a bulk superconductor in a field H, the Gibbs free energy per unit volume is

$$G_s(H) = G_s(0) + \frac{H^2}{8\pi}$$

The existence of positive interphase boundary energy indicates that the free energy of a superconductor is increased if ψ, the "degree of order" of the superconducting state, is forced to vary over small distances in space. To take this phenomenon into account, the expression for $G_s(H)$ must be amended by the inclusion of a term in grad ψ.

On the basis of quantum mechanical arguments Ginzburg and Landau (1950) postulated that the amended free energy expression should be written

$$G_s(H) = G_s(0) + \frac{H^2}{8\pi} + \frac{1}{2m}\left[-i\hbar\,\nabla\psi - \frac{e^*}{c}A\psi \right]^2 \qquad (3.25)$$

where m and e^* are respectively the effective mass and charge of the superelectrons. The order parameter ψ is a complex quantity. $\psi\psi^* = |\psi|^2$ may be identified with the volume density n_s of the superelectrons.

Before this equation can be applied it is necessary to specify $G_s(0)$ explicitly as a function of the order parameter ψ. According to a general theory for second-order phase transitions[8] the free energy of a superconductor near T_c may be expanded in powers of ψ^2. Ginzburg and Landau (1950) write

$$G_s(0) = G_n(0) + \alpha(T)\psi^2 + \tfrac{1}{2}\beta(T)\psi^4 \qquad (3.26)$$

The equilibrium value of ψ^2 in Equation 3.26 is that which leads to a minimum value of $G_s(0)$. Differentiating Equation 3.26 and setting

$$\frac{\partial G_s(0)}{\partial \psi} = 0$$

gives the equilibrium value of ψ (in the absence of an applied field) as

$$\psi_0{}^2 = -\frac{\alpha}{\beta} \qquad (3.27)$$

---

[8] Landau and Lifshitz (1958).

Substituting this into Equation 3.26 and rearranging gives

$$G_s(0) - G_n(0) = -\frac{1}{2}\frac{\alpha^2}{\beta}$$

$$= \frac{H_c^2}{8\pi}$$

Hence

$$\frac{H_c^2}{4\pi} = \frac{\alpha^2}{\beta} \tag{3.28}$$

where H_c is the thermodynamic critical field for a bulk superconductor.

We will solve Equation 3.25 for the simple case of an infinite superconducting sheet lying in the $y - z$ plane. The applied field H may be assumed to be in the z direction, so that $\mathbf{A}$ has only a y axis component, which varies with x. Hence $H = dA/dx$. Grad ψ lies in the x direction, so that $\mathbf{A} \cdot \text{grad } \psi = 0$.

Under these conditions the expression for $G_s(H)$ becomes

$$G_s(H) = G_s(0) + \frac{1}{8\pi}\left(\frac{dA}{dx}\right)^2 + \frac{1}{2m}\left[\hbar^2\left(\frac{d\psi}{dx}\right)^2 + \left(\frac{e^*A}{c}\psi\right)^2\right] \tag{3.29}$$

It is necessary to find those functions of ψ and A that minimize the volume integral of $G_s(H)$. It can be shown[9] that this is achieved by solving the two Euler equations:

$$\frac{\partial G_s(H)}{\partial \psi} - \frac{d}{dx}\frac{\partial G_s(H)}{\partial \psi_x} = 0$$

$$\frac{\partial G_s(H)}{\partial A} - \frac{d}{dx}\frac{\partial G_s(H)}{\partial A_x} = 0$$

where

$$\psi_x \equiv \frac{d\psi}{dx} \quad \text{and} \quad A_x \equiv \frac{dA}{dx}$$

Applying this procedure to Equation 3.29 leads to the two coupled non-linear equations,

$$\frac{d^2\psi}{dx^2} = \frac{m}{\hbar^2}\frac{\partial G_s(0)}{\partial \psi} + \left(\frac{e^*A}{\hbar c}\right)^2\psi \tag{3.30}$$

and

$$\frac{d^2A}{dx^2} = \frac{4\pi e^{*2}}{mc^2}\psi^2 A \tag{3.31}$$

---

[9] See Margenau and Murphy, *The Mathematics of Physics and Chemistry*, 2nd ed. New York: Van Nostrand, 1956, Ch. 6.

These two equations replace the London equation

$$\frac{4\pi}{c} \lambda_L{}^2 \mathbf{J}_s = -\mathbf{A} \qquad (3.32)$$

Since curl $\mathbf{H} = -\dfrac{4\pi}{c}\mathbf{J}$ and curl curl $\mathbf{A} \equiv -\nabla^2\mathbf{A}$ if div $\mathbf{A} = 0$,

$$\frac{d^2A}{dx^2} = -\frac{4\pi}{c} J_s$$

in this geometry. Substituting for d^2A/dx^2 in Equation 3.31 gives,

$$J_s = \frac{e^{*2}}{mc}\psi^2 A \qquad (3.33)$$

For weak fields the order parameter may be assumed invariant with x and equal to ψ_0. Under these circumstances Equation 3.33 assumes the form of Equation 3.32, proving that the Ginzburg-Landau theory reduces to the London theory in the weak field limit. By substituting for ψ^2 in Equation 3.33, using Equation 3.27, we obtain

$$J_s = \frac{e^{*2}}{mc}\left(-\frac{\alpha}{\beta}\right)A$$

Comparing this with the London Equation 3.32 gives

$$\frac{\alpha}{\beta} = -\frac{m}{4\pi}\left(\frac{c}{e^*\lambda_L}\right)^2 \qquad (3.34)$$

where λ_L is the temperature dependent London function for the penetration depth. Equations 3.28 and 3.34 determine α and β in terms of experimental parameters. By substituting for α and β in Equation 3.26, differentiating to obtain $\partial G_s(0)/\partial\psi$ and substituting this into Equation 3.30 we obtain after some simplification

$$\frac{d^2\psi}{dx^2} = \frac{\kappa^2}{\lambda_L{}^2}\left[-\left(1 - \frac{\frac{1}{2}A^2}{H_c{}^2\lambda_L{}^2}\right)\psi + \frac{\psi^3}{\psi_0{}^2}\right] \qquad (3.35)$$

This equation uses the dimensionless parameter κ that has been introduced in connection with the interphase boundary in Section 7 and which is defined by

$$\kappa = \frac{\sqrt{2}e^*H_c\lambda_L{}^2}{\hbar c}$$

The expressions 3.31 and 3.35 constitute the two fundamental equations of the Ginzburg-Landau theory. They can be solved subject to various boundary conditions, and have been applied to the calculation of inter-phase boundary energy, supercooling, the critical fields of thin films, the variation of the penetration depth with field, and the properties of super-conductors at high frequencies.[10] Expressions have also been derived for the critical current of thin films (see Sec. 14.2), for the dependence of the energy gap on field and temperature,[11] and for the theory of super-conducting alloys (see Sec. 7.4).

Perhaps the most remarkable prediction of the theory is that of the existence of Class II superconductors that remain superconducting above the thermodynamic critical field. This prediction is based on the fact that Equation 3.35 can be shown to possess a non-zero solution for ψ in a field $H_e \geqslant H_c$. For this solution $\psi \ll \psi_0$. Hence $H(z) \sim H_e$. Since $H = dA/dx$, we have

$$A(x) = H_e x$$

Under these conditions Equation 3.35 reduces to

$$\frac{d^2\psi}{dx^2} = -\frac{\kappa^2}{\lambda_L^2}\left(1 - \frac{H_e^2 x^2}{2H_c^2 \lambda_L^2}\right)\psi$$

This is similar to the Schrödinger equation for a simple harmonic oscillator that has real, periodic solutions[12] provided that

$$\frac{H_e}{H_c} = \frac{\kappa\sqrt{2}}{2n+1}$$

where n is an integer.

The maximum value of H_e/H_c occurs for $n = 0$ giving

$$\frac{H_1}{H_c} = \kappa\sqrt{2}$$

Since the Ginzburg-Landau theory predicts negative-interphase boundary energy for $\kappa > 1/\sqrt{2}$, this result indicates that this type of material will remain superconducting up to a field $H_1 > H_c$ without exhibiting the Meissner effect. As described in Section 7, this prediction is in good agreement with experiment.

Gorkov (1959, 1960a,b) has been able to derive equations almost identical to those of the Ginzburg-Landau theory starting from the BCS microscopic theory. He found that $e^* = 2e$ where e is the charge of the

---

[10] For a review of these topics see Bardeen (1956) or Ginzburg (1955).
[11] See for instance Douglass (1961).
[12] See for instance Margenau and Murphy, *op. cit.*, Sec. 11.11.

electron, that κ varies with electron mean free path, and that for a pure superconductor

$$\kappa \sim 0.96 \frac{\lambda_L(0)}{\xi_0}$$

Here $\lambda_L(0)$ represents the London value of the penetration depth at absolute zero, and ξ_0 is the coherence length for the pure metal.

The microscopic theory shows that the relation between $\mathbf{J}_s$ and $\mathbf{A}$ must be non-local except very close to T_c. This limits the validity of the Ginzburg-Landau theory to a temperature region for which $\xi_0 \ll \lambda_L$. Ginzburg (1958) has noted however that for calculations involving surface energy and supercooling, the theory is applicable over the far larger temperature range for which $\lambda_L/\kappa \gg \xi_0$.

10.8   The Pippard Non-Local Theory

A number of experimental facts led A. B. Pippard (1950a, 1953) to propose a modification to the London theory which involves the concept of a range of coherence. He suggested—and this has been borne out by the BCS microscopic theory—that the electrons in a pure bulk super-conductor act coherently over distances ξ that may be large compared to the penetration depth. One piece of evidence for the existence of long-range coherence forces is the sharpness of the phase transition of super-conductors in zero field. This suggests that large numbers of electrons act coherently to reduce the effect of local temperature fluctuations that would tend to broaden the phase transition. Another piece of evidence is the large interphase boundary energy. In general this is equal to approximately

$$\xi \frac{H_c^{\,2}}{8\pi}$$

where ξ is a constant having the dimensions of length with a magnitude of the order of 10^{-4} cm. We may identify this with the maximum distance over which correlation effects can occur.

The final piece of evidence which led Pippard to propose his modification of the London equation was his discovery[13] that the addition of less than 3 per cent of indium to pure tin produced a very strong increase in the penetration depth. This is not predicted by the London theory, according to which (see Eq. 3.17) λ is a function of only the electron effective mass and density, neither of which would be strongly changed by the introduction of small amounts of impurity.

---

[13] Pippard (1953).

Pippard showed that the dependence of λ on impurities could be accounted for by replacing the London Equation 3.17d', which relates the current density to the vector potential at the same point, by a non-local equation in which the current density at a point is dependent on the value of A averaged over a surrounding region of radius ξ. λ now becomes a function of ξ as well as of the electron mass and density. It was found that the experimentally observed dependence of λ on impurity concentration could be explained by assuming that ξ varies with the electron m.f.p. l according to the relation

$$\frac{1}{\xi} = \frac{1}{\xi_0} + \frac{1}{\alpha l} \tag{3.36}$$

ξ_0 is the range of coherence for the pure metal and was assumed to vary only slightly with temperature, and α is a constant of order unity.

For the equation relating $\mathbf{J}$ and $\mathbf{A}$, Pippard adopted an existing expression[14] for metallic surface impedance, in the anomalous frequency region. This region is defined as that of frequencies high enough for the skin depth to be reduced below the electron m.f.p., so that the electric field varies strongly over distances comparable to l. In this region the linear Ohm's law $J = \sigma E$ has to be replaced by an equation of the type

$$\mathbf{J}(0) \propto \iiint \mathbf{r} \frac{(\mathbf{E} \cdot \mathbf{r})}{r^4} \, dv$$

Pippard (1953) proposed a similar equation

$$\mathbf{J}_s(0) = \text{const.} \iiint \mathbf{r} \frac{\mathbf{A}(r) \cdot \mathbf{r}}{r^4} \, dv$$

to replace the London Equation 3.17d. This equation is justified as follows.

Consider the influence on the current density at the origin, of the component of $\mathbf{A}(r)$ that acts along a line segment $\mathbf{dr}$ at a point $\mathbf{r}$ (See Fig. 3.3). We assume that momentum $\delta \mathbf{p}$ along the line $\mathbf{r}$ is communicated to the electrons at the origin according to the equation

$$\delta \mathbf{p} \propto \mathbf{r}_1 A \cos \theta e^{-r/\xi}$$

$\mathbf{r}_1$ is the unit vector in the direction of $\mathbf{r}$, and the exponential term ensures that the effect of $\mathbf{A}$ at distances much larger than the correlation distance

---

[14] See A. B. Pippard, "Metallic Conduction at High Frequencies" *Advances in Electronics*, Vol. VI, ed. L. Marton. New York: Academic Press, 1954.

becomes negligible. Writing the equation in vector notation we obtain

$$\delta \mathbf{p} \propto \frac{(\mathbf{A} \cdot \mathbf{r})\mathbf{r}}{r^2} e^{-r/\xi}$$

therefore

$$\mathbf{p} \propto \int_0^{\infty} \frac{(\mathbf{A} \cdot \mathbf{r})\mathbf{r}}{r^2} e^{-r/\xi} \, dr \qquad (3.37)$$

The current $\mathbf{J}_s$ at the origin will be proportional to the electron momentum
$\mathbf{p}$ integrated over a sphere, that is,

$$\mathbf{J}_s(0) \propto \int^{4\pi} \mathbf{p} \, d\Omega \qquad (3.38)$$

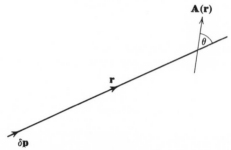

Fig. 3.3

$d\Omega$ is a segment of solid angle that is related to a volume segment by the
expression

$$r^2 \, d\Omega \, dr = dv \qquad (3.39)$$

Substituting for $d\Omega$ from Equation 3.39 into Equation 3.38 gives

$$\mathbf{J}_s(0) \propto \int \mathbf{p} \frac{1}{r^2} \frac{dv}{dr}$$

By substituting for $\mathbf{p}$ using Equation 3.37 we obtain

$$\mathbf{J}_s(0) = \text{const.} \int \frac{(\mathbf{A} \cdot \mathbf{r})\mathbf{r}}{r^4} e^{-r/\xi} \, dv$$

The integration is over the volume of the superconductor only, since the
electrons outside it cannot correlate with those inside. Pippard wrote
this equation in the form

$$\mathbf{J}_s(0) = \frac{-3}{4\pi c \Lambda(T)\xi_0} \int \frac{(\mathbf{A} \cdot \mathbf{r})\mathbf{r}}{r^4} e^{-r/\xi} \, dv \qquad (3.40)$$

where $\Lambda(T)$ is given by Equation 3.17e and ξ is related to l and ξ_0 by
Equation 3.36. It is shown below that under circumstances such as

temperatures close to T_c where $\mathbf{A}$ varies little over distances of the order ξ, $\mathbf{A}$ can be taken outside the integration sign in Equation 3.40, which then reduces to a local form. The constant $-3/4\pi c\Lambda(T)\xi_0$ is chosen so that in this case Equation 3.40 reduces to the local London Equation 3.17d.

The microscopic theory has lent support to the non-local Pippard equation. Even before the development of the BCS theory, it was shown by Bardeen (1956) that any theory that involved an energy gap in the electronic spectrum was bound to lead to a non-local relation between current and vector potential. The BCS theory leads to a relation very similar to Equation 3.40, namely

$$\mathbf{J}_s = -\frac{3}{4\pi c\Lambda(T)\xi_0}\int \frac{\mathbf{r}(\mathbf{r}\cdot\mathbf{A})}{r^4}\, e^{-r/l}\, J(r,T)\, dv \qquad (3.41)$$

This expression is seen to be identical to Equation 3.40 except that the function $J(r,T)$ in the BCS equation replaces the function e^{-r/ξ_0} in the Pippard equation. This function is defined so that for all temperatures below T_c

$$\int_0^\infty J(r,T)\, dr = \int_0^\infty e^{-r/\xi_0}\, dr = \xi_0$$

Hence for all purposes of practical calculation the BCS and Pippard equations are identical. For the correlation distance the BCS theory leads to the expression

$$\xi_0 = 0.18\,\frac{\hbar v_f}{kT_c} \qquad (3.42)$$

where v_f is the electron Fermi velocity[15] that can be calculated from measurements of the anomalous skin effect in the normal metal.

10.9 The Non-Local Penetration Depth

The decrease of magnetic field inside a semi-infinite superconductor predicted by the non-local theory is compared to the exponential decrease predicted by the London theory in Figure 3.4. The most striking difference is that the internal field predicted by the non-local theory goes very slightly negative at large distances from the surface.[16]

To interpret experimental results in terms of the non-local equation, it becomes convenient to define an effective penetration depth

$$\lambda = \frac{1}{H(0)}\int_0^\infty H(z)\, dz \qquad (3.43)$$

where $H(0)$ is the field outside the superconductor and $H(z)$ is the field at a distance z inside it. Using the BCS form of the non-local equation, λ/λ_L has been calculated as a function of ξ_0/λ_L, where λ_L is the London

---

[15] This term is defined in Sec. 11.1.

[16] Drangeid and Sommerhalder (1962) have presented experimental evidence for this phenomenon.

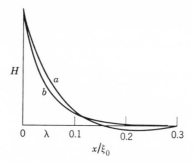

Fig. 3.4 Penetration of magnetic field at a plane boundary, (Pippard, 1953). (*a*) Pippard theory with specular reflection at the surface. (*b*) London theory.

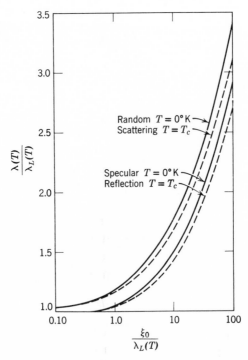

Fig. 3.5 λ/λ_L versus $\xi_0/\lambda_L(T)$ calculated from the BCS theory (Bardeen et al., 1957).

value of the penetration depth given by the semi-empirical relation[17]

$$\lambda_L(T) = \lambda_L(0)\left[1 - \left(\frac{T}{T_c}\right)^4\right]^{1/2}$$

The results of this calculation are shown in Figure 3.5. Two somewhat different values for λ are obtained depending on whether the conduction electrons are assumed to suffer specular reflection at the specimen boundaries or whether they are assumed to be scattered randomly after impact. For most pure metals ξ_0 is of the order of 10^{-4} cm, that is, much larger than λ except very near T_c. The figure shows that under these circumstances the ratio λ/λ_L is almost constant throughout the temperature range from absolute zero to slightly below T_c. Hence, the temperature variation of λ calculated from the non-local equation is of the same form as that calculated from the London equation, which itself is known to be in agreement with experiment. Values of ξ_0 calculated from Equation 3.42, and values of $\lambda(0)$, the penetration depth at absolute zero, calculated from Equation 3.41, are shown in Table 3.1 for some common super-

TABLE 3.1
(After Bardeen and Schrieffer, 1961)

		Calculated London Value	Calculated BCS Values		Observed Values	
	T_c	$10^6\lambda_L(0)$	$10^4\xi_0$	$10^6\lambda(0)$	$10^6\lambda(0)$	$10^{-8}v_f$
	°K	cm	cm	cm	cm	cm/sec
Sn	3.73	3.55	0.23	5.6	5.1	0.65
Al	1.18	1.57	1.6	5.3	5.15, 4.9	1.32
Pb	7.15	3.7	0.083	4.8	3.9	0.50

conductors. Shown for comparison are values of $\lambda_L(0)$, the London penetration depth at absolute zero, calculated from Equation 3.51 derived below, as well as observed values of $\lambda(0)$ and v_f. Although the BCS value for the penetration depth is not vastly different from the London value, it is clear that in no case is $\lambda(0) \gg \xi_0$. Hence for these metals, the simple local equations are only correct very close to T_c where λ tends to infinity.

For alloys or films, where ξ is reduced due to electron scattering, the London equation will, however, hold over a larger temperature range. This happens because if ξ is reduced for any reason, λ is increased over the value for the pure metal.[18] The dependence of λ on l/ξ_0 for tin,

---

[17] An expression for $\lambda_L(0)$ in terms of experimentally measurable parameters is derived in Sec. 11.1.

[18] This property of the non-local equation (i.e., that $\lambda \propto 1/l$), is proved in the following paragraphs.

calculated by Miller (1959) from the BCS version of the Pippard equation is shown in Figure 3.6.

Under conditions where λ is either very much larger or very much smaller than ξ, the non-local Pippard Equation 3.40 reduces to simpler local forms. This is fortunate since the complexity of the non-local

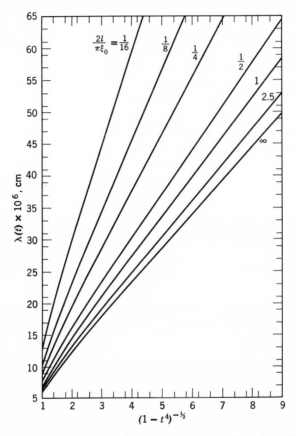

Fig. 3.6 The BCS penetration depth for tin versus a function of $t = T/T_c$, for various values of the dimensionless parameter $2l/\pi\xi_0$ (Miller, 1959).

equation limits its usefulness. One case where $\lambda \gg \xi$ is that of a pure superconductor at temperatures just below T_c, where λ approaches infinity. Another is that of an alloy or thin film where ξ is limited by a short electron m.f.p. (see Eq. 3.36).

If $\lambda \gg \xi$, $A(r)$ in Equation 3.40 will vary very little over the region $r < \xi$, that is, over the region in which the term $e^{-r/\xi}$ is significantly larger than zero. Hence it can be taken outside the integral and given its value at the origin. This leads to

$$J_s(0) = \frac{-3A(0)}{4\pi c \Lambda(T)\xi_0} \int \frac{(\mathbf{a}_1 \cdot \mathbf{r}_1)\mathbf{r}_1 e^{-r/\xi}}{r^2} \, dv \qquad (3.44)$$

where $\mathbf{a}_1$ and $\mathbf{r}_1$ are unit vectors of $\mathbf{A}$ and $\mathbf{r}$ respectively and the integral is carried out over the volume of the superconductor. If the superconductor has dimensions large compared to ξ, the term $[e^{-r/\xi}]/r^2$ will become vanishingly small at values of r small compared to the dimensions. Hence we may set the limits of the above integral at infinity without changing its value.

It is shown in Appendix 35.1, that

$$\int_0^\infty \frac{(\mathbf{a}_1 \cdot \mathbf{r}_1)\mathbf{r}_1}{r^2} e^{-r/\xi} \, dv = -\frac{4\pi}{3} \mathbf{a}_1 \xi$$

Substituting this result into Equation 3.44 gives

$$\mathbf{J}_s(0) = \frac{A(0)\xi}{c\Lambda(T)\xi_0} \qquad (3.45)$$

This equation is seen to be of the local type where $\mathbf{J}_s$ at a given point depends on $\mathbf{A}$ at that point only. Comparison with the London relation 3.17d shows that the penetration depth for the case $\lambda \gg \xi$ may be written as

$$\lambda = \lambda_L \sqrt{\xi_0/\xi} \qquad (3.46)$$

where λ_L is the London value of the penetration depth.[19] This equation shows that λ is increased when ξ is reduced by impurities or geometry.

For the opposite limit $\lambda \ll \xi_0$, which holds for most pure bulk superconductors at temperatures not too close to T_c, Faber and Pippard (1955) have shown that

$$\lambda_\infty = \left[\frac{\sqrt{3}}{2\pi} \xi_0 \lambda_L^2 \right]^{1/3}$$

11. THE MICROSCOPIC THEORY OF SUPERCONDUCTIVITY

The phenomenological theories discussed above are successful in accounting for many of the electromagnetic and other properties of superconductors in terms of a small number of empirical equations added to

---

[19] A more exact analysis by Miller (1959) gives for the limit $l \ll \xi_0$,

$$\lambda_L^2/\lambda^2 = l\Delta/\xi_0\Delta_0 \tanh \Delta/2kT$$

where Δ is the energy gap at temperature T, and Δ_0 its value at absolute zero.

those that describe the behavior of normal metals. A deeper understanding of superconductors has been gained with the advent of the microscopic theory of Bardeen, Cooper and Schrieffer (1957), which has been able to account for the unique properties of superconductors in terms of quantum mechanics. Not only does the theory account for the electromagnetic properties of superconductors, but it also explains effects such as acoustic attenuation, and superconducting tunneling, for which no phenomenological theories have been developed.

The behavior of the electrons in superconductors as deduced from the microscopic theory is described qualitatively in Section 11.2, using the terminology of the electron theory of metals. A brief review of this terminology is given in Section 11.1, which follows. The BCS model is used to analyze the zero resistance phenomenon in Section 11.3, and the phenomenon of superconductive tunneling in Sec. 11.4.

11.1 The Free Electron Theory of Metals

It was shown in Section 9.1 that the electrical and thermal conductivity of metals can be partly explained on the basis of a model that assumes that

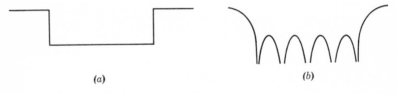

(a)   (b)

Fig. 3.7

the current is carried by the so-called conduction electrons that are free to move through the lattice and whose density has the order of magnitude of the lattice ions. A more precise description of the properties of metals and of the differences between the normal and the superconducting state requires knowledge of the distribution of kinetic energy among these electrons.

A good approximation to the energy distribution in real metals is given by the theory due to Sommerfeld,[20] which treats the conduction electrons of a metal as an electron gas. The ionic forces acting on the electrons are taken into account by postulating that the electrons cannot escape from the metal. The simplifying assumption is made that the force acting on an electron within the metal is zero. This is equivalent to assuming that the potential within a metal is constant as shown in Figure 3.7a. In a real

---

[20] See for instance Mott and Jones, *op. cit.*, p. 51.

metal, the potential will be related to the ion positions somewhat as shown in Figure 3.7b.

According to the Sommerfeld model, each electron of mass m and energy E is assigned a wave function ψ which is the solution of the Schrödinger wave equation

$$V^2\psi + \frac{2m}{\hbar^2}E\psi = 0$$

If we consider the electrons as contained in a cube of unit size, then ψ must vanish on the sides of this cube, that is, when x, y and z are equal to either zero or unity. The wave functions are therefore of the form

$$\psi = \sin \pi l_1 x \;\; \sin \pi l_2 y \;\; \sin \pi l_3 z$$

where l_1, l_2, and l_3 are integers. By substituting this function in the wave equation it is possible to show that solutions exist for energy values

$$E = \frac{\hbar^2}{2m}\pi^2(l_1{}^2 + l_2{}^2 + l_3{}^2).$$

These are known as the "eigenvalues" of the wave equation. They are the *only* energy values or states which the electrons can have, and each corresponds to a specific momentum $\mathbf{k}$ that is defined by the equation

$$E = \frac{\hbar^2 k^2}{2m}$$

The number Σ of energy states having an energy less than E is equal to the number of sets of positive integers l_1, l_2, and l_3 such that

$$\frac{\hbar^2}{2m}\pi^2(l_1{}^2 + l_2{}^2 + l_3{}^2) < E$$

Some thought will show that this number is equal to the volume of $\frac{1}{8}$ of a sphere of radius $(2mE)^{\frac{1}{2}}/\hbar\pi$. Therefore,

$$\Sigma = \frac{1}{8}\frac{4\pi}{3}\left(\frac{2m}{\hbar^2}\frac{E}{\pi^2}\right)^{\frac{3}{2}} = \frac{1}{6\pi^2}\left(\frac{2m}{\hbar^2}\right)^{\frac{3}{2}}E^{\frac{3}{2}} \tag{3.47}$$

The number of states in the energy range E to $E + dE$ is defined as $N(E)\,dE$ and is obtained by differentiating Σ with respect to E, that is,

$$N(E)\,dE = \frac{1}{4\pi^2}\left(\frac{2m}{h^2}\right)^{\frac{3}{2}}E^{\frac{1}{2}}dE \tag{3.48}$$

$N(E)$ is known as the density of states function and is shown in Figure 3.8.

The electrons are distributed statistically among these energy states, tending to lower energies as the temperature decreases. If the electronic behavior were governed by the classical Boltzmann statistics, they would all occupy the lowest energy level at absolute zero. Since, however, the electrons in a metal obey "Fermi-Dirac" statistics, only two electrons (of opposite spin) can occupy a given energy state. At room temperature the

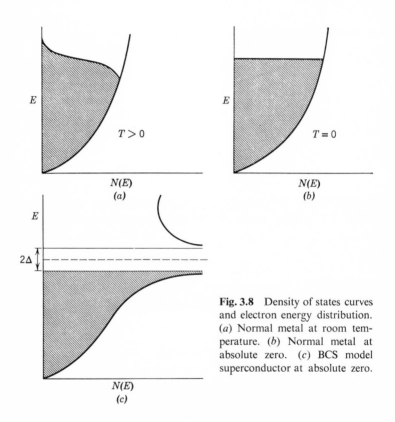

Fig. 3.8 Density of states curves and electron energy distribution. (*a*) Normal metal at room temperature. (*b*) Normal metal at absolute zero. (*c*) BCS model superconductor at absolute zero.

electron distribution among the energy states is somewhat as shown in Figure 3.8a. In a normal metal, at absolute zero, the electrons would reduce their kinetic energy as much as possible subject to the limitations of Fermi-Dirac statistics by occupying all the lowest energy states somewhat as shown in Figure 3.8b.

If n is the density of the conduction electrons, the number of states occupied at absolute zero is $\Sigma = \frac{1}{2}n$.

By substituting for Σ in Equation 3.47, we find that the energy E_f of the highest occupied state at absolute zero is

$$E_f = \left(\frac{3}{\pi}\right)^{2/3} \frac{\pi^2 \hbar^2}{2m} n^{2/3} \qquad (3.49)$$

E_f and the corresponding velocity are known as the "Fermi Energy" and "Fermi velocity" respectively.

$$E_f = \tfrac{1}{2} m v_f^2 \qquad (3.50)$$

As shown in Figure 3.8a, the number of electrons excited to higher energy states at normal temperatures is small because E_f, which is equal to several electron volts, is much larger than the thermal energy of each electron.

The above equations make it possible to express $\lambda_L(0)$, the London penetration depth at absolute zero, in terms of $N(E_f)$ and v_f. These parameters can be determined experimentally using specific heat and high frequency surface impedance measurements[21] respectively. From Equation 3.17e,

$$\lambda_L{}^2(0) = \frac{mc^2}{4\pi n e^2}$$

Substituting for n from Equation 3.49, we obtain an expression that includes E_f. Substituting for E_f and m by means of Equations 3.48 and 3.50 respectively we obtain finally

$$\lambda_L{}^2(0) = \frac{3c^2}{8\pi e^2 N(E_f) v_f{}^2} \qquad (3.51)$$

where $N(E_f)$ stands for the density of states of one spin at the Fermi surface.

The shape of the density of states curve given by Equation 3.48 is found to be approximately correct for real metals. To account for the differences between metals and for the existence of insulators, it is necessary to take the periodic variation of the electron potential into account.[22] This leads to the result that the electrons in a lattice are restricted to certain ranges or "bands" of energy whose extent and dimensions depend on the crystal structure. The more detailed properties of metals and insulators can be explained in terms of the band shape, and the degree to which each band is occupied by the available electrons. As is well known for instance, a material with completely filled bands is an insulator, whereas a material which contains a partly filled band behaves as a conductor.

The BCS theory, some of whose conclusions are described below,

---

[21] See for instance Pippard (1954).
[22] See Mott and Jones, op. cit.

considers an idealized model of a metal and neglects the existence of band structure. Such a theory can successfully account for the properties of superconductors because they obey the "principle of similarity." For instance, curves of H_c v T for the common superconductors differ from one another only in scale. Since the superconducting properties of the soft superconductors differ less than the normal properties, which depend on the details of their band structure, they can be accounted for by a model such as that of the BCS theory, which ignores band structure.

11.2   The Bardeen-Cooper-Schrieffer Theory

The development of the microscopic theory of superconductivity was assisted by a number of deductions suggested by experimental facts. One of these was based on the success of the two-fluid models in accounting for thermodynamic properties of superconductors. This had made it seem plausible that a portion of the conduction electrons in a super-conductor was condensed into a lower energy phase. The fact that the superconducting state can only exist below a critical temperature T_c indicates that the energy difference between these phases at absolute zero must be of the order kT_c per electron where k is Boltzmann's constant. For a critical temperature of $4°K$, $kT_c = 3.0 \times 10^{-4}$ ev. This energy difference is much smaller than the Fermi energy E_f, which is of the order of 3–10 ev. The experimental finding that the electronic portion of the specific heat of superconductors showed an exponential dependence on temperature near absolute zero was shown to indicate that the condensed electron phase must be separated from the normal phase by an "energy gap," that is, that a certain minimum energy Δ must be required to excite a single electron from the condensed to the normal phase.

Following some earlier unsuccessful attempts by others to identify the low-temperature electron condensation mechanism believed to be associ-ated with superconductivity, Fröhlich in 1952 developed a theory that attempted to show that an electron could condense into a low energy state at low temperatures by distorting the adjacent portion of the lattice. This theory was later shown to be incorrect, but one of its predictions—the dependence of critical temperature on isotopic mass (see Ch. 2), was experimentally verified for mercury almost immediately. This proved that the electron condensation mechanism of this superconductor had to be associated in a very direct way with some type of electron-lattice inter-action, although not necessarily the specific type examined by Fröhlich. Some years later, Cooper (1956) calculated that pairs of electrons could condense into a lower energy phase provided that there was some attrac-tion, however weak, between them. Shortly afterwards, Bardeen, Cooper, and Schrieffer (1957) were able to show that such an attraction does exist between electron pairs due to electron-phonon[23] interaction. In qualitative terms this electron-electron attraction may be thought of as due to the lattice distortions produced by the two electrons. In their theory, usually referred to as the BCS theory, Bardeen, Cooper, and Schrieffer were able to account quantitatively for most of the phenomena of superconductivity on the basis of the Cooper pairing mechanism. The attractive interaction (which in quantum mechanical terms is said to be due to "virtual phonon exchange") can exist between two electrons of energies E_k and $E_{k'}$ excited above the Fermi "sea," provided that $E_k - E_{k'} < \hbar\omega$ where ω is the "Debye" or resonance frequency of the lattice. Bardeen, Cooper, and Schrieffer assumed that the attractive interaction that gives rise to super-conductivity takes place between electrons of opposite spins, and equal and opposite momenta, $\hbar\mathbf{k}$ and $-\hbar\mathbf{k}$. These paired electrons can carry current. For a current corresponding to an average electron velocity $\mathbf{v}$, the virtual phonon exchange coupling occurs between electrons having momenta $m\mathbf{v} + \hbar\mathbf{k}$ and $m\mathbf{v} - \hbar\mathbf{k}$. It is found that the density-of-states curve of the conduction electrons, which in the normal state approximates the parabolic curve shown in Figure 3.8b, changes to the form shown in Figure 3.8c in the superconducting state. In this state a forbidden energy region of width 2Δ makes its appearance, centered on the Fermi energy of the normal metal. This region is called the "energy gap." The density of states now goes to infinity at $E = E_f \pm \Delta$.

In spite of the change in the energy distribution curve, the total number of states below the Fermi level is unchanged. Hence at $T = 0$, all the electrons have energies equal or less than $E_f - \Delta$, and are coupled together as virtual pairs. At $T > 0$ some electrons are excited across the gap; these correspond to the normal component of the two-fluid model.

In the normal metal with a density of states corresponding to Figure 3.8a an arbitrarily small energy increment is sufficient to excite an electron from the top of the Fermi "sea" to a state of larger energy. However, in the superconducting state, the minimum energy required to disrupt the two electrons of a Cooper pair and excite them to the "normal" band is 2Δ, equal to the width of the energy gap. The theory predicts that the width of this gap decreases from $3.52kT_c$ at $T = 0$ to zero at T_c. The width of the energy gap can be determined by tunneling and in other ways. For the common superconductors, the experimental values of 2Δ range from 3.5 to $4.5kT_c$.

The concepts of the BCS model that have been presented in this section are sufficient to discuss those properties of superconductors presented in

---

[23] A phonon is defined as a quantum of vibrational or acoustic energy, in analogy with the definition of a photon as a quantum of electromagnetic radiation energy.

this book. A more detailed account of the microscopic theory, and of its applications to various phenomena of superconductivity, is given in the review by Bardeen and Schrieffer (1961), and in the book by Lynton (1962).

11.3 Calculation of the Electron Depairing Velocity

By using the BCS model it is possible in a straightforward manner[24] to deduce the destruction of superconductivity by a critical current density. The argument runs as follows.

In a metal the conduction electrons are in motion even at absolute zero since they occupy states of finite kinetic energy. When carrying a current, the conduction electrons assume a net velocity in the current direction. In a normal metal any of these electrons can be scattered to unoccupied velocity states by interacting with an oscillating lattice ion or a lattice irregularity. If the electron is scattered to a lower velocity, it loses kinetic energy to the lattice, which appears as heat. It is this scattering of current-carrying electrons to lower velocities, accompanied by energy transfer to the lattice, that gives rise to the ohmic resistivity of the normal state.

In the superconducting state, current is carried by electrons paired with a binding energy 2Δ. Electron scattering to a different velocity state must be accompanied by electron de-pairing that results in an increase 2Δ in the potential energy of the electrons. It is shown in the following paragraphs that for electron velocities below a critical value, the maximum decrease in electron kinetic energy that can be achieved by scattering to a lower velocity is outweighed by the increase in electron potential energy due to de-pairing. Under these circumstances, the conduction electrons cannot lose energy to the lattice by scattering, so that the ohmic resistance is zero. The current-induced phase transition takes place when the current density becomes so large that the electron velocity exceeds the critical value for de-pairing.

In Chapter 1 it was pointed out that the critical current in a bulk superconductor is that which produces a surface field H_c. This suggests that the critical field rather than the critical current is fundamental in causing the phase transition. The above reasoning shows that the opposite is the case. In fact, it is found that the critical field corresponds to that which induces a screening current of critical density in the surface of a superconductor; and it is shown in Chapter 4 that the critical field of a thin film is therefore inversely proportional to its thickness and rises indefinitely as the film thickness is reduced. Clearly, therefore, it is the critical current density rather than the critical field that is fundamental in both the current and field-induced superconducting transition.

---

[24] Bogoliubov et al. (1958).

The critical velocity for electron de-pairing will be calculated at $T = 0$ and for the case of a film much thinner than the penetration depth, so that any current carried by the film can be assumed to be uniformly distributed throughout its thickness. It is convenient to use the representation shown in Figure 3.9a. Every point in this diagram represents a particular velocity state that can be occupied by no more than two electrons (of opposite spin). At absolute zero all the momentum states within the "Fermi

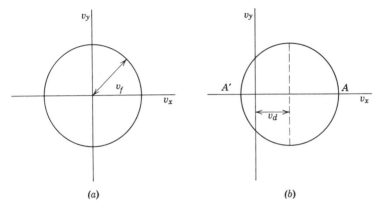

(a)   *(b)*

Fig. 3.9 Distribution of the conduction electrons among velocity states. *(a)* Zero net current. *(b)* Current density $J = nev_d$.

sphere" of radius v_f are occupied, and all those outside the sphere are unoccupied. In other words, at absolute zero all the electrons have velocities equal or less than $|v_f|$.

The so-called Fermi energy corresponding to the maximum velocity is $E_f = \frac{1}{2}mv_f^2$ where m is the effective electron mass. In the superconducting state the maximum energy of the electrons is reduced to $E_f' = E_f - \Delta$. $\Delta \ll E_f$, so that the effect of the energy gap on the Fermi energy can be neglected in this calculation.

For each electron of a virtual pair having velocity v, the kinetic energy will be reduced by the binding energy Δ, so that the total energy per electron is $E = \frac{1}{2}mv^2 - \Delta$. Assume an electron current of density J flowing through the lattice. This will be associated with a mean electron drift velocity v_d so that $J = env_d$. If J is along the x axis, the Fermi sphere will be displaced a distance v_d along this axis (Fig. 3.9b). In the normal metal, some of the electrons moving through the lattice will be scattered to unoccupied states of lower velocity giving up energy to the lattice.

The scattering process involving the greatest loss of velocity and therefore the greatest loss of energy to the lattice is one in which an electron at point A in momentum space having velocity $v_d + v_f$ is scattered to point A', that is, to a velocity $v_d - v_f$. In the normal metal such a scattering process would involve a change in the energy of the scattered electron of

$$\Delta E_n = \tfrac{1}{2}m(v_d + v_f)^2 - \tfrac{1}{2}m(v_d - v_f)^2$$
$$= -2mv_dv_f$$

In the superconducting state, the electron at point A' in momentum space is coupled to that at point A with binding energy -2Δ. Hence the scattering process in the superconducting state would involve a change in electron binding energy of

$$\delta E_s = \delta E_n + 2\Delta$$
$$= 2\Delta - 2mv_dv_f \tag{3.52}$$

By the second law of thermodynamics such scattering processes can only occur when they tend to equate the energy distribution between the electrons and the lattice by reducing the energy of the former, that is, when δE_s is negative. Equation 3.52 shows that this occurs when the average electron velocity v_d is equal or larger than the critical value

$$v_c = \frac{\Delta}{mv_f} \tag{3.53}$$

Below this velocity it is not possible for the electrons to give up energy to the lattice. In the normal metal where the energy gap Δ is zero, the critical velocity given by this expression is zero, which can be interpreted to mean that these metals exhibit ohmic resistance even for vanishingly small currents.

Since $J = nev_d$, Equation 3.53 shows that the critical current density at absolute zero is

$$J_c = -\frac{ne\Delta}{v_f m} \tag{3.54}$$

A thermodynamic method of calculating the critical current density at any temperature is presented in the next chapter.

11.4   The BCS Model Applied to Superconductive Tunneling

It was mentioned in Chapter 2 that when two metals are brought close together, conduction electrons, owing to their wave nature, can tunnel from one metal to the other across the intervening gap. The dependence of tunneling current on applied voltage was shown to change strongly if one or both metals become superconducting. It is the purpose of this section to explain these phenomena in terms of the BCS model.

To examine tunneling between two normal metals it is helpful to consider Figure 3.10a, which represents their density-of-state curves. If an external potential is applied across the two metals, the Fermi levels are shifted with regard to one another and current flows. It is found experimentally that this tunneling current varies linearly with voltage and that dI/dV is almost independent of temperature.

If one of the tunneling metals becomes superconducting, its density-of-states curve changes to the one shown in Figure 3.10b. It can be shown[25] that in this case the current will be proportional to the product of the density of electrons at a particular energy in the emitter metal and the density of unoccupied states at the same energy level, in the absorber metal. Most of the Fermi electrons of the normal metal are now seen to be opposite the forbidden energy region of the superconductor. It is clear that the potential across the junction must be raised to Δ_1/e in either a positive or negative sense before a significant tunneling current can flow. This is illustrated in the right-hand curve of Figure 3.10b. It is found that the largest value of dI/dV occurs when $eV = \Delta_1$. This phenomenon provides a simple measure of the energy gap of superconductors.

Figure 3.10c can be used to analyze tunneling between two superconductors having widely different energy gaps. If a potential is applied that lowers the energy of the electrons of metal-1 having the larger energy gap Δ_1, some of the electrons which are temperature excited across the gap of metal-2 will now be able to flow to the empty states just above the gap of metal-1. This leads to the first increase in tunnel current, shown at potential $(\Delta_1 - \Delta_2)/e$ in the figure. However, as the potential across the junction is increased further, the tunnel current decreases, due to the decrease of the density of available states in metal-1 with increasing energy above the gap. This process produces the region of negative slope in the current-voltage characteristic. Finally, as the applied potential is increased to $(\Delta_1 + \Delta_2)/e$ the main body of unexcited electrons in metal-2 is brought opposite the empty states of metal-1, thus leading to the major current increase shown in the right-hand curve. It is left to the reader to show that a similar current-voltage characteristic results if an opposite potential is applied to the junction, such that the electrons of metal-1 are increased in energy with respect to those of metal-2. If the two superconductors have equal energy gaps, the negative impedance region of Figure 3.10c is strongly reduced, so that a rectangular curve similar to that shown schematically in Figure 3.10d results.

---

[25] Bardeen (1961a).

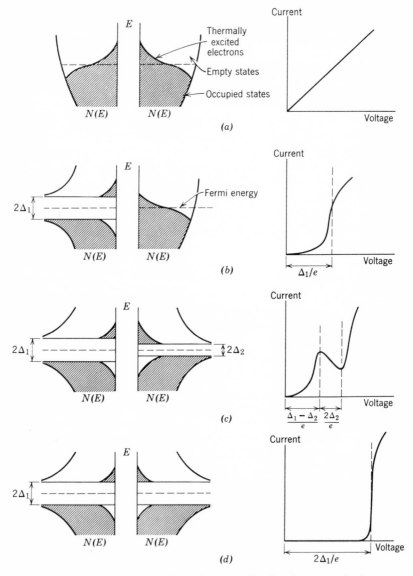

Fig. 3.10 Density of states curves for various tunneling junctions near absolute zero. (a) Both metals normal. (b) One metal superconducting, one metal normal. (c) Both metals superconducting. (d) Two identical superconducting metals.

The above conclusions are representative of situations where the temperature is much below the critical temperatures of the superconductors involved. If this is not the case, the experimental current-voltage tunneling characteristics are less angular, and approach the straight line ohmic case.

12. APPLICATIONS OF POTENTIAL THEORY TO CURRENT FLOW IN SUPERCONDUCTORS

In Chapter 2, mathematical analogies between superconductors and ferromagnets were established and used to calculate the surface field of a superconducting ellipsoid in a magnetic field. In this section we establish analogies between electrically charged bodies and current-carrying superconductors, and use these analogies to calculate the surface field of the latter. We start by showing in Section 12.1, that for certain geometries, the surface current distribution in a current carrying bulk superconductor is the same as the surface charge distribution on an electrostatically charged perfect conductor of similar shape. Current flow in two such geometries, that is, in superconductors of cylindrical symmetry, and in superconducting sheets, is analyzed in Sections 12.2 and 12.3 respectively. In Section 12.4, we derive the image theorem for current near superconductors and apply it to a problem of practical importance.

12.1   Analogies to Electrostatics

Some of the parameters used in electrostatic potential theory are shown in the first column of Table 3.2. The analogous magnetic quantities are

TABLE 3.2

Electric Quantities		Magnetic Quantities	
Electrostatic Potential	Φ	Magnetic Vector Potential	$\mathbf{A}$
Electric Field	$\mathbf{E}$	Magnetic Field	$\mathbf{H}$
Volume Density of Charge	ρ	Volume Current Density	$\mathbf{J}$

shown in the second column. The interrelations connecting the various quantities are shown in Table 3.3, again in correspondence with one

TABLE 3.3

Electric Fields	Magnetic Fields
1. $\operatorname{grad} \phi = -\mathbf{E}$	$\operatorname{curl} \mathbf{A} = \mathbf{H}$
2. $\operatorname{div} \mathbf{E} = 4\pi\rho$	$c \operatorname{curl} \mathbf{H} = 4\pi\mathbf{J}$

another. In free space both electric charge and current are zero, so that Equations 2 of Table 3.3 reduce to

$$\text{div grad } \phi = 0 \qquad (3.55)$$

and

$$\text{curl curl } \mathbf{A} = 0$$
$$\text{div grad } \mathbf{A} - \text{grad div } \mathbf{A} \equiv \qquad (3.56)$$

Choosing a gauge in which div $\mathbf{A}$ is identically equal to zero, we can write Equation 3.56 as

$$\text{div grad } \mathbf{A} = 0 \qquad (3.57)$$

Equations 3.55 and 3.57 show that a formal analogy exists for electric and magnetic fields in free space. This analogy breaks down on the

TABLE 3.4

	Charged Conductors	Current-Carrying Superconductors
On the surface	$\mathbf{E}_s = 4\pi\sigma\mathbf{n}$	$\mathbf{H}_s = 4\pi\mathbf{g} \times \mathbf{n}$
In free space	div grad $\phi = 0$	div grad $\mathbf{A} = 0$

surface and in the interior of normal conductors since the electrostatic field inside a conductor is zero, whereas the magnetic field is not. The analogy becomes perfect however, for the magnetic field in the vicinity of bulk superconductors, since the internal magnetic field of a superconductor is always zero.

The equation

$$\mathbf{E}_s = 4\pi\sigma\mathbf{n}$$

relating the surface field $\mathbf{E}$ and surface charge density σ of a conductor, is closely analogous to that relating the surface field and surface current density of a superconductor,

$$\mathbf{H}_s = 4\pi\mathbf{g} \times \mathbf{n}$$

The two sets of analogous equations for the electric and magnetic fields and potentials outside conductors and superconductors are collected in Table 3.4.

Since $\mathbf{A}$ is a vector, div grad $\mathbf{A}$ does not in general have a simple form. However, in the case of geometries where $\mathbf{A}$ has only a single component so that it can be treated as a scalar, div grad $\mathbf{A}$ reduces to a form identical to div grad ϕ so that the analogy between the electrostatic and superconductive case becomes complete. Under such circumstances solutions of electrostatic problems can be rewritten for superconductors of similar geometry. Two such geometries are treated below.

12.2 Cylindrical Coordinate Systems

Systems where current flow is along one direction can be treated using cylindrical coordinates with the z axis as the direction of current flow.

In such a system the direction of H lies in the x-y plane. Since the curl of any vector is at right angles to that vector and since $H = \text{curl } A$, A must lie along the z axis. Hence in this as in all similar systems, A_x and A_y are zero and A_z is a scalar. By definition, no quantities vary along the z axis so that $\partial/\partial_z = 0$, hence

$$iH_x + jH_y = i\frac{\partial A_z}{\partial y} - j\frac{\partial A_z}{\partial x} \tag{3.58}$$

Since A_z is a scalar we can define its gradient

$$\nabla A_z = i\frac{\partial A_z}{\partial x} + j\frac{\partial A_z}{\partial y}$$

∇A_z and H are at right angles. This can be proved by using Equation 3.58 to show that their scalar product is zero, that is,

$$\nabla A_z \cdot H \equiv \frac{\partial A_z}{\partial x}H_x + \frac{\partial A_z}{\partial y}H_y = 0$$

Since H and ∇A_z are at right angles, H is parallel to lines of constant A_z. From Equation 3.58

$$H = |\nabla A_z|. \tag{3.59}$$

Thus we can identify A_z with the magnetostatic potential and the conductor surfaces with lines of constant A_z. Hence the problem of finding the field distribution is solved by finding a solution for

$$\frac{\partial^2 A_z}{\partial x^2} + \frac{\partial^2 A_z}{\partial y^2} = 0,$$

with the surfaces at constant vector potential. At any surface, from Equation 3.59,

$$H = 4\pi g_z/c = |\nabla A_z|$$

By definition g_x and g_y are zero.

The results of this section may be summarized as follows.

For electrostatic and superconducting systems that can be described by cylindrical coordinates

1. Surfaces are lines of constant electrostatic potential and vector potential respectively.
2. E and H are respectively perpendicular and parallel to the surfaces and are respectively proportional to surface charge and surface current density.

3. Inside solid bodies **E** and **H** are identically zero.
4. The magnitudes of **E** and **H** are respectively equal to the gradients of the electrostatic and vector potentials.

By using these equivalences many results of electrostatic theory can immediately be applied to superconductors.

12.3 Current Flow in Flat Sheets

Another case that can be treated by simple methods is that represented in Figure 3.11 of current flowing into and out of a flat superconducting sheet. The z axis is taken to be normal to the sheet. Since any magnetic

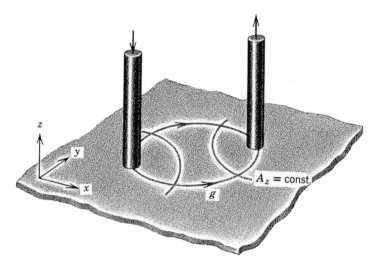

Fig. 3.11   Current flow in a superconducting sheet.

field must be parallel to a superconducting surface, H_z is zero. Since **A** is normal to **H**, A_x and A_y must be zero. This geometry represents another case where **A** is in one direction throughout.

Above the sheet all quantities are constant with respect to z. Hence, the equation curl **A** = **H** again reduces to

$$H_x = \partial A_z / \partial y \quad \text{and} \quad H_y = -\partial A_z / \partial x$$

and the sheet surface current density **g** is given by

$$4\pi g / c = H = |\nabla A_z|$$

By the arguments of the previous Section, it can be shown that A_z is the magnetostatic potential and that the intercepts of the conductors with the sheet form curves of constant A_z. The magnetostatic potential lines between these curves are drawn schematically in Figure 3.11 and are seen to correspond to the lines of constant electrostatic potential between two infinite charged conductors having the same cross section as the given curves. They can thus be derived by standard methods. The orthogonal system of lines of constant ∇A_z are in this case parallel to the direction of the current flow and normal to the direction of the field.

12.4   The Image Theorem for Superconductors

When a negative point charge is brought close to a semi-infinite conductor, surface charges are induced in its surface that produce a field outside it. The image theorem of electrostatics states that this field is

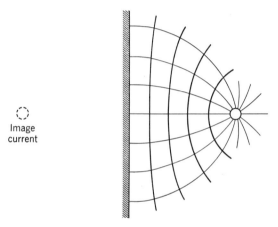

Image
current

Fig. 3.12   Field due to current flow near a superconducting plane, *or* potential due to a line of charge near a conducting plane.

equivalent to that produced by a positive "image" point charge situated as far behind the surface of the conductor as the negative charge is in front. By extension, a *line* of negative charge parallel to a semi-infinite conductor will give rise to surface charges whose effect is the same as that of an *image line* of positive charge. The lines of force near a charged cylinder whose radius is small compared to the distance separating it from the conducting plane are shown in Figure 3.12.

Due to the analogy that holds between electrostatic systems, and superconducting systems where the current flow is along one direction only, Figure 3.12 can equally well represent a current-carrying superconducting cylinder near a semi-infinite superconducting plane. In this case the image current flows in the opposite direction to the current in the cylinder.

The current-image producing property of a superconductor still holds

if the semi-infinite superconductor is replaced by a semi-infinite superconducting sheet provided that this is thick compared to the penetration
depth. The image effect clearly reduces H everywhere except between the
conductor and the plane: this reduces the self-inductance of any conductor brought close to such a plane, a property which is useful in reducing
the inductance of superconducting circuits.

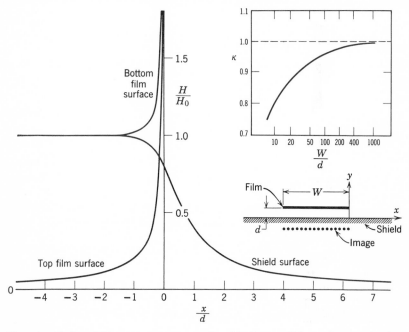

Fig. 3.13 Surface fields near a current-carrying thin film parallel to a superconducting
shield plane.

The theorem of images derived above can be used to analyze the field
distribution around a current-carrying film, whose surface is parallel to
that of an infinite superconducting shield plane. The geometry occurs in
many superconducting devices and is shown in cross section in Figure
3.13. A current I is assumed to flow in the film of width W. It is assumed
that the magnetic field generated by this current on the shield plane is
everywhere less than H_c, and that the separation d between the film and
the shield plane is much larger than the shield plane penetration depth,
so that magnetic field penetration into the shield plane can be neglected.
Since the shield is assumed superconducting the field between it and the
film must be parallel to both. By drawing an image, shown dotted in
Figure 3.13 it is apparent by inspection that the fields due to the actual

current and the image add in the region between the film and the shield and cancel everywhere else. Hence the field between the film and the shield is uniform and falls to zero within a distance of the order of d outside the edge of the film. The shield screening current, whose integral is equal to I must therefore be uniformly distributed over that portion of the shield surface covered by the film. Hence the field between the middle of the film of width W and the shield is,

$$H_0 = \frac{\kappa 4\pi I}{cW} \tag{3.60}$$

where κ is a function of d/W that approaches unity for $d/W \ll 1$. The dependence of κ on d/W has been calculated[26] using standard potential theory, and is shown in Figure 3.13.

References

For further material on the theory of metallic resistivity as well as on the band theory of metals and semiconductors, see for instance,

C. Kittel, *Introduction to Solid State Physics*, 2nd ed. New York: Wiley, 1956.
N. F. Mott and H. Jones, *The Theory of the Properties of Metals and Alloys*. New York: Dover, 1958.
A. H. Wilson, *Theory of Metals*. Cambridge University Press, 1953.

For details on the phenomenological theories of superconductivity, see for instance,

J. Bardeen, "Theory of Superconductivity" in *Encyclopedia of Physics*, Vol. XV, ed. S. Flügge. Berlin: Springer, 1956.
F. London, *Superfluids*, Vol. I, with an epilogue by M. J. Buckingham. New York: Dover, 1961.

For an account of the BCS theory, see for instance,

J. Bardeen, and J. R. Schrieffer, "Recent Developments in Superconductivity," in *Progress in Low Temperature Physics*, Vol. III, ed. C. J. Gorter. New York: Interscience, 1961.
E. A. Lynton, *Superconductivity*. New York: Wiley, 1962.

---

[26] Newhouse Bremer and Edwards (1960).

chapter 4

Superconductive Films

13. INTRODUCTION

Since the properties of the soft superconductors depend very little on crystal direction, impurities, or strain, it is relatively easy (as compared to the case of magnetic films for instance), to prepare them in the form of films having well reproducible properties.

Films whose thickness is smaller than the penetration depth differ strongly from bulk superconductors and can be used to test various theoretical predictions such as the influence of a shortened electron m.f.p. on the penetration depth, etc. Many other investigations that involve parameters not directly dependent on specimen size can only be conveniently carried out on thin films. Typical of the latter are experiments where the material has to be rapidly switched between the normal and superconducting states using a magnetic field. In these cases thin films or small particles of superconductor must be used because eddy current phenomena limit the switching speed of superconductors of large dimensions.[1]

The high switching speed of superconductive films compared to that of bulk superconductors has led to their use in superconductive computer devices. Because of their device applications and theoretical interest they have been studied intensively so that a good deal of information about their behavior has recently become available. It is the object of this chapter to present the more basic properties of superconductive films. These are also the properties that most decisively influence device performance. References to other phenomena that may play an important part in future devices but whose interpretation is complex or in doubt are given at the end of the chapter.

We begin our treatment in Section 14 by using the theories developed

---

[1] See Sec. 25.2.

in Chapter 3, to analyze the dependence of the resistivity, critical current, and critical field of a film on its thickness. It is established, that as the film thickness d becomes small compared to λ, the critical current per unit width of film decreases proportionately to d/λ, and that the critical field increases proportionately to λ/d. The treatment is carried out for the simplest case of cylindrical films where edge effects are absent. In practice, films are most conveniently deposited on flat surfaces and in such a geometry that the effect of the edges can not be neglected. The behavior of the critical field and current of such flat films and their dependence on film geometry are described in Sections 15 and 16 respectively.

Current-induced phase transitions in superconducting films are accompanied by pronounced joule heating. This gives rise to interesting and important phenomena that are described and analyzed in Section 17.

Both the joule heating effects and many of the operational characteristics of the film devices described in later chapters are a function of the film resistivity when in the normal state. The dependence of the resistivity and of certain other properties of superconductive films on the details of preparation are described in Section 18, which concludes this chapter.

14. THEORETICAL DEPENDENCE OF ELECTRICAL PROPERTIES ON FILM THICKNESS

14.1 Film Resistivity

It was established in the previous chapter that the resistivity of a normal metal can be expressed in the form

$$\rho = \frac{mv_f}{\tfrac{1}{2}ne^2}\frac{1}{l}$$

where only l, the mean free path of the conduction electrons, is a function of temperature. At "high" temperatures,[2] l is limited by lattice vibrations, and therefore increases with decreasing temperature, until, close to absolute zero, it reaches an upper limit determined by impurities or specimen dimensions. This limiting value of the m.f.p. corresponds to the residual resistivity ρ_r. Typical values range from 10^{-2} cm for very pure bulk metals to 10^{-5} cm for thin films.

Most metal surfaces appear to scatter internal conduction electrons diffusely. As the thickness of such a metal film or wire is reduced to a length comparable to the m.f.p. in bulk material, the effective resistivity, as determined from the measured resistance and specimen dimensions,

---

[2] I.e., at temperatures high compared to the so-called Debye temperature.

increases.[3] This effect can be taken into account by replacing the bulk m.f.p., l_∞, by an effective m.f.p. calculated from the specimen dimensions.

For a wire it can be seen intuitively that the effective m.f.p. must approach the diameter when this becomes much smaller than l_∞. For a film the situation is more complex because electron scattering is reduced in one dimension only. The dependence of mean free path on film thickness has been derived by Fuchs (1938), and is shown and plotted in Figure

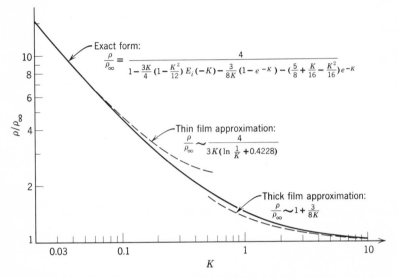

Fig. 4.1 Reduced resistivity ρ/ρ_∞ as a function of reduced film thickness. $K = d/l_\infty$. Solid line represents exact equation, broken lines represent thick and thin film approximations (Mayer, 1959).

4.1 in terms of the reduced resistivity, ρ/ρ_∞. Limiting forms of ρ/ρ_∞ for very thin and very thick films and wires are given in Table 4.1.

It was shown in Section 9.2 that $d\rho/dT$ is approximately independent of material purity for bulk specimens. It can be shown that this is true for "thick" films also. This provides a useful method of estimating film thickness using measurements of the resistance variation with temperature.

To prove that $d\rho/dT$ is independent of film thickness for thick films, we rewrite the expression for the resistivity of thick films shown in Table 4.1 as

$$\rho = \rho_\infty + \frac{3}{8}\frac{l_\infty}{d}\rho_\infty \tag{4.1}$$

[3] Gold films have been prepared with a resistivity no larger than the bulk value. This is attributed to specular reflection of the conduction electrons from the film surfaces.

Equation 3.3 of the previous chapter shows that $l_\infty \rho_\infty$ is a constant, independent of temperature. Hence differentiating Equation 4.1 with regard to temperature, we obtain

$$\frac{d\rho}{dT} = \frac{d\rho_\infty(T)}{dT}$$

which is independent of film thickness.

TABLE 4.1

Limiting Values of ρ/ρ_∞ for Wires and Films

$$(K = d/l_\infty)$$

	Films (thickness d)	Wires (diameter d)
$K \gg 1$	$\dfrac{\rho}{\rho_\infty} = 1 + \dfrac{3}{8K}$	$\dfrac{\rho}{\rho_\infty} = 1 + \dfrac{3}{4K}$
$K \ll 1$	$\dfrac{\rho}{\rho_\infty} = \dfrac{4}{3K\left(\ln\dfrac{1}{K} + 0.4228\right)}$	$\dfrac{\rho}{\rho_\infty} = \dfrac{1}{K}$

For a film of resistance R,

$$\frac{dR}{dT} = \frac{d\rho}{dT}\frac{\text{film length}}{\text{width} \times \text{thickness}}$$

Since $d\rho/dT$ is a constant of the material, the film thickness can be estimated from measured values of dR/dT if the width and length are known.

14.2 Critical Current Density

In a flat superconducting film carrying current, an intense magnetic field is created near the film edges that has a complex effect on the current-induced transition. To concentrate attention on the effect of material properties on the critical current, we will, in this section, only consider geometries where the current is distributed uniformly over the whole film so that edge effects are negligible. Two examples of such geometries are a film deposited on a cylinder much longer than its radius, which itself is much larger than the film thickness; and a flat film adjacent and parallel to a much larger superconducting plane of higher critical temperature.

In the case of a current-carrying film much thicker than λ, deposited on a cylinder, the current flows in an outer region of approximate depth 3λ. In accordance with Silsbee's rule, the critical current in this case is that which produces a surface field H_c outside the cylinder. The field on the inside surface of the film should be zero for all currents since the current is assumed to be distributed uniformly around the cylinder. For a film much thinner than λ, the current is distributed approximately uniformly throughout the film thickness and the surface field H_I corresponding to the critical current, is smaller than H_c. The transition to the normal state now occurs when the critical velocity, which causes the virtual electron pairs to split up, is exceeded. This velocity was calculated in Chapter 3 and used to derive the critical current at absolute zero of a film much thinner than λ. To calculate the critical current at finite temperatures we use a thermodynamic method based on the supposition that in a thin film the kinetic energy of the critical current equals the difference in the free energies of the normal and superconducting states. This rule has been established by Bardeen (1958) on the basis of the BCS theory.

To calculate the KE of the superconducting current we recall that in the presence of a current of density $\mathbf{J}_s$, the conduction electrons have an imposed drift velocity $\mathbf{v}_s = \dfrac{\mathbf{J}_s}{en_s}$ but that their velocities relative to one another remain unchanged. This leads to a KE increase of

$$E = \tfrac{1}{2}n_s m v_s^{\,2}$$

Substituting for v_s,

$$E = \frac{1}{2}\frac{m}{e^2 n_s}J_s^{\,2}$$
$$= \tfrac{1}{2}\Lambda_L J_s^{\,2}/c \tag{4.2}$$

where Λ_L is the parameter of the London theory (see Eq. 3.17e).

As mentioned above, we may suppose that the current-induced superconducting-to-normal transition will take place when the KE of the current-carrying electrons just cancels the free energy that accompanies the transition to the normal state. This argument assumes that the transition causes no change in the magnetic field energy, that is, that the magnetic field distribution is the same in the superconducting and normal state. This is true for a film much thinner than the penetration depth.

Let the critical current density for the film be J_c. From Equation 4.2, the corresponding KE is

$$E_c = \tfrac{1}{2}\Lambda_L J_c^{\,2}/c$$

The increase in free energy per unit volume of the film associated with the superconducting-to-normal transition is $H_c^2/8\pi$ where H_c is the critical field of the *bulk* material. Hence

$$\frac{H_c^2}{8\pi} = \frac{\frac{1}{2}\Lambda_L J_c^2}{c}$$

Substituting for Λ_L from Equation 3.17e we have

$$J_c = \frac{cH_c}{4\pi\lambda} \tag{4.3}$$

According to Bardeen (1962), the factor λ in this expression should be interpreted as the non-local value given by Equation 3.46. Hence

$$J_c(T) \sim \frac{cH_c}{4\pi\lambda_L}\left(\frac{\xi}{\xi_0}\right)^{\frac{1}{2}} \tag{4.4}$$

where λ_L is the London value of the penetration depth. This value for J_c is slightly too large, since the slight variation of the energy gap with current has been neglected. A more exact calculation by Bardeen (1962) for the limit $T \sim T_c$ modifies the above result by a multiplying factor $(2/3)^{\frac{3}{2}}$. At $T = 0$ for $l \ll \xi_0$, Bardeen derives the multiplying factor $2/3$. From Equation 4.4 we see that $J_c(T)/J_c(0)$ is independent of l and ξ_0. That is,

$$\frac{J_c(T)}{J_c(0)} = \frac{H_c(T)/H_c(0)}{\lambda_L(T)/\lambda_L(0)}$$

By using the identities

$$H_c(T) = H_c(0)\left[1 - \left(\frac{T}{T_c}\right)^2\right]$$

$$\lambda_L(T) = \lambda_L(0)\left[1 - \left(\frac{T}{T_c}\right)^4\right]^{-\frac{1}{2}}$$

we obtain

$$J_c(T)/J_c(0) = (1 - t^2)^{\frac{3}{2}}(1 + t^2)^{\frac{1}{2}}$$

where

$$t = T/T_c$$

This relation is plotted in Figure 4.2. Near T_c, H_c varies as $(T_c - T)$ and λ_L varies as $(T_c - T)^{-\frac{1}{2}}$; hence $J_c(T)$ varies as $(T_c - T)^{\frac{3}{2}}$.

To calculate the surface field H_I present outside a film of thickness d carrying a current of density J_c, we assume that it is deposited on a cylinder of radius $r \gg d$. Using Ampere's law and integrating H_I around the circumference we have

$$2\pi r H_I = \frac{4\pi}{c}2\pi r d J_c$$

Hence

$$H_I = \frac{4\pi}{c} J_c d \qquad (4.5)$$

independent of r. Eliminating J_c between Equations 4.4 and 4.5 gives the surface field corresponding to the critical current in a thin film as

$$H_I = \frac{H_c d}{\lambda} \qquad (4.6)$$

Near T_c where H_c varies as $(T_c - T)$ and λ varies as $(T_c - T)^{-\frac{1}{2}}$, $H_I \propto (T_c - T)^{\frac{3}{2}}$.

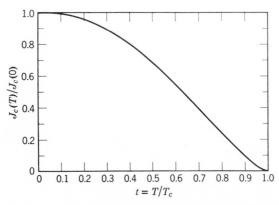

Fig. 4.2   Dependence of the reduced critical current density parameter on temperature.

This formula applies to a geometry such as that of a film deposited on a cylinder, or a flat film deposited on a superconducting shield plane (see Sec. 4.2 below), where the field produced by the current is present *on one side* of the film only. If the field is present on both sides $H_I = H_c d/2\lambda$.

14.3   Critical Field

The result derived above, that the film critical surface current decreases with film thickness at constant temperature, is intuitively understandable in terms of electron "scarcity" in a very thin film. In this section we derive the less obvious result that the critical field of a thin film *increases* with decreasing thickness at constant temperature.

In physical terms this result can best be understood by recalling that the magnetic field applied to a bulk superconductor is forced to pass around it. This increases the magnetostatic energy of the system containing the superconductor. As the applied field is increased this excess magnetostatic energy eventually exceeds the free energy increase associated with the superconducting-to-normal transition. This transition then takes place, defining the "thermodynamic critical field".

In a very thin film, an applied magnetic field is only very imperfectly excluded. Therefore for a given applied field the excess of magnetostatic energy per unit volume of superconductor is smaller than that for a bulk superconductor. Hence the field causing a superconducting-to-normal transition should be correspondingly larger than the bulk value. This argument makes the reasonable assumption that the free energy difference between the superconducting and normal state is the same in a thin film as in bulk material. The critical field of a thin film is usually calculated by this thermodynamic method. We will use a less rigorous derivation which provides a picture of the microscopic processes that accompany a field-induced transition.

The exclusion of any applied magnetic field from a superconducting film must be associated with the presence of circulating screening currents in the film. The critical field is the value of applied field that generates circulating currents equal to the critical density. In Section 10.3 the density of the surface screening current in a bulk superconductor exposed to a surface field H has been shown to be given by

$$J = \frac{cH}{4\pi\lambda}$$

According to the London theory, λ is independent of film thickness, hence we may assume that the critical surface current density for *any* film thickness is given by

$$J_c = \frac{cH_c}{4\pi\lambda} \tag{4.7}$$

where H_c is the bulk critical field.

Consider now a film of thickness d exposed to a field H_e, parallel to the surface. According to the London theory the field inside such a film is given by[4]

$$H = H_e \frac{\cosh x/\lambda}{\cosh d/2\lambda}$$

where the direction of x is normal to the film surface and the origin of coordinates is taken at the center of the film. By using the Maxwell relation curl $\mathbf{H} = (4\pi/c)\mathbf{J}$, which reduces to $dH/dx = 4\pi J/c$ in this geometry, we find the surface screening current density as

$$J(x) = \frac{c}{4\pi} \frac{H_e}{\lambda} \frac{\sinh x/\lambda}{\cosh d/2\lambda}$$

---

[4] See Sec. 10.4.

At the film surface $x = d/2$, hence the surface screening current density is

$$J = \frac{cH_e}{4\pi\lambda} \tanh \frac{d}{2\lambda}$$

J will equal the critical current density when the applied field reaches the film critical value H_F, that is,

$$J_c = \frac{cH_F}{4\pi\lambda} \tanh \frac{d}{2\lambda}$$

Substituting for J_c from Equation 4.7, and transposing, we find the critical field for a film of thickness d given by

$$H_F(d) = H_c \coth \frac{d}{2\lambda} \sim 2H_c \frac{\lambda}{d}$$

for $d \ll \lambda$. The thermodynamic derivation leads to the expression

$$H_F = H_c \left[1 - \frac{2\lambda}{d} \tanh \frac{d}{2\lambda} \right]^{\frac{1}{2}} \sim \sqrt{12}\, H_c \frac{\lambda}{d} \qquad (4.8)$$

Clearly H_F increases with decreasing film thickness. Near T_c where H_c varies as $(T_c - T)$ and λ varies as $(T_c - T)^{-\frac{1}{2}}$, H_F varies as $(T_c - T)^{\frac{1}{2}}$. Eliminating the term λ/d from Equations 4.6 and 4.8, we find

$$H_F H_I = \sqrt{12} H_c^2 \qquad (4.9)$$

This expression is particularly useful because it contains only directly measurable parameters.

Equation 4.8 and 4.9 have here been derived on the basis of the London theory, which is only exact in the weak field limit. A calculation using the Ginzburg-Landau theory which is known to be correct at temperatures near T_c leads to equations of the same form with slightly different numerical constants. For $d \ll \lambda$ it is found that

$$H_F = \sqrt{24} \frac{\lambda}{d} H_c \qquad (4.10)$$

where

$$\lambda = \lambda_L \left(\frac{\xi_0}{\xi} \right)^{\frac{1}{2}}$$

and

$$H_I H_F = \tfrac{8}{3} H_c^2 \qquad (4.11)$$

For $d \gg \lambda$, the Ginzburg-Landau theory gives

$$H_F = H_c \left(1 + \frac{\lambda}{d} \right) \qquad (4.12)$$

More complex equations applicable over a wider temperature range have been derived by Bardeen (1962).

15. MAGNETIC FIELD INDUCED TRANSITIONS

In the theoretical treatment of the critical field of films given above it is implicitly assumed that the field induced transition is sharp. It is the purpose of this section to examine the extent to which real superconducting films conform with this assumption and to explain the divergencies as far as possible. Section 15.1 deals with the behavior of films subjected to a field parallel to the surface. This behavior is relatively simple and well understood. Section 15.2 describes some of the more complex and less understood phenomena that occur when films are subjected to fields normal to their surface.

15.1 Field Parallel to Film Surface

The field-induced transition in this case can conveniently be studied by its effect on the film resistance. In this type of experiment the film is oriented parallel to the applied field and allowed to carry a current small

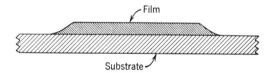

Fig. 4.3 Cross-section of an evaporated metal film that "wets" the substrate.

compared to the critical value. The resistance is then measured as a function of the applied field. Most measurements of the field-induced transition have been carried out on films deposited on flat, as opposed to cylindrical, substrates. The edges of flat films are found to exert a disturbing effect on critical field measurements, unless precautions are taken.

A flat film of a low melting-point metal such as tin evaporated on clean glass at room temperature "wets" the glass and consequently has a profile of the type shown in Figure 4.3. Since the critical field of films varies inversely with film thickness, the thin edges of the film have a much higher critical field than the thicker central region. For a film of this cross section the dependence of resistance on applied field will therefore be equivalent to that of a number of narrower strips of different thicknesses connected in parallel. The variation of resistance with field will thus be highly current dependent. For a measuring current larger than the critical current of the thin edges, the film will start to exhibit resistance at a low field corresponding to the critical field of the central region. In the presence of a much lower measuring current, film resistance will only appear at a relatively high field corresponding to the critical field of the edge regions. For both currents the field-induced transition will be very broad.

One method of eliminating edge effects in flat films, described by Delano et al. (1960), is to cut off the edges mechanically. Another method described by Behrndt et al. (1960) is to deposit the film on a substrate

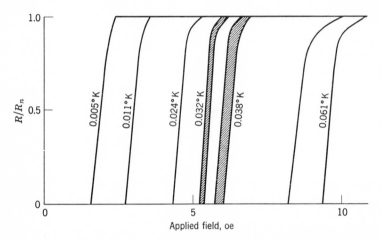

Fig. 4.4 Field induced phase transitions of a tin film, 105 microns thick, at different temperatures. $T_c = 3.777°K$, $T_c - T$ is shown with each curve (Zavaritsky, 1951).

heated close to the film melting point. This causes the metal to agglomerate in relatively large nuclei, which leads to a broken edge structure. A simple method due to Appleyard et al. (1939) is to solder current and voltage leads to the central region of a relatively wide film, thus avoiding the short circuiting action of the edges. Well-annealed and reasonably pure flat films of the "soft" superconductors in which edge effects have been eliminated show resistive transitions that are sharp and relatively independent of measuring current. ("Reasonably pure" in this connection is defined as deposition at pressures of 10^{-6} tor and rates of 50 Å per sec.) A typical series of measurements for tin films is shown in Figure 4.4. It is seen that as the temperature is lowered, the transition sharpens and hysteresis appears. A series of critical field measurements of tin films of various thicknesses is shown in Figure 4.5. The breaks in these curves are associated with the onset of hysteresis. It is seen that the thicker the film, the higher the temperature below which hysteresis occurs.

The occurrence of hysteresis indicates that the field-induced transition is of the first order type involving latent heat which is believed to be associated with positive interphase boundary energy. As shown in Section 7 this energy is believed to be positive for $\lambda < \xi$ and negative for $\lambda > \xi$. Since

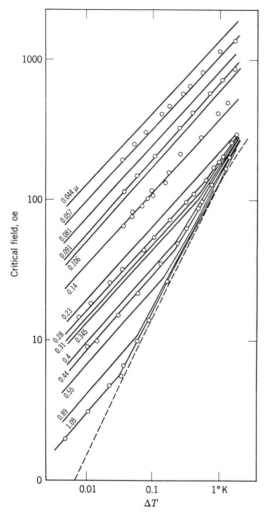

Fig. 4.5 The dependence of critical field on temperature for tin films of various thicknesses (Zavaritsky, 1951).

both λ and ξ depend on the mean free path of the normal electrons, the temperature at which hysteresis appears may depend on grain size as well as film thickness. This problem has been treated theoretically by Gorkov (1960a,b), Douglass (1962), and Bardeen (1962).

The importance of factors such as grain size that affect the m.f.p. is brought out by the results of Behrndt et al. (1960), who have shown that the hysteresis phenomena in tin films depend strongly upon the conditions of preparation. For instance, by depositing films at a substrate temperature of around 100°C they have produced strongly agglomerated films that exhibit hysteresis at higher temperatures than those described by Zavaritsky.

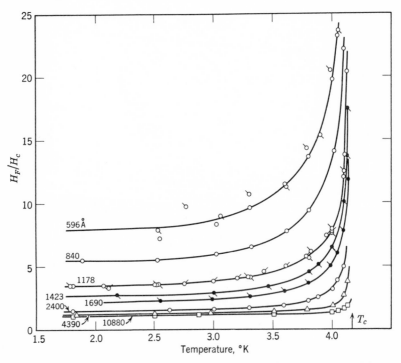

Fig. 4.6 Temperature variation of H_F/H_c for mercury films of various thicknesses (Appleyard et al., 1939).

The theoretical Equations 4.10, 4.11, and 4.12 for the critical field of films much thinner than λ have been verified experimentally by a number of different investigators.[5] In particular it is found that at a specific temperature the critical field of a thin film varies inversely with film thickness, and that for a specific film the critical field is proportional to $(T_c - T)^{1/2}$.

Since λ approaches infinity near T_c a film of given thickness can behave like bulk material at temperatures close to zero with $H_F/H_c \sim 1$, and yet

---

[5] See for instance Zavaritsky (1951a,b), Sebastyanov (1961), and Khukareva (1962).

exhibit "thin" film properties with $H_F/H_c \gg 1$ at temperatures close to T_c. This dependence of effective thickness on temperature is brought out in Figure 4.6.

15.2   Field Normal to Film Surface

According to the theory of Section 5, an ellipsoid of demagnetizing factor N exposed to a field H_0 develops an internal field

$$H_i = \frac{H_0}{(1 - N)}$$

A flat circular film can be approximated by a very oblate ellipsoid of rotation for which $N \sim \left(1 - \dfrac{d}{w}\right)$ where d is the thickness and w the diameter. Hence $H_i \sim H_0\, d/w$, so that flux penetration should occur for very small values of applied field.

DeSorbo and Newhouse (1962) have investigated the penetration of a normal field through lead films using the optical method described in Section 7. The flux penetration phenomena observed on a circular lead film whose circumference includes two tab-like film-free regions, are reproduced in Figure 4.7. In this series of pictures the optical system was arranged so that high-field and low-field regions show up as bright and dark areas respectively.

As the field is increased from zero, it tends to be diverted around the outside of the film. If the field is decreased to zero at this stage, no visible trapped flux remains in the film. If the field is increased further as shown in Figure 4.7a irregular and irreversible flux penetration occurs near the tabs in the film edges where the field intensity is highest. As the field is increased still further, the boundaries of the superconducting regions shrink towards the center of the film in a jerky and irregular manner which is reminiscent of the boundary behavior in bulk samples of the so-called hard superconductors, such as impure niobium. (In bulk samples of lead and of the other soft superconductors, boundary movement is relatively smooth.) If the field applied to the lead film is raised to a high value comparable to the critical field of bulk material, separate domains disappear. If the applied field is now returned to zero, a complex pattern of trapped flux remains in the film as shown in Figure 4.7i. The patterns shown in Figure 4.7 are unlikely to correspond to the domains found in bulk superconductors, and can probably be best explained by a filamentary model of the kind used to account for the properties of high-field super-conductors.[6] Any domains that might exist in these thin films would

---

[6] See Sec. 20.

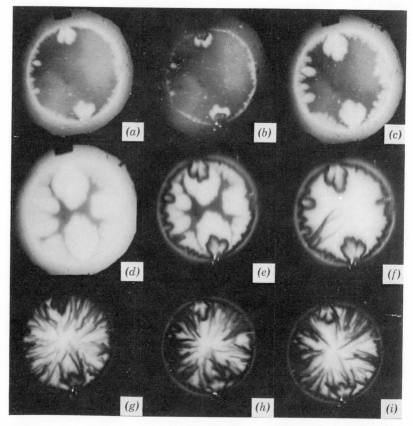

Fig. 4.7 Flux penetration through a 1 micron thick lead film at 1.43°K exposed to a field normal to the surface. (*a*) Applied field 40 oe, peripheral field 135 oe; (*b*) *H* reduced to zero; (*c*) *H* = 59 oe. Abrupt boundary motion occurs; (*d*) *H* = 190 oe; (*e*) *H* reduced to zero; (*f*) *H* = 0 after having been increased to 422 oe. (*g*) *H* = 0 after having been decreased to −428 oe. (*h*) After cycling to ±515 oe; (*i*) after cycling to ±710 oe. (DeSorbo and Newhouse, 1962).

almost certainly be too small to be viewed with either the powder or the optical method.

A thorough study of the resistance transitions of tin films in transverse fields was made by Rhoderick (1962). The transitions were found to be relatively sharp, strongly dependent on measuring current, but to exhibit no hysteresis.[7]

---

[7] It is shown in Sec. 28 that the critical current of a tin film, at least a film with untrimmed edges, is strongly affected by trapped flux. However, this flux is destroyed if the current through the film is increased sufficiently to drive the film fully normal.

By using a Hall-effect probe, Broom and Rhoderick (1962) found that in transverse fields, complete flux penetration occurs at fields far lower than those at which resistance appears (see Fig. 4.8). These data, together with the strong dependence of the resistive transition field on current, indicate that a tin film in a transverse magnetic field contains filaments that remain superconductive after most of the film has become normal.

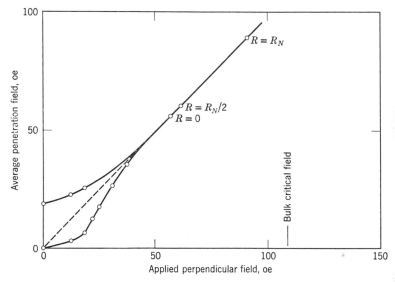

Fig. 4.8 Field normal to the surface of a 2000Å thick tin film at 3°K, as a function of applied transverse field. Note that resistance is fully restored far below the bulk critical field. (Broom and Rhoderick, 1962.)

Tinkham (1963) has been able to account for the flux penetration results by means of the Ginzburg-Landau theory, treating the film as a class II superconductor.

Studies of the resistance transition of relatively thick tin and tantalum foils in transverse fields have been carried out by Davies (1960) and Reeber (1960) respectively. In both cases, the resistance transition was found to start at fields well below H_c, as would be expected from a "soft" superconductor.

16. CURRENT INDUCED TRANSITIONS

In Section 14.2 we calculated the critical current of cylindrical films much thinner than the penetration depth, under conditions where edge effects could be neglected. In this section we describe and analyze the current-induced transitions of more complex geometries that are of device interest, such as flat films, and films thicker than the penetration depth.

16.1   Flat Films

The properties of superconductors make it possible to use a particularly simple geometry, shown in Figure 4.9, for measuring the current-induced transition in flat films of tin or indium. The wide ends of the dumb-bell shaped films to be measured are covered with a vacuum-deposited film of lead which, having a higher critical temperature than the tin or indium film, can be assumed to remain superconducting for all experimentally applied currents and temperatures. The current and potential leads are soldered or pressed to this lead film. The width of that portion of the film whose critical current is to be measured is deliberately made much smaller than that of the remainder. Since the critical current is found to depend on film width, this portion of the film will become resistive at currents at which the wider regions remain super-conducting. This ensures that the alloyed regions at the edge of the lead film do not affect the measurements.

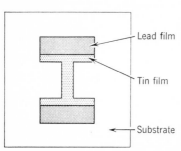

Fig. 4.9 Geometry for measuring current induced transitions in flat films.

The process of the current-induced transition for a thin film carrying a uniformly distributed current was described in Section 14.2. The current-induced transition for flat films, which is analyzed in this section, is more complex and less well understood but plays an important role in the action of superconductive film devices deposited on flat surfaces.

In the case of uniformly distributed current flowing through a film, the field due to the current is uniform over the film surface and parallel to it. We will now show that when current flows in a flat film, the surface field and current density vary from point to point of the surface, and that if the film is thin compared to the penetration depth, fields normal to the surface are present.

By making use of one of the analogies proved in Section 12, it can be seen that current carried in a long flat superconducting strip is distributed over its surface in the same way as electric charge would be distributed over the surface of an electrostatically charged strip of the same shape, provided that field penetration into the superconductor is neglected. Using conformal mapping techniques the surface current density at a distance x from the center of a strip of width $2w$ carrying current I can be shown to be[8]

$$J(x) = \frac{I}{2\pi(w^2 - x^2)^{1/2}}$$

This expression is plotted in Figure 4.10. Since the superconducting strip has been assumed to be perfectly diamagnetic, the field outside the film is everywhere parallel to the surface. Since the film thickness has been neglected, the calculated current density approaches infinity at the film

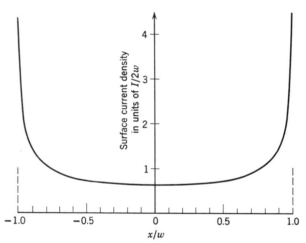

Fig. 4.10 Calculated surface current per unit width in a flat superconducting film of width $2w$ and thickness d, carrying current I. $w \gg d \gg \lambda$.

edges. Rhoderick and Wilson (1962) have shown that this approximation does not strongly affect the calculated perpendicular field outside the film, and they have found that the measured perpendicular field near a 1.5 mm wide, 2000 Å thick, lead film at 4.2°K agrees to within the experimental error with that calculated from the current distribution shown in the figure.

It is now clear that the measured critical current density of a flat film must be much less than that calculated assuming uniform current distribution, since the requirement that the surface field generated by the current be parallel to the film surface, leads to the very uneven current distribution shown in Figure 4.10. If the current through a film is increased to a point where an appreciable portion of the film edges become normal, the extra current will flow through the center of the film, producing a more uniform current distribution. This leads to the generation of a field component

[8] See Appendix 35.2.

normal to the film. When the current through the film is large enough to drive it fully normal, the current will be distributed uniformly across the film, and strong fields normal to the plane of the film will be present.[9]

The superconducting films whose transitions have been studied most carefully are indium and tin films of a thickness comparable to the penetration depth. If the current through such films is increased slowly, resistance begins to appear, as shown in Figure 4.11, at a current value I_c that is

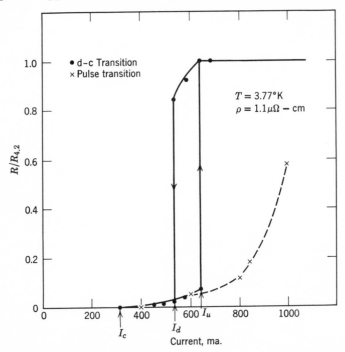

Fig. 4.11 Current induced transitions in a 3000Å thick, 4 mm wide tin film deposited on single crystal sapphire. $T_c - T = 0.08°$K (Bremer and Newhouse, 1959).

found to be proportional to the film width, and that has approximately 10 per cent to 20 per cent of the magnitude calculated by assuming uniform current distribution.[10] If the current is increased further, the resistance continues to increase reversibly up to a current value I_u beyond which it increases abruptly and irreversibly[11] to the full normal value. To return the film to the superconducting state the current has now to be decreased to a value I_d that may be considerably smaller than I_u. The transition to

---

[9] These fields are calculated in Sec. 28.
[10] See for instance Feigin and Shalnikov (1956).
[11] Irreversible is here used in the thermodynamic sense.

the superconducting state that takes place at this current is again abrupt and irreversible. It is shown in Section 17 that these abrupt resistance changes and the accompanying hysteresis are exclusively due to joule heating produced in the film, and depend on the film resistivity and substrate thermal conductivity rather than on the superconducting characteristics of the film.

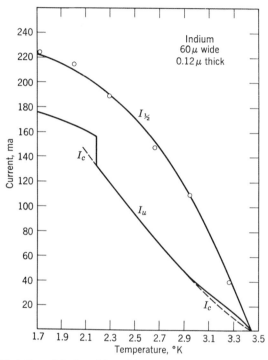

Fig. 4.12 Variation of I_c, I_u and $I_{1/2}$ with temperature for a typical film of a soft superconductor (Crittenden et al., 1960). I_c is current corresponding to onset of resistance, I_u is current corresponding to onset of thermal propagation (see Sec. 17), and $I_{1/2}$ is current corresponding to midpoint of isothermal transition.

By measuring the current-induced transition with short current pulses and using a substrate such as single crystal quartz, or sapphire, which has a high thermal conductivity, it is possible to suppress joule heating phenomena in the presence of the small critical currents obtained near the critical temperature.[12] Transitions measured in this manner are found to be very broad, as shown in the broken line of Figure 4.11, and will be

---

[12] Bremer and Newhouse (1959). See also Kolchin et al. (1961), who report the existence of hysteresis effects that may be due to redistribution of current in the film during a pulse.

referred to as "iso-thermal" transitions. Their breadth, as well as other evidence presented below, indicates that the surface current distribution at which resistance first appears, is quite non-uniform.

For the 0.3 micron thick tin films investigated, it was found that the shape of the isothermal transition was independent of film resistivity over a range of values of 3 to 1, and that the value of (pulse) current $I_{1/2}$ at which the film resistance attained half its normal value agreed with that predicted from Equation 4.11, provided that T was so close to T_c that the penetration depth was equal or larger than the film thickness. Since this formula was derived for a uniformly distributed current, this agreement indicates that the film current at the half-resistance point is distributed approximately uniformly across the width of the film.

Crittenden et al. (1960) have measured I_c, I_u, and $I_{1/2}$ for a number of thicknesses of tin and indium films over a wide temperature range. Representative curves are shown in Figure 4.12. It is seen that the curve for I_c is concave upwards near T_c where λ is larger than the film thickness, as predicted by the theories discussed in Section 14.2. The curves for I_c and I_u merge at a temperature just below T_c because the evolution of joule heat becomes excessive, so that thermal "runaway" occurs as soon as the film starts to exhibit resistance.[13] The curves separate once more at the λ point, below which the thermal conductivity of liquid helium rises by an order of magnitude.

16.2 Cylindrical and Shielded Films

If current flows along a film deposited in the form of a hollow cylinder, the edge effects that create a non-uniform current distribution for flat films must disappear. It is not certain however that other effects leading to a non-uniform current distribution may not be present, associated with current spiraling around the cylinder axis.

This may be the reason why experiments on cylindrical tin films by N. I. Ginzburg and A. I. Shalnikov (1960) give critical current magnitudes that are only 22 per cent of the theoretical value.

A geometry that is easier to fabricate than a cylinder and in which neither edge effects nor circulating current effects can occur, is that of a film deposited on a flat insulated "shield plane" made of a superconductor with a higher critical temperature. This case was analyzed in Section 12, where it was shown that current flowing through such a film must be uniformly distributed over its surface except for a region comparable to the film-shield separation, near the edges. The average surface current density I_c at which resistance appears should thus be higher for a shielded

---

[13] In this region even I_c has to be determined by pulse methods, since the heat evolved by a fully normal film in the presence of d.c. is sufficient to destroy it.

film than for an unshielded film of the same thickness, since a uniform current distribution can not exist in an unshielded superconducting film.

This conclusion has been verified experimentally[14] as illustrated by Figure 4.13. This shows that I_c for a shielded tin film is considerably larger than that for an identical unshielded film at all temperatures below T_c. For the shielded film, I_c is closely proportional to $(T_c - T)^{3/2}$ as

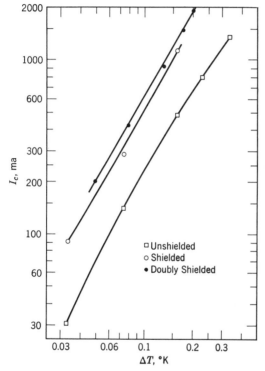

Fig. 4.13 Currents corresponding to the onset of resistance for 3000Å × 2 mm unshielded, singly shielded, and doubly shielded tin films on glass. 10,000Å thick lead films insulated by 9,000Å of SiO were used for shielding (Edwards and Newhouse, 1962).

predicted by theory for films thinner than the penetration depth. However, the magnitudes of I_c although larger than those found by Ginzburg and Shalnikov for cylindrical films of the same thickness, are still somewhat smaller than the values predicted by Equation 4.11.

As shown in Figure 4.13 it is found that I_c for a shielded tin film can be increased by depositing an insulated second lead shield film on top of it, that is, by forming a sandwich of lead-insulator-tin-insulator-lead.

---

[14] Edwards and Newhouse (1962).

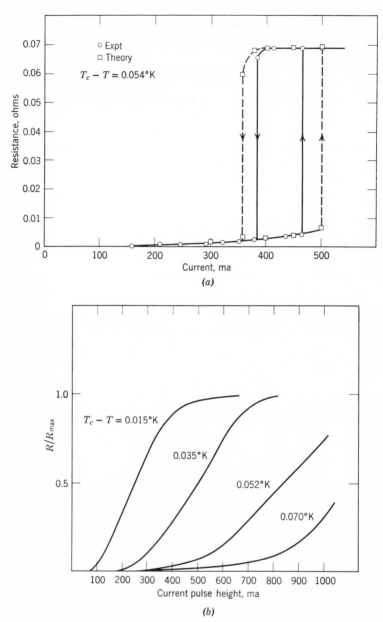

Fig. 4.14 Current-induced phase transitions for a 3000 Å × 3.75 mm tin film deposited on single crystal sapphire (Bremer and Newhouse, 1959). (a) Experimental and calculated d-c transitions. (b) Isothermal transitions measured with 12 microsecond pulses.

This result is explained by reference to Figure 3.13, which shows that the field on the side opposite the shield plane of a shielded, current-carrying film is approximately zero. This effect is due to the canceling action of the film current and the shield screening currents and must therefore be true even for films much thicker than the penetration depth. In a current-carrying shielded film whose thickness is comparable to the penetration depth, the current will be distributed approximately uniformly throughout the film thickness. However, if the thickness is much greater than λ, all the current will flow on that side of the film adjacent to the shield plane since the film surface field on the other side is zero. Since, for such a film, Silsbee's condition should hold, the film will enter the intermediate state and begin to exhibit resistance at the current at which the field between it and the shield plane reaches H_c.

If a film thick compared to λ is sandwiched between two shield planes, symmetry considerations show that any current passed through the film will divide itself uniformly between the two surfaces. Hence for a given input current, the surface current density and thus the field on each side of a doubly shielded film will only be half of that on the shield side of a singly-shielded film. It is for this reason that I_c for a doubly-shielded film much thicker than λ should be approximately double that for a singly-shielded film.

17. JOULE HEATING EFFECTS

As mentioned in Section 16.1, joule heating causes a discontinuous increase in the resistance and temperature of a superconductive film carrying a slowly increasing current. Furthermore the transition from the superconducting to the normal state takes place at higher currents than the normal-to-superconducting transition. This hysteresis phenomenon, which is often called thermal latching, is described and analyzed in Section 17.1.

The dynamics of the heat-induced transitions are examined in Section 17.2 where it is shown that a small normal region in a current-carrying film can propagate over the remainder in a process called thermal propagation.

17.1   Thermal Latching

The hysteresis effect produced by joule heating during the current-induced phase transition of superconductive films is illustrated in Figure 4.14a. A graphical method[15] of deriving the d-c hysteresis curve from the isothermal transition data will be described.

---

[15] Bremer and Newhouse (1959).

Consider a film with a temperature and current-dependent resistance R, carrying a current I, immersed in helium at temperature T_0. The heat evolved will be I^2R and the film and the substrate immediately underneath it will be at a temperature T that is far enough above T_0 that the heat loss to the helium is equal to the evolved heat. The heat loss to liquid helium is found to be of the form $FA(T - T_0)$ where $F =$ approximately 200

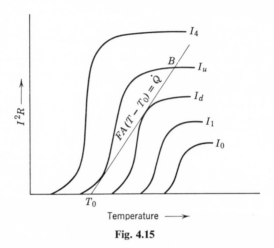

Fig. 4.15

mw/cm²/degree K.[16] Hence the equilibrium temperature and resistance of the film are given by the equation

$$I^2R = FA(T - T_0) \tag{4.13}$$

This equation can be solved graphically using the isothermal transition curves of Figure 4.14b. The results are first replotted as curves of I^2R versus T, shown schematically in Figure 4.15. For a particular current, the solution of Equation 4.13 is then given by the intercept of the corresponding current curve with the straight line, which represents the right-hand side of the equation. For a current increasing from zero, the equilibrium temperature and resistance of the film are given by the lower intercept of this line with the I^2R curve. At a current I_u the straight line becomes tangential to the I^2R curve. For higher currents the equilibrium becomes unstable and the temperature and film resistance increase discontinuously to values corresponding to the upper intercept B. In the case illustrated, this transition corresponds to the temperature region where the film resistance varies only slowly with temperature. If the current is now

---

[16] Karagounis (1956).

reduced, the downward discontinuous transition occurs at a lower value of current I_d.

From this treatment we see that the discontinuous transitions occur when

$$\left(\frac{\partial(I^2R)}{\partial T}\right)_I = FA$$

that is, when

$$I^2\left(\frac{\partial R}{\partial T}\right)_I = FA \qquad (4.14)$$

A hysteresis curve calculated with this method, using the isothermal curves of Figure 4.14b is shown dotted in Figure 4.14a and can be seen to provide reasonable agreement with experiment.

We can convert Equation 4.14 into a form independent of the film width and length l. If the resistance of the film per square is r ohms, and if i is the current per unit width, then

$$R = \frac{rl}{w}$$

$$I = iw$$

and

$$A = wl$$

Substituting these quantities into Equation 4.14 gives $i^2(\partial r/\partial T)_i = F$. This shows that the current corresponding to the abrupt resistance transitions is proportional to film width provided that the film is much wider than the substrate thickness. This prediction is confirmed by experiment, for films on substrates of high thermal conductivity such as single crystal sapphire.

It is apparent that in the graphical analysis carried out above, the temperature was assumed constant over the whole film. This is equivalent to assuming that the whole of the film undergoes a transition at the same time. It is shown in the next section that the transition actually starts at the hottest point of the film (usually midway between the ends) and proceeds progressively towards the ends. The assumption of uniform temperature used in the above calculation is justified however provided that the temperature difference between the center and the ends of the film is always small compared to the width of the isothermal transition at constant (pulse) current. This can be calculated to be true for the case analyzed above.

Hysteresis in the current-induced phase transition for tin films on glass substrates is even more pronounced than that shown in Figure 4.14a. This happens because the thermal conductivity of glass at liquid helium temperatures is approximately 0.01 per cent that of single crystal sapphire. It is also found that the loop shape is no longer independent of film width, presumably because the temperature is not constant over the film surface.[17]

17.2 Thermal Propagation

Curves such as Figure 4.14a illustrate that a current-carrying tin film can exhibit two equilibrium values of temperature and resistance. It was shown by Bremer and Newhouse (1958) that, in the presence of a suitable constant film current, a transition from the low to the high-resistance state can be initiated by generating heat at any point of the film. Once a sufficiently hot normal nucleus has been formed, heat conduction makes the adjacent parts of the film normal. These produce additional joule heat causing further growth of the normal region, which rapidly covers the whole film. This phenomenon is called thermal propagation and can take place at velocities of up to 10^6 cm/sec.

A convenient method of initiating thermal propagation employs a current-carrying wire placed transversely to an insulated superconducting film. The magnetic field from the wire produces a resistive region in the adjacent part of the film. If the film carries current, joule heat will be developed in the resistive region, producing a local rise in temperature. If the current through the film is made sufficiently large, the rise in temperature will increase the resistive region, which will then start to grow spontaneously at a speed determined by the joule heating and by the thermal diffusivity of the film and substrate.

The results of an experiment of this type are shown in Figure 4.16. The values of the nucleating wire current I_N are those required to initiate thermal propagation at the corresponding film current I_M. It can be calculated that the minimum size of nucleus sufficient to initiate thermal propagation varies inversely with the magnitude of the film current. This is the reason why larger values of nucleating current are required at the lower values of film current. Thermal propagation can only take place at film currents for which two equilibrium resistance values exist.

The dynamics of this process have been studied with a specimen consisting of a tin film on glass crossed by two lead nucleating wires as shown in Figure 4.17a. A broad current pulse is passed through the tin film. Shortly after the start of the current a much narrower nucleating pulse is passed through one or both of the nucleating wires. The variation with time of voltage across the film is measured with an oscilloscope and appears as shown in Figure 4.17b, c, or d, depending on which wire or wires is used to nucleate.

---

[17] Bremer and Newhouse *op. cit.*

Figure 4.17b corresponds to the case where the central wire 2 is pulsed. This creates two phase boundaries that propagate in opposite directions along the film and reach the ends simultaneously. Since the number of boundaries and their velocity is constant, film resistance increases uniformly with time. Consider now the case where wire 1 is used as a nucleus. Let it be assumed that the normal-superconducting boundaries are at all times parallel to the nucleating wire and move at constant speed along the film. A break in the voltage-versus-time curve would then be

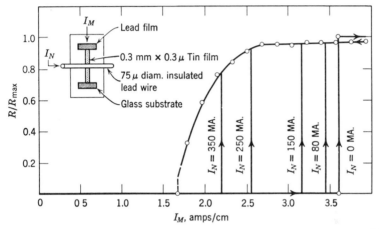

Fig. 4.16 Phase transitions in a current carrying tin film deposited on glass; initiated by currents I_N in a 75 micron diameter superconducting lead wire placed transverse to the film. $T_c - T = 0.28°K$. (Bremer and Newhouse, 1958.)

expected when one of the boundaries reaches the nearest end of the film. Since nucleating wire 1 is at a distance of one quarter of the film length from one end, the break should occur at half the maximum resistance. This prediction is found to be confirmed as shown by the curve of Figure 4.17c, indicating the correctness of the assumptions made with respect to the shape and velocity of the interphase boundaries.

Figure 4.17d shows the case where both nucleating wires are pulsed simultaneously. Point k in this picture corresponds to the disappearance of the two central boundaries as they meet. Points i and j indicate the arrival of the two remaining boundaries at the ends of the specimen.

If the current pulse through the film is made large enough to cause a spontaneous superconducting-to-normal transition, a curve similar to Figure 4.17b is obtained. This proves that spontaneous transitions normally start midway between the ends of the film. This probably happens because the temperature of a current-carrying film is a maximum

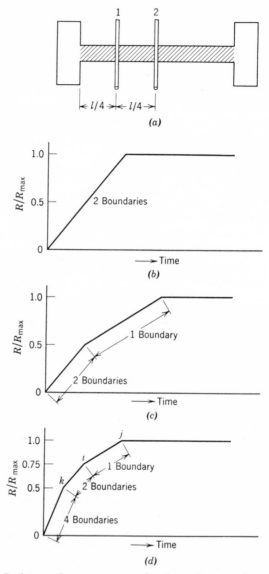

Fig. 4.17 Resistance changes accompanying thermal propagation (Bremer and New-house, 1958). (*a*) Superconducting film crossed by two insulated nucleating wires. (*b*) Nucleation of normal region at midpoint of film (wire 2). (*c*) Wire 1 used for nucle-ation. (*d*) Simultaneous nucleation with both wires.

at the center. If the film contains a narrow region where the current density is high, thermal propagation starts there. The distance of the nucleation site from the nearest end of the film can be deduced from the fraction of the maximum voltage at which the break in the voltage-time curve occurs.

17.3 Thermal Propagation Velocity

The velocity of the phase boundaries during thermal propagation depends on the joule heating, on the thermal properties of the substrate, and on the efficiency of heat transfer from the film to the substrate. The propagation velocity can be calculated as follows.[18]

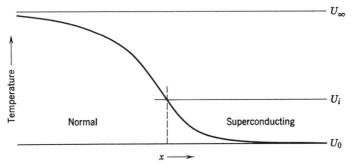

Fig. 4.18 Schematic of the temperature profile moving from left to right during thermal propagation.

Consider an infinitely long current-carrying film of unit width deposited on a substrate that is so thin that the temperature variation normal to its surface can be neglected. If a normal region is formed in the film and starts to propagate, it can be assumed that the phase boundary velocity will eventually reach a constant value. The boundary will then be characterized by a moving temperature profile of constant form, approximately as shown in Figure 4.18. It is the form and velocity of this profile that will be calculated here.

The main parameters used in the calculations are as follows:

t time
x distance along strip
v phase boundary velocity
D substrate thickness
ρ substrate density
s substrate specific heat

---

[18] Broom and Rhoderick (1960), Cherry and Gittleman (1960), Schmidlin and Crittenden (1960).

k substrate thermal conductivity
F heat loss coefficient
U_0 bath temperature
U_n, U_s, and U_i film temperature in the normal and superconductive regions and at the phase boundary respectively
U_c film critical temperature
U_∞ maximum film temperature
r film resistance per square
i film current per unit width
I_c film critical current per unit width

Since we may assume that most of the heat is carried by the substrate, we can neglect the thermal conductivity and specific heat of the film. For the sake of simplicity it is assumed that the width of the temperature-induced transition at current density i is so small that the transition region between the normal and superconducting phase is small compared to the width of the temperature profile shown schematically in Figure 4.18.

The various terms that determine the heat balance in the film and substrate are derived as follows. The thermal conductivity is defined so that the heat flow across any surface at temperature U and position x in the substrate is equal to $Dk(\partial U/\partial x)$. Hence the net increase in heat per unit time due to heat conduction in a segment of unit width and of length Δx is equal to $Dk(\partial^2 U/\partial x^2)\,\Delta x$. The heat loss to the helium is equal to $2\,\Delta x F(U - U_0)$, and the joule heat produced in the normal region is $i^2 \Delta x\, r$. Furthermore the heat inflow into a region exhibiting a temperature rise $\partial U/\partial t$ is equal to $\Delta x\, Ds\rho(\partial U/\partial t)$.

Combining all these terms and simplifying we find that the thermal equilibrium in the superconducting region is given by the equation

$$\frac{\partial U_s}{\partial t} = \frac{k}{\rho s}\frac{\partial^2 U_s}{\partial x^2} - \frac{2F}{D\rho s}(U_s - U_0) \tag{4.15}$$

In the normal region we have

$$\frac{\partial U_n}{\partial t} = \frac{k}{\rho s}\frac{\partial^2 U_n}{\partial x^2} - \frac{2F}{D\rho s}(U_n - U_0) + \frac{i^2 r}{D\rho s} \tag{4.16}$$

The assumption that the temperature profile does not change with time enables us to eliminate the time-dependent terms in the above expressions provided that we use a reference frame moving at the boundary velocity. Taking the boundary as the origin of coordinates we have

$$\frac{\partial U}{\partial t} = -v\frac{\partial U}{\partial x} \tag{4.17}$$

Substituting for $\partial U/\partial t$ in Equations 4.15 and 4.16 we obtain the ordinary differential equations

$$\frac{k}{v\rho s}\frac{d^2 U_s}{dx^2} + \frac{dU_s}{dx} - \frac{2F}{v\,D\rho s}(U_s - U_0) = 0 \qquad (4.18)$$

and

$$\frac{k}{v\rho s}\frac{d^2 U_n}{dx^2} + \frac{dU_n}{dx} - \frac{2F}{v\,D\rho s}(U_n - U_0) + \frac{i^2 r}{v\,D\rho s} = 0 \qquad (4.19)$$

In the normal region far away from the phase boundary the temperature reaches the equilibrium value U_∞ determined by the equation

$$2F(U_\infty - U_0) = i^2 r \qquad (4.20)$$

With this expression we are able to simplify Equation 4.19 to the form

$$\frac{k}{v\rho s}\frac{d^2 U_n}{dx^2} + \frac{dU_n}{dx} - \frac{2F}{v\,d\rho s}[U_n - U_\infty] = 0 \qquad (4.21)$$

By standard methods we find the solutions of 4.18 and 4.21 to be

$$U_s - U_0 = A \exp\left[-mx(1 + \sqrt{1 + \eta})\right]$$

and

$$U_n - U_\infty = B \exp\left[-mx(1 - \sqrt{1 + \eta})\right]$$

where

$$m = \frac{v\rho s}{2k} \quad \text{and} \quad \eta = \frac{8Fk}{D(v\rho s)^2}.$$

A and B are constants of integration that can be determined in terms of the temperature at the phase boundary. This procedure gives

$$U_s - U_0 = (U_i - U_0) \exp\left[-mx(1 + \sqrt{1 + \eta})\right]$$

and
$$\qquad (4.22)$$
$$U_n - U_\infty = (U_i - U_\infty) \exp\left[-mx(1 - \sqrt{1 + \eta})\right]$$

These equations still contain the unknown parameter v. This is determined by using the condition that the heat flow across the moving phase boundary must be continuous in the absence of a latent heat term, that is,

$$DK\frac{dU_n}{dx} = DK\frac{dU_s}{dx}$$

at $x = 0$.

Applying this condition to Equations 4.22 and simplifying, we obtain finally

$$v = \frac{\alpha - 1}{\sqrt{\alpha}}\frac{1}{\rho s}\sqrt{\frac{2Fk}{D}} \qquad (4.23)$$

where

$$\alpha = \frac{U_\infty - U_i}{U_i - U_0} \tag{4.24}$$

These equations enable us to describe three limiting cases by inspection. Clearly $v = 0$, for $\alpha = 1$. This corresponds to a condition of static boundary equilibrium. An experiment demonstrating boundary equilibrium is described below.

If $U_i = U_0$, $\alpha = \infty$ and $v = \infty$. This corresponds to the case where the current through the film is increased to such a value that the whole film becomes resistive simultaneously. In practice, a finite time would of course be required even in this case for the substrate to heat up. The result $v = \infty$ is due to the assumption that the film has a negligibly wide temperature-induced transition.

We will finally consider the case of an infinite film held in the normal state at temperature U_∞ by joule heating. If the film current were gradually reduced, the transition to the superconducting state would not take place until the current fell below the value of I_c corresponding to the temperature U_∞. (The fact that U_∞ is itself a function of I_c does not affect this argument.) The transition would clearly take place simultaneously over the whole film. Viewed analytically, $U_\infty = U_i$, hence $\alpha = 0$ so that $v = -\infty$. The infinite value for the velocity is again due to the assumption of a negligible transition width. In the case of a finite normal film with central temperature U_∞ but having "cool" ends, the collapse of the normal region would take place at *higher* values of film current than the critical, that is, as soon as the film current fell below the value corresponding to $\alpha = 1$, and would then occur at finite velocity.

To obtain the velocity as a function of film current, we must substitute for U_∞ and U_i in Equation 4.24 in terms of their dependence on i. The dependence of U_∞ on i is given in Equation 4.20. To represent U_i, we will make the simplifying assumption that the film critical current varies linearly with $U_c - U$, that is,

$$\frac{i}{I_c} = \frac{U_c - U_i}{U_c - U_0} \tag{4.25}$$

Using Equations 4.20 and 4.25 to substitute for U_∞ and U_i in Equations 4.24, and simplifying, we obtain

$$\alpha = \frac{i^2}{I_c - i} \xi - 1 \tag{4.26}$$

where

$$\xi = \frac{I_c r}{2F(U_c - U_o)} \tag{4.27}$$

Broom and Rhoderick (1960) have calculated the expression $(\alpha - 1)/\sqrt{\alpha}$ that occurs in Equation 4.23 for v, for the condition that $i = \frac{1}{2}I_c$ for $v = 0$, that is for $\alpha = 1$. From Equation 4.26 this is equivalent to putting

$$\xi = \frac{4}{I_c} \tag{4.28}$$

This makes α into a non-dimensional function of i/I_c.

The result of this calculation is shown in Figure 4.19. In accordance with the initial assumption $v = 0$ when $i = \frac{1}{2}I_c$; v approaches infinity as i/I_c approaches unity.

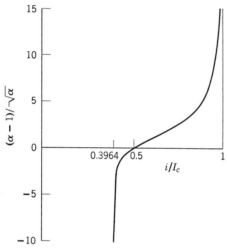

Fig. 4.19 The thermal propagation velocity constant of Eq. 4.23 calculated as a function of i/I_c for the case $U_\infty - U_i = U_i - U_0$ at $i = \frac{1}{2}I_c$ (Broom and Rhoderick, 1960).

By setting the condition $\alpha = 0$ (which corresponds to $v = -\infty$), in Equation 4.26, we find that this occurs as $i \rightarrow 0.396I_c$. From Equations 4.20, 4.25, 4.27, and 4.28, it can be verified that $U_i = U_\infty$ for this value of i, as would be anticipated from the preceding discussion.

In view of the simplifying assumptions made in the analysis, exact agreement with experiment cannot be expected. Measurements of the thermal propagation velocity in a tin film are shown in Figure 4.20, and are seen to fall on curves similar to the positive portion of the theoretical curve.

The prediction that the thermal propagation velocity can be reduced to zero has been confirmed by Broom and Rhoderick (1960). In their experiment a steady current corresponding to $v = 0$ is passed through a superconducting film. If an additional current pulse is then superimposed on this film, a normal region is produced that remains stable or almost stable for a period of at least several microseconds. Successive "ignition" pulses produce corresponding increases in the size of the normal region

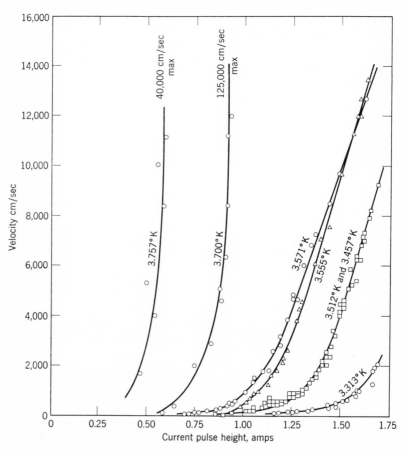

Fig. 4.20 Thermal propagation velocity in a 1000Å × 0.5 mm tin film, $T_c = 3.87°K$, residual resistance 7 milliohms/mm. Substrate unknown (Cherry and Gittleman, 1960).

(or regions). The reverse quenching process is initiated by an opposed pulse that temporarily reduced the film current to zero. The length of this quenching pulse is determined by the cooling time of the film and substrate. Cooling times for tin and lead films on various substrates are found to vary between approximately 50 nanoseconds for tin films on mica, to 5 microseconds for lead films on glass.

18. DEPENDENCE OF FILM PROPERTIES ON PREPARATION

Many properties of superconductive films such as grain size and impurity concentration, which affect the correlation length and normal resistivity, are strongly dependent on the method and conditions of preparation. In Section 18.1, which follows, we briefly survey the best known methods of film fabrication.

The method that has been studied and used most extensively is that of vacuum deposition. The effect of vacuum deposition conditions on film properties is therefore examined in some detail in Section 18.2, which concludes the chapter.

18.1 Miscellaneous Methods

ROLLING.   Thin foil of many metals can be prepared by repeated rolling of sheets of bulk material. Foils of the soft superconductors down to less than 1 mil in thickness can be easily prepared by this method. Annealing treatment is often unnecessary since metals such as lead, tin and indium anneal at room temperature.

ETCHING.   Another method of preparing metallic foil from bulk material, which is used to prepare small area specimens for transmission microscopy, is that of electrolytically etching away a spot in the center of a disk of metal.

ELECTRODEPOSITION.   Electrolytic deposition in liquids has been used to form a superconducting film on non-superconductive conducting substrates.[19] It can also be used on insulating substrates that are previously covered with a thin conducting layer (usually a sputtered gold film). The method has been displaced by vacuum deposition in popularity but is quite practicable for many applications.

SPUTTERING.   In this method the metal to be deposited is made the cathode of an electric discharge in a low pressure gas. Ions of the cathode material are formed due to ionic bombardment. These ions can be caused to fall onto a suitably placed substrate. Sputtering is particularly convenient for the deposition of the refractory metals such as tantalum and niobium, whose boiling points are too high for convenient evaporation from a crucible.[20]

PYROLYSIS.   This method, which is particularly useful for the deposition of refractory materials of high boiling point, involves the formation of a compound of the metal that has a lower boiling point than the pure metal. The vapor of this compound can be arranged to decompose on a substrate held at a temperature high enough for decomposition. A related method

---

[19] See for instance Misener (1936).
[20] See for instance Whohareva and Shalnikov (1954).

that uses electron beam bombardment for the selective deposition of tin obtained by the decomposition of the vapor of organic tin compounds, has been reported by Christy (1962).

18.2   Vacuum Deposition

EFFECT OF DEPOSITION RATE AND SUBSTRATE TEMPERATURE.   In this, the most widely used method for the preparation of superconducting films, the metal is boiled off from an electrically heated source in vacuum and allowed to deposit on a cooler substrate.[21]

The pressures used for vacuum deposition are 10^{-5} tor or less, depending on the extent of the permissible gas contamination of the film. Variously shaped masks can be placed between the source and substrate, allowing metals to be deposited in complex patterns. The metal atoms that are boiled off from the source and land on the substrate do not lose all their kinetic energy immediately. Instead they move on the substrate and occasionally re-evaporate to an extent determined by chemical affinity and temperature. Under suitable conditions the evaporant agglomerates as discrete islands that form a continuous film after an adequate amount of metal has been deposited. For instance it was found by Niebuhr (1952) that when evaporating tin on room temperature quartz at pressures between $2 \cdot 10^{-6}$ and 10^{-5} tor, an amount of tin corresponding to a mean thickness of approximately 1000 Å had to be deposited before a continuous film is formed. For a substrate at liquid nitrogen temperature (78°K) on the other hand, the minimum mean thickness continuous film that could be formed was reduced to a lower limit of approximately 30 Å. In general, low substrate temperatures and high rates of deposition are necessary for the formation of very thin continuous films. After depositing a film at a reduced substrate temperature it can often be annealed without damage by bringing it to a temperature closer to the mp since surface tension effects prevent it from re-agglomerating. For tin and lead films, annealing takes place at room temperature.

EFFECT OF RESIDUAL GASES.   It can be calculated that for deposition from normal sources at pressures in the 10^{-6} to 10^{-5} tor range, between 1 per cent and 50 per cent of the particles striking the substrate are gas atoms. In systems that can be baked out it is possible to vacuum deposit at pressures of the order of 10^{-9} tor where gas contamination is negligible. Caswell has used such a system to investigate the effect of specific contaminating gases on evaporated tin[22] and indium.[23]

---

[21] For a description of vacuum deposition equipment and methods, see L. Holland, *Vacuum Deposition of Thin Films.* New York: Wiley, 1956.
[22] Caswell (1961a).
[23] Caswell (1961b).

It is known that in general the adhesion of metals to glass substrates due to Van der Waal forces is small, and that the main part of the adhesion of metals other than the noble metals is due to the formation of chemical bonds with the glass.[24] Caswell found, as might be expected, that the adhesion of tin evaporated onto a baked-out substrate in a very low vacuum was much impaired, and that the tendency to agglomerate was increased. It was found difficult to prepare continuous films less than 2000 Å thick under these extremely clean conditions. The edges of films deposited through a mask under these conditions of high surface mobility presented a broken-up appearance. It was determined that if the ratio of oxygen atoms to tin atoms hitting the substrate is greater than 0.1 per cent, the tin surface mobility is reduced, so that it "wets" the glass, forming drawn-out edges. Since the edges of a flat film have a strong effect in determining the value of magnetic field at which such a film becomes resistive when carrying a small current, the condition of these edges is important (see Sec. 15.1). Caswell finds that if oxygen atoms hitting the substrate are 10 per cent or less of the tin atoms, the edge of the film is the only point that is contaminated. If this edge is removed mechanically, the electrical properties of the film become indistinguishable from those of a film evaporated in the absence of oxygen. It is possible to produce a broken-up edge structure even in the presence of oxygen by evaporating onto a heated substrate,[25] preferably using additional nucleation sites[26] or by annealing the film after evaporation.[27]

Caswell found the effect of all the other gases commonly present in evaporators to be negligible except for water vapor, whose effect is about 10 per cent of that due to oxygen. He therefore concludes that to produce tin films that are indistinguishable from those produced at 10^{-9} tor it is possible to use pressures as high as 10^{-5} tor provided the partial pressures of O_2, CO_2, and H_2O are kept below the values

$$\text{for oxygen} \quad 5 \times 10^{-8} \text{ tor}$$

$$\text{for } H_2O \quad 4 \times 10^{-7} \text{ tor}$$

$$\text{and for } CO_2 \quad 8 \times 10^{-7} \text{ tor}$$

using specific pumping agents. Indium films were found to have a smaller sensitivity than tin to oxygen and water vapor, and to be unaffected by CO_2.

---

[24] See Benjamin and Weaver (1960).
[25] Behrndt et al. (1960).
[26] Holland *op. cit.*
[27] Kahan et al. (1960).

EFFECT OF SUBSTRATE STRUCTURE.   The effect of the substrate thermal conductivity on the current-induced transition has already been discussed (see Sec. 17), as has the effect of a superconducting substrate in increasing I_c (see Sec. 16).   The other substrate parameter of measurable effect is the expansion coefficient with temperature, which affects the film critical temperature.

The films of the soft superconductors partially anneal at room temperature, which tends to relieve stresses.   On cooling, the film usually contracts more than the substrate.   This produces a tensile stress in the film which is often strong enough to cause plastic deformation.   For tin films deposited on glass, this increases the critical temperature by as much as $0.23°K$ above the bulk value.[28]

In the case of indium which has a lower yield stress than tin, substrate contraction increases T_c by less than $0.06°K$ above the bulk value.[29] For both tin and indium, thin films show the greatest increase in T_c. This is believed to be due to the fact that thin films have a higher yield stress than thick films because of dislocation pinning at the film surfaces and grain boundaries.

References

A number of important topics that have had to be omitted for various reasons are described in the following references.

The transmission of infrared radiation through superconducting films; see for instance Tinkham (1960).

The carry-over of properties between adjacent normal and superconducting films; see for instance Simmons and Douglas (1962).

The effect of electrostatic charging on the critical temperature of superconducting films; Glover and Sherrill (1960).

Radiation induced transport of magnetic flux along a superconducting sheet; Marchand (1962).

---

[28] Blumberg and Seraphim (1962).
[29] Toxen (1961).

chapter 5
_____

Superconducting Solenoids and Magneto-Mechanical Devices

19. INTRODUCTORY SUMMARY

Magnetic fields of several hundred oersteds generated with conventional solenoids are widely employed for various laboratory and engineering purposes. Larger fields are generated by winding the solenoid on an "iron" core, that is, on a metal of high magnetic permeability, and in addition by shaping the magnet pole pieces so as to concentrate the magnetic flux in the vicinity of the air gap.

Conventional ferromagnets saturate at fields in the vicinity of 25 koe so that their presence leads to no advantage at fields above this value. Higher fields are therefore generated with air core solenoids, using some form of liquid cooling to dissipate the large amounts of heat that are evolved in the windings. An early and widely used design evolved by Bitter (1939) used water as a coolant and could develop 100 koe in a space $1\frac{1}{8}$ inches in diameter and 4 inches long. This field requires an electrical generating capacity of 1.7 megawatts together with pumps and cooling towers capable of handling approximately 1000 gallons of water per minute.

Due to the development of superconducting alloys with critical fields above 100 kilogauss, fields of this order of magnitude can now be generated with zero steady-state power dissipation by means of superconducting solenoids. By operating the solenoids at a fraction of the critical current for zero field, it is possible to generate steady magnetic fields approaching the critical field of the windings, without driving them into the normal state.

The advantages of superconducting solenoids were recognized as soon as superconductivity was discovered, but interest remained limited since

145

at that time only the soft superconductors having critical fields of a few hundred oersteds were known. Interest in superconducting electromagnets was revived when de Haas and Voogd (1931) discovered that Pb-Bi retained some superconductivity at fields of 20 koe. However, attempts to construct a high field magnet from this material[1] were abandoned.

The first report of a successful high-field superconducting electromagnet appears to be by Yntema (1955), then at the University of Illinois, who attained a field strength of 7.1 koe using a solenoid of unannealed niobium wire. Several niobium wire wound electromagents are described in detail in a paper by Autler (1960), which includes a description of an iron core electromagnet capable of producing 14 koe. It is reported by Kropshot and Arp (1961) that with a later design, again using ferromagnetic enhancement, Autler was able to obtain 25 koe using an iron core magnet wound with niobium wire having a critical field of approximately 9 koe. Unannealed niobium was used in preference to annealed material because it is found that the critical field of mechanically hard superconductors such as niobium is considerably increased by cold working.[2]

The next outstanding development was the discovery by Kunzler and others[3] that various superconducting alloys can be prepared so as to exhibit critical fields in excess of 10^5 oersteds. These materials will be described as "filamentary" superconductors. Their properties and methods of preparation are discussed in Section 20.1.

Filamentary superconductors can be used to construct solenoids that generate fields in the vicinity of 10^5 oersteds. Such high-field solenoids can be operated in conventional helium cryostats or in special cryostats of the type shown in Figure 5.1, in which the working space of the solenoid is isolated from the liquid helium environment. A typical design can be operated with a persistent current of up to 20 A, has an inner diameter of 2 inches, an outer diameter of 4.62 inches, is 8 inches long and can generate 60 koe at 4.2°K. This is to be compared with the water-cooled 100 koe magnet described above, which requires continuous excitation of 1.7 Mw. As well as replacing laboratory magnets of this type, superconducting magnets are being used in connection with masers, and are being considered for numerous other applications including nuclear accelerators, plasma containment devices, and satellite instrumentation. The design and operation of high-field superconducting solenoids are discussed in Section 21.

Some devices in which superconductors are respectively used to guide and compress magnetic flux are described in Section 22. In the first of these, a superconducting shield is used to increase the efficiency of an iron core

[1] Keesom (1935).
[2] This phenomenon is discussed in Sec. 20.1.
[3] Kunzler et al. (1961); Berlincourt et al. (1961).

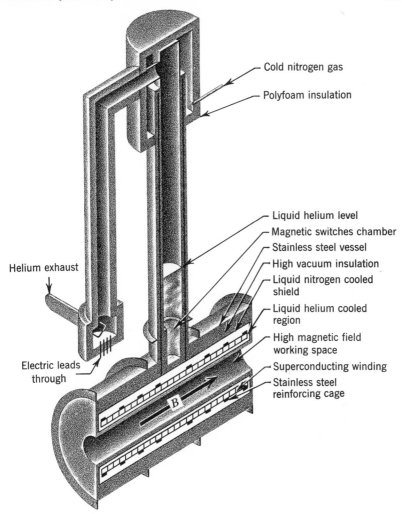

Fig. 5.1   An electromagnet cryostat (Donadieu and Rose, 1962).

magnet by reducing leakage flux. In the second device, a superconducting plunger is used to compress the magnetic flux in a superconducting cavity and thus intensify the magnetic field in this region. In principle these devices can use brittle superconductors to produce intense magnetic fields, since the superconducting material does not have to be drawn into wire but need merely be machined. The section concludes with a description of a flux pump equipped with valves so as to be capable of multi-stroke operation.

A superconductor that exhibits the Meissner effect is subjected to a surface pressure in the presence of an external magnetic field. This phenomenon, which makes it possible to suspend a field-excluding superconductor in a steady magnetic field, has been applied by Buchhold and collaborators to the construction of superconducting bearings and accelerometers.[4] Superconducting bearings have extremely low drag compared to conventional designs. They are described and analyzed in Section 23, where it is shown that the bearing materials should have as high a critical field as possible. Since the bearings must completely exclude magnetic flux in order to avoid eddy-current losses, it is not possible to take advantage of the very high critical fields of the filamentary superconductors.

Another application of the pressure exerted by a magnetic field on a superconductor is to the construction of superconducting motors. These are described in Section 24. Here also superconductors exhibiting a good Meissner effect are required.

20. THE FILAMENTARY SUPERCONDUCTORS

20.1   General Properties

The superconducting alloys that may be considered for magnet construction can be divided into two categories. The first of these consists of brittle materials having the so-called β-wolfram structure, and includes the alloys Nb_3Sn, V_3Si and V_3Ga. All of these have critical fields above 10^5 oersteds. Since they are brittle, they cannot be formed into wire by the conventional methods of drawing or swaging, but must instead be prepared by special methods (see Sec. 21.2). The other category of alloys has the body-centered cubic crystal structure that is flexible at all temperatures. This includes Mo_3Re and Nb-Zr alloys. These materials have somewhat lower critical fields than the brittle β-wolfram alloys, but can be prepared and handled using conventional techniques.

All these filamentary superconductors allow flux penetration at fields far below the critical, and exhibit strong flux trapping if a field causing flux penetration is applied and then removed. At fields comparable to the critical, current flowing through a filamentary superconductor is found to be distributed through the body of the material. This in contrast to the behavior of perfectly diamagnetic soft superconductors in which current flow takes place along surfaces only.

Many of the properties of filamentary superconductors can be analyzed on the basis of a phenomenological model due to Mendelssohn (1935),

---

[4] Buchhold (1960, 1961).

which assumes them to consist of a "sponge" of very fine filaments of very high critical field, embedded in a lower critical field class I superconductor. In terms of this model, the initial penetration of flux occurs at the critical field of the class I superconductor, whereas the complete disappearance of superconductivity occurs at the far higher critical field of the filaments.

As mentioned in Section 7.4, filamentary superconductors that are prepared in an extremely homogeneous manner approach the properties

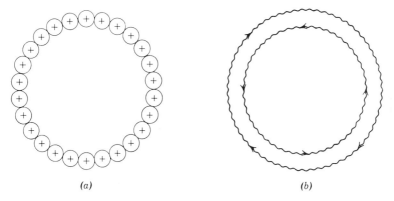

(a)   (b)

Fig. 5.2 (a) A ring of pinned fluxons (schematic). (b) Equivalent persistent current representation.

of an Abrikosov-type class II superconductor. This suggests that[5] the conventional filamentary superconductors consist of class II superconductors containing gross inhomogeneities. These are believed to "pin" the flux quanta or fluxons which, in an ideal class II superconductor, can move freely throughout the material. From a macroscopic standpoint, a ring of fluxons, shown schematically in Figure 5.2, is indistinguishable from a circumferential filament of supercurrent.

The property of high-field superconductors that is of greatest interest from the standpoint of magnet construction is the dependence of critical current on applied magnetic field, where "critical current" is defined as the current corresponding to the onset of resistance. Three curves, representing results for various mechanical treatments of typical filamentary alloys, are shown schematically in Figure 5.3. It can be seen that severe mechanical deformation increases critical current at high fields and produces a curve with a characteristic "knee." This is the optimum characteristic for magnet construction. It is significant from a theoretical standpoint that little effect is produced on the field at which the critical current vanishes.

---

[5] See for instance Friedel et al. (1963).

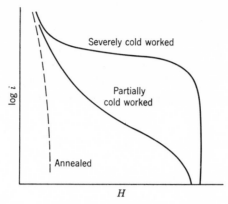

Fig. 5.3 Dependence of quenching characteristic on strain in a typical filamentary superconductor.

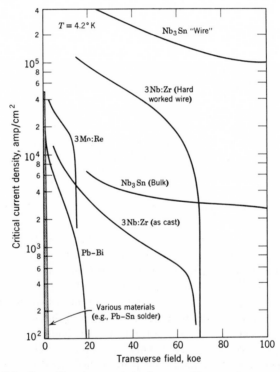

Fig. 5.4 Quenching characteristics for some filamentary superconductors.

Prolonged annealing is seen to reduce the critical current severely. This behavior is not universal, however, since it is found that heat treatment can produce an increased critical current in the niobium-zirconium alloys.[6] This is believed to be due to annealing processes such as phase dissociation or precipitation hardening which increase internal stresses and inhomogeneities.

Curves of critical current density versus transverse field for a number of filamentary superconductors are shown in Figure 5.4.[7] It is seen that

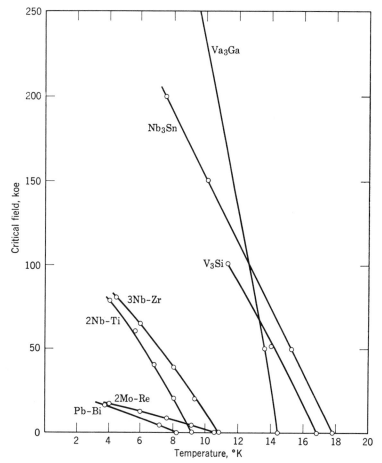

Fig. 5.5 Dependence of critical field on temperature for some filamentary superconductors (Kunzler, 1962).

[6] The superconducting behavior of these alloys and its dependence on heat treatment is discussed by Treuting et al. (1962) and Kneip et al. (1962).

mechanical cold-working increases the critical current density of the Nb-Zr alloy. The term Nb_3Sn "wire" refers to a material prepared by packing powdered niobium and tin into a cylinder of niobium that is then drawn down to a smaller diameter and fired.[8] This material is seen to have a critical current density larger by an order of magnitude than that of the unswaged material. The critical field of a number of filamentary

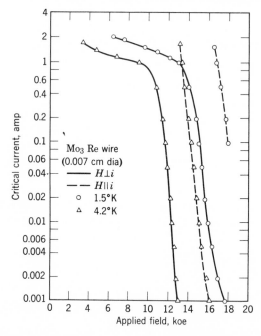

Fig. 5.6 Critical current density versus transversely applied magnetic field, for Mo_3Re (Kunzler, 1961).

superconductors plotted as a function of temperature is shown in Figure 5.5. As in soft superconducting wires, a parallel magnetic field is less effective in quenching superconductivity than a transverse one. This is illustrated in Figure 5.6. The field generated in a superconducting solenoid is normal to the direction of current flow, so that the dependence of critical current on transverse fields is more critical than that on parallel fields.

A "synthetic" filamentary superconductor has been prepared[9] by forcing

---

[7] Taken from the review by Kunzler (1962).

[8] Kunzler et al. (1961).

[9] Bean, Doyle, and Pincus (1962).

mercury (which in bulk form behaves like a soft superconductor) into a type of silica containing pores that are approximately 20 Å in diameter. Since the surface tension at a mercury-silica interface is $\sim$500 dynes/cm² this process requires a pressure of greater than $P = \gamma/2R \sim 1500$ atmospheres where R is the pore radius and γ the surface tension. By applying a pressure of 3000 atmospheres at room temperature and cooling within a few minutes after reducing the pressure, a material was produced that exhibited critical fields of above 20 koe at approximately 2°K.[10] This represents an increase with regard to bulk mercury by a factor of at least 67:1, a result which supports the hypothesis that the properties of filamentary superconductors can be represented by the Mendelssohn sponge model.

20.2   The Mendelssohn Sponge Model

Many of the properties of filamentary superconductors can be derived on the basis of this simple model. It is particularly appropriate for calculating the magnetic flux penetration phenomena which are of importance in connection with devices for flux confinement and compression.

The filamentary or sponge model analyzed in the following paragraphs is a simplified version of one treated by Bean (1962). The superconductor is assumed to consist of a network of interconnected filaments having infinite critical field and possessing a critical current density of J_c A/cm², which is independent of applied field. The critical field of the material between the filaments is assumed to be negligibly small.

The specimen shape to be considered is that of an infinite plate of thickness $2D$ exposed to an external field H parallel to the surface. As this field is applied, screening currents will be induced in the surface in the directions shown in Figure 5.7a, and with the distribution shown in Figure 5.7b. It can be seen that except in four narrow transition regions, the screening current is either $\pm J_c$ or zero. The precise width of these regions depends on the details of the filament structure assumed. It can be neglected in this treatment.

By using the circuital form of Ampere's Law, $0.4\pi J = \text{curl } \mathbf{H}$, we find that in two dimensions

$$0.4\pi J = \frac{dH}{dx} \tag{5.1}$$

where J is in amperes and where x is taken normal to the plate surface. This equation shows that the penetrating field must decrease linearly (since $J = J_c$), rather than exponentially as in a London superconductor.

---

[10] Magnetic measurement techniques that did not require current contacts were used to determine H_c.

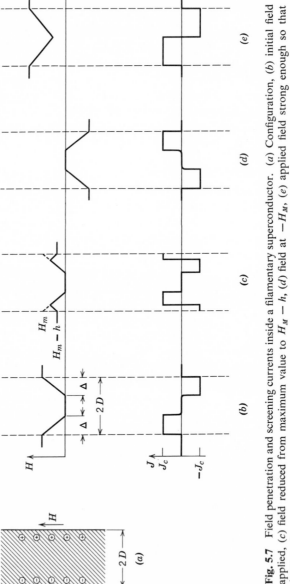

Fig. 5.7 Field penetration and screening currents inside a filamentary superconductor. (*a*) Configuration, (*b*) initial field applied, (*c*) field reduced from maximum value to $H_M - h$, (*d*) field at $-H_M$, (*e*) applied field strong enough so that $\Delta(H) > D$.

By integrating Equation 5.1 inward from the surface we find that the depth of penetration Δ is connected with the applied field H by the relation

$$0.4\pi J_c \, \Delta = H \tag{5.2}$$

For a filamentary superconductor with a critical current density of $10^4 A/cm^2$, this equation predicts a penetration depth of approximately 1 mm per koe. This is to be contrasted with the almost field independent penetration depth of 10^{-5} to 10^{-4} cm, found in class I superconductors.

A useful way of comparing the predictions of the filamentary theory with experiment is by using the theory to calculate the average flux penetration into the specimen. This quantity can be readily measured experimentally by standard magnetic methods involving search coils connected to a ballistic galvanometer.[11]

The average magnetic flux B in the specimen is defined in terms of the internal field H_i averaged over the volume, that is,

$$B = \frac{\mu_0 \iiint H_i \, dv}{\iiint dv} \tag{5.3}$$

μ_0 is the permeability of free space and can be taken as unity. Applying Equation 5.3 to the field distribution shown in Figure 5.7b gives

$$B = \frac{1}{2}\frac{H\Delta}{D}$$
$$= \frac{1}{2}\frac{H^2\delta}{D} \tag{5.4}$$

where δ is defined as the penetration depth for unit applied field, that is, $\delta = \Delta/H$. From Equation 5.2

$$1/\delta = 0.4\pi J_c$$

If a field is applied to a filamentary superconductor initially storing no flux, the internal field and screening currents will be as shown in Figure 5.7b, and the dependence of average penetrating flux on field will be given by Equation 5.4. This is shown as OA in Figure 5.8. If a field H_M is applied and then decreased by an amount h, the resultant field distribution will be as shown in Figure 5.7c. The corresponding decrease in average penetrated flux below the maximum value B_M can be shown to be

$$b = (\tfrac{1}{2}h)^2 \frac{\delta}{D}$$

<hr/>

[11] See for instance Bozorth, *Ferromagnetism*. New York: Van Nostrand, 1951, Ch. 19.

Hence the flux curve for decreasing field, shown as AC in Figure 5.8, is given by the relation

$$B = B_M - \frac{1}{4} H^2 \frac{\delta}{D} \tag{5.5}$$

Combining Equations 5.4 and 5.5 shows that the remanent flux at zero field is $\frac{1}{2}B_M$. When the applied field has been reduced to $-H_M$ the field distribution in the superconductor will be as shown in Figure 5.7d

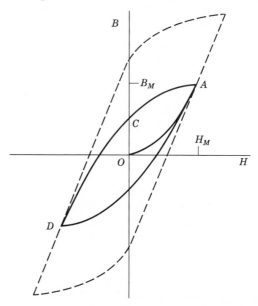

Fig. 5.8 Hysteresis loops calculated using the filamentary model. The broken curve is for the case where $\Delta(H) > D$.

corresponding to point D in Figure 5.8. Using symmetry arguments it can be seen that an increase in field to $+H_M$ will produce a flux change corresponding to DA, thus closing the hysteresis loop.

The above analysis only holds provided the penetration depth Δ never exceeds the half-thickness D of the plate. If $\Delta > D$ the internal field distribution assumes the form shown in Figure 5.7e. It can be shown that under these conditions the predicted hysteresis loop assumes the form shown in the broken line of Figure 5.8.

In the above calculation the model used has been kept deliberately simple by assuming that the critical field of the material filling the interstices between the filaments is zero and that the critical field of the filaments themselves is extremely large. These simplifying assumptions can of course be removed when attempting to predict the detailed behavior of the common filamentary superconductors (Bean, 1962). In spite of its simplicity, the model analyzed above brings out the important features of filamentary superconductors, including their large penetration depth, and the consequent dependence of magnetic behavior on specimen size. These predictions are borne out by the experiments described in the next section.

20.3   Application as Permanent Magnets

The magnetic hysteresis loops predicted by the filamentary model and shown in Figure 5.8 can be verified experimentally for bulk specimens of real filamentary superconductors such as Nb_3Sn and Va_3Ga.[12] However,

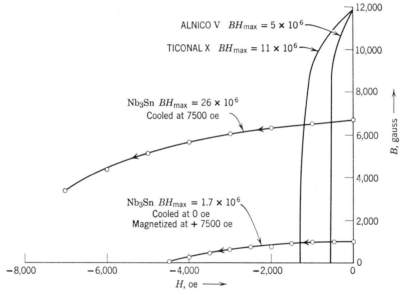

Fig. 5.9 Demagnetizing curves for the best conventional permanent magnet materials compared with that of Nb_3Sn. (Bean and Doyle, 1962.)

many specimens exhibit abrupt jumps in magnetic induction with changes in applied field. It is found[13] that this flux-jumping is related to the difference between the frozen-in field strength and the applied field strength, that is, to the magnitude of the screening currents flowing in the specimen. It is possible that the effect is due to eddy current heating that occurs when a bundle of flux is torn away from a pinning site due to forces generated

---

[12] See for instance Swartz (1962).
[13] Swartz and Rosner (1962).

by the applied field. Conceivably, the rise in temperature due to such an event could become high enough to start a thermal propagation process analogous to that which can take place in current-carrying superconducting films.

The flux-trapping properties of a filamentary superconductor allow it to be regarded as a permanent magnet. A convenient measure of the quality of permanent magnet materials is provided by the product of the magnetic induction and the corresponding applied field. Filamentary superconductors have values of $(BH)_{max}$ that are larger than those of any known ferromagnetic. This is illustrated in Figure 5.9, which compares the hysteresis loop produced in a 0.48 cm diameter rod of sintered Nb_3Sn cooled in a field of 7.5 koe with the loops produced in two of the best available permanent magnet materials by exposure to a saturating magnetic field. The figure also shows that for fields much smaller than the critical, more flux can be trapped in a superconductor by cooling it in the field than by cycling it in the field after cooling.

21. SUPERCONDUCTING SOLENOIDS

21.1   Coil Optimization

In the design of superconducting solenoids for high fields, no provision need be made for heat dissipation. However, it is desirable to minimize the winding thickness required for a given field so as to avoid excessive refrigeration requirements. In any solenoidal electromagnet the generated field varies from its maximum value near the inside surface of the winding to a very low value at the outside. Since the critical current of filamentary superconductors decreases strongly with increasing field, a superconducting solenoid can be optimized by allowing the inner windings, which are exposed to a high field, to carry a smaller current than the outer windings. The improvement obtainable from such a procedure may be calculated as follows.[14]

The field in oersted produced inside a multilayer coil of N turns per unit length excited with I amperes is

$$H = \frac{4\pi}{10} NI$$

Alternatively

$$I = \frac{10}{4\pi} \frac{H}{nd} \tag{5.6}$$

where n is the number of turns per unit cross-sectional area of a winding of thickness d. This relation is plotted as a solid line in Figure 5.10, which

---

[14] Gauster and Parker (1962).

also shows the quenching characteristic of the wire, and a cross section of a three layer coil. If the coil is to remain superconducting, the largest current that it can carry is that corresponding to the intercept of Equation 5.6 with the critical current curve. At this current the field H_0 produced inside the coil is just sufficient to render it normal.

To demonstrate the improvement obtained with non-uniform current excitation, it will be assumed that the coil is split into three layers each of

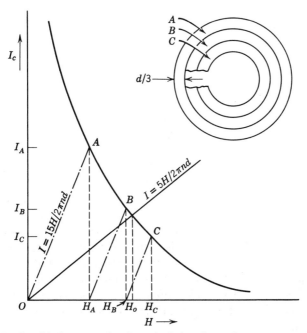

Fig. 5.10 Graphical construction for calculating the optimum currents for a super-conducting magnet coil split into three layers. (After Gauster and Parker, 1962.)

thickness $d/3$, shown as A, B and C in the figure. From Equation 5.6 it can be seen that the current-field relation for the outer layer A can be displayed by a line OA with slope $15/(2\pi nd)$. The largest field that can be produced inside this layer is clearly equal to H_A and is produced by an exciting current I_A. The next inner layer B is exposed to the field H_A. Hence in the presence of a current I the field inside layer B is given by

$$H = H_A + \frac{2\pi nd}{15} I$$

This line intersects the critical current curve at point B. The maximum current that can be carried by layer B in the superconducting state is given by I_B, and produces a net internal field of H_B. By a similar argument it can be shown that the maximum current that the innermost winding C can carry is I_C. In the presence of currents I_A, I_B and I_C in their respective windings, the net field in the core of the solenoid is given by H_C. This is seen to be somewhat larger than the field H_0 which could be obtained by operating the three layers A, B and C in series.

21.2 Solenoid Construction and Operation

Popular materials for use in high-field superconducting solenoids are the flexible niobium-zirconium alloys. When appropriately prepared[15] these have useful critical current densities at 70 koe (see Fig. 5.4); coils that generate fields slightly smaller than this can be layer-wound from these alloys in a conventional manner. It has been found by a number of investigators,[16] that the critical current of niobium-zirconium wire wound in a coil is smaller than that of an isolated wire and has the type of field dependence shown schematically in Figure 5.11. Although this phenomenon does not prevent the generation of fields close to the critical field of the material, it prevents the application of the multilayer optimization technique described above. Niobium-zirconium superconducting solenoids are nevertheless often wound in separate layers so that the occurrence of a "weak" spot in the wire will only affect a portion of the winding.

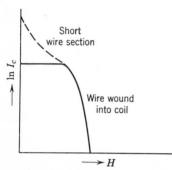

Fig. 5.11 Dependence of critical current on applied field for Nb-25% Zr. (Schematic.)

The superconductors with the highest critical fields, such as Nb_3Sn, V_3Si and V_3Ga are brittle and cannot be drawn into wire by conventional means. Solenoids of Nb_3Sn have been prepared by Kunzler et al. (1961) by drawing down niobium cylinders filled with a near stoichiometric niobium-tin powder mixture, winding this "wire" into solenoids, and heat-treating the completed solenoid at temperatures between 850 and 950°C for many hours. Coils using this process do not show the reduction in critical current associated with niobium-zirconium. However, the heat treatment required after winding necessitates the use of special insulation. A simpler process of preparing Nb_3Sn in which tin is diffused into previously degassed niobium wire has been developed by Sauer and Wurm

---

[15] See for instance Treuting et al. (1962) and Kneip et al. (1962).
[16] See for instance Autler (1962) and Hulm et al. (1962).

(1962) and by W. de Sorbo.[17] It has also proved possible to deposit Nb_3Sn by pyrolysis onto a vitreous substrate.[18] It is reported that coils wound from material formed in this way do not require heat treatment after winding.

The pressure exerted by a field H on a diamagnetic is equal to the energy per unit volume in free space $H^2/8\pi$.[19] This gives rise to a pressure of 100 atmospheres at 50 koe. Although this pressure is not sufficient to stretch the filamentary superconductors appreciably, it can lead to movement of the windings which can cause fracture and insulation damage. Superconducting solenoids must therefore be wound so that the windings are constrained as much as possible.

Superconducting solenoids are usually equipped with a shunt consisting of a superconductor, which can be driven normal by the application of heat or of a magnetic field. When the current through the coil has reached the desired value, this shunt can be made superconducting and the external current supply switched off, thus allowing the electromagnet to be excited by a persistent current.

It is easy to show that if a current I is applied to a coil of inductance L shunted by a resistance R, energy $\frac{1}{2}LI^2$ is dissipated in the shunt while the current is established. This indicates that the resistance of the shunt should be made as high as possible, so as to minimize the power dissipated in it. The shunt must also be able to carry the full excitation current, and may therefore have to be screened from the field of the solenoid. Such screening can be provided by a hollow thick-walled cylinder of a high field superconductor. An energized solenoid may transform magnetic energy into heat energy at a dangerously rapid rate, if a large portion of it ever becomes normal. To limit the maximum rate of heat production, coils may be encased in a copper cylinder which acts as a low resistance short-circuit in the presence of sudden flux changes.

22. MAGNETIC FLUX CONFINEMENT AND COMPRESSION

The flux-excluding properties of superconductors can be used to confine and control magnetic flux so as to considerably increase the efficiency of iron-cored electromagnets. Filamentary superconductors can be used for this purpose provided that their appreciable penetration depth (see Eq. 5.2) is allowed for. Such an application[20] is illustrated in Figure 5.12 in which

[17] Private communication.
[18] Hunak et al. (1962).
[19] This is proved in Sec. 23.
[20] Cioffi (1962).

the air gap of an iron-core electromagnet is surrounded by a super-conducting cylinder, composed of a layer-wound sheet of the high field superconductor Pb-Bi. The sheet is insulated to avoid the formation of a shortened turn. In this design, the electromagnet is turned on when the Pb-Bi tube is superconducting. The absence of a shortened turn in this tube allows the magnetic flux to penetrate the magnet air gap, but confines it within the tube, thus reducing the leakage flux by a factor of ten and greatly increasing the field homogeneity in the working area of the magnet.

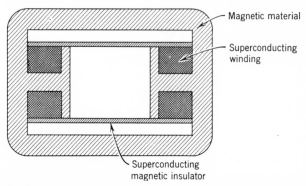

Fig. 5.12   Use of a sheet of filamentary superconductor to reduce leakage flux (Cioffi, 1962).

Cioffi finds that in this way a 750 lb Alnico-V room-temperature maser magnet can be replaced by a cryogenic magnet containing only 10 lbs of magnetic material. The possibilities inherent in such a weight reduction for magnetic field generators may influence the design of satellites and space vehicles.

Superconductors can be used to intensify magnetic fields by compressing flux trapped in a superconducting cavity. This method bears some similarity to the "implosion" method that has been used to generate fields of several million gauss for microsecond periods at room tempera-ture. In this method a magnetic field is generated in a conducting cavity that is then imploded. The rapid movement of the imploding cavity walls leads to the generation of eddy currents that cannot decay fast enough for the trapped flux to escape. Since the flux in the imploding cavity is there-fore conserved, the field in it is temporarily intensified[21] until the eddy currents decay or the cavity collapses completely.

The fact that "eddy" currents induced in the surface of a superconductor persist, allows flux compression to be performed slowly. Attempts to

---

[21] See for instance Fowler et al. (1962).

generate high fields by this method have been described by Swartz and
Rosner (1962), who used a Nb_3Sn cylinder containing a "figure eight"
cavity as shown in Figure 5.13. Flux of intensity up to 6000 gauss was
trapped in the cylinder by cooling in the presence of a permanent magnet
which was then withdrawn, or by other methods. After the flux had been
trapped, a superconducting Nb_3Sn mandrel was inserted into the larger

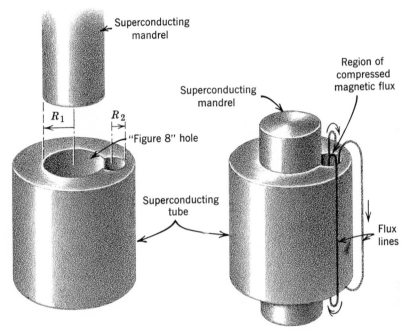

Fig. 5.13   A flux compressor (Swartz and Rosner, 1962).

hole that had a diameter of 0.5 in. This compressed the trapped flux into
the smaller hole that had a diameter of 0.125 in.

   If the areas of the large and small holes are A_1 and A_2 respectively,
and if the finite penetration into the filamentary material is neglected,
then the compression should increase the flux density and thus the field
strength in the small hole by a factor of $(A_1 + A_2)/A_2$. By this reasoning
the compressor described above should have provided a sixteen-fold
increase in field intensity on compression. The finite flux penetration into
the walls reduces this factor. Experimentally it was found impossible to
exceed 15 koe, due to flux-jumping phenomena. Various suggestions for
measures to minimize or prevent flux-jumping are given in the original
paper by Swartz and Rosner (1962).

The flux intensification ratio obtainable by the one-stroke flux compressor of Figure 5.13 is simply the ratio of the cross-sectional area available to the flux before and after compression. It follows that to produce an intense magnetic flux in a large working volume, an even larger piston volume is required. Hildebrandt et al. (1962) have shown that by the addition of two superconductive valves to the flux compressor

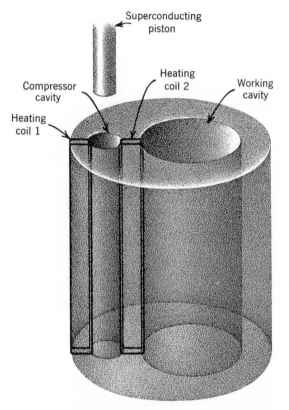

Fig. 5.14   Cyclical flux pump.

a multi-cycle flux pump becomes possible. Such a device is shown in Figure 5.14. The valves consist of heating coils that can be used to drive portions of the cavity peripheries normal.

The cycle of operation is as follows: The entire system is made superconducting and a field H_0 is induced in both cavities, using an external field coil that is not shown in the figure. The piston, of cross-sectional area A_1, is now pushed into the compressor cavity, which has a slightly larger cross-sectional area A_2. The flux in this cavity is compressed into the small remaining space of area $A_2 - A_1$. The field intensity in this space is

$$H_M = H_0 \frac{A_2}{A_2 - A_1}$$

if penetration effects are neglected. Heating coil 2 is now activated, driving the wall between the two cavities normal. This allows the compressed flux to expand into the working cavity, slightly increasing the field there. Heating coil 2 is then turned off, trapping the increment of flux in the working cavity. Heating coil 1 is turned on and the piston is withdrawn. Heating coil 1 is then switched off, and the whole cycle is repeated. The field in the working cavity increases with each cycle, approaching the value H_M asymptotically.

Hildebrandt and co-workers have demonstrated the feasibility of the flux pump using Nb_3Sn as a working material, and have attained 22 koe over a volume of several cubic centimeters. Flux pumps using magnetic valves and intended to 'pump up' a large persistent current in superconducting solenoids have been described by Hildebrandt et al. (1962), Volger and Admiraal (1962), van Beelen et al. (1963), and Laquer (1963).

23. SUPERCONDUCTING BEARINGS

23.1 Introduction

The surfaces of a perfectly diamagnetic superconductor placed in a magnetic field experience an inward pressure due to the fact that the field inside the superconductor is zero. The magnitude of this pressure on an element of surface is $H^2/8\pi$ dynes/cm² where H is the surface field at that point. To prove this, assume that unit surface area of the superconductor collapses a distance δx and that the external field is maintained constant during this process. Since the volume energy of a field H in free space is $\mu_0 H^2/8\pi$, the work done in increasing the space occupied by the field is

$$\delta W = \mu_0 \frac{H^2}{8\pi} \delta x$$

Also

$$\delta W = P \, \delta x$$

where P is the inward pressure exerted by the field on unit area of the superconductor. Combining these two equations, we obtain finally

$$P = \mu_0 \frac{H^2}{8\pi} \text{ dynes/cm}^2$$

$$\sim \left(\frac{H}{5000}\right)^2 \text{ kgm/cm}^2 \tag{5.7}$$

where H is in oersteds, and μ_0, the permeability of free space, is taken as unity.

This effect makes possible superconducting suspensions or bearings. Since a superconducting bearing must exclude magnetic flux, its surface field must not exceed H_c. Hence the maximum bearing load per unit area is $H_c^2/8\pi$.

As illustrated in Chapter 1 superconductors can be stably supported in three dimensions by means of suitably shaped magnetic fields. Several such schemes are described below, and it is shown that the shapes of the flux lines surrounding the suspended object resemble the flow lines of a liquid jet supporting an object of similar shape. An analogous suspension scheme for conducting bodies at room temperature is obtained by the use of alternating magnetic fields. These produce eddy currents in the surface of the suspended conductor, which prevent field penetration.

It is feasible to evacuate the cavity containing a suspended super-conductor, maintaining the temperature constant by radiation cooling. In this way it is possible to produce bearings with extremely small drag.[22] By spinning such a suspended superconductor using methods analogous to those used in electrical motors, a superconducting gyroscope is obtained. Due to the low losses of superconducting bearings and the complete dimensional stability available at low temperatures[23] it may prove possible to develop superconducting gyroscopes of extremely small "drift."

23.2   Planar Bearings[24]

The properties of superconducting bearings can be established with a minimum of mathematical complexity by analyzing the bearing shown in Figure 5.15 which consists of a superconducting disk a, supported by a superconducting coil b, embedded in a flat cylinder of iron, c. The coil may be made of a filamentary superconductor with very high critical field, and is assumed to consist of N turns carrying a current of I amperes. This produces a magnetic field in the region B, which exerts an upward thrust on the disk. The disk is attached to a shaft guided by mechanical bearings, d.

To calculate this field we employ Ampere's circuital law $\oint \mathbf{H} \cdot d\mathbf{s} = 0.4\pi NI$ and integrate around the cross section of the coil, which is assumed to be of width l_0. Since the part of this path that falls within the iron can

---

[22] The residual drag appears to be mainly due to trapped flux, and a-c losses in the superconducting bearing surface.

[23] Due to the fact that most materials contract very little between 70°K and absolute zero.

[24] This section is based on a paper by T. A. Buchhold (1961).

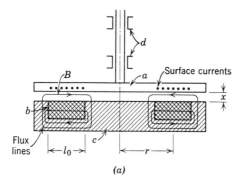

(a)

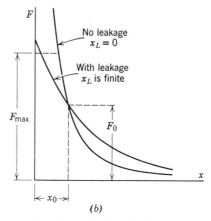

(b)

Fig. 5.15 Basic superconducting thrust bearing (Buchhold, 1961). (a) Cross section, (b) bearing force as a function of gap.

be neglected owing to its high magnetic permeability we have, to first order,

$$H \sim \frac{0.4\pi NI}{l_0} \qquad (5.8)$$

Taking the exposed area of the coil as A, and using Equation 5.7 we derive the upward thrust on the disk as

$$F = A \frac{H^2}{8\pi} \text{ dynes} \qquad (5.9)$$

Substituting for H from Equation 5.8,

$$F = \frac{\pi A}{50} \left(\frac{N}{l_0}\right)^2 I^2$$

This formula shows that for constant current through the coil, F is independent of the gap x between the top surface of the coil and the disk. Alternatively a current can be trapped in the coil by means of a magnetic field-operated or heat-operated shunt. In that case the trapped flux, rather than the coil current, will remain constant as the disk is moved. Hence

$$2\pi r H x = k_0 \tag{5.10}$$

where r is the radius of the coil and k_0 is a constant. In this case the field is inversely proportional to the gap, so that the coil current must increase as the disk is depressed. Hence from Equations 5.9 and 5.10,

$$F = \frac{A}{8\pi}\left(\frac{k_0}{2\pi r x}\right)^2 \tag{5.11}$$

In a real bearing not all the coil flux ϕ goes through the gap. That is

$$\phi = 2\pi r H x + \phi_L$$

where ϕ_L is the leakage flux. This may be rewritten as

$$\phi = 2\pi r H (x + x_L)$$

where x_L is a term that represents the effect of leakage flux and varies slightly with x. With leakage flux taken into account Equation 5.11 is rewritten as

$$F = \frac{A}{32\pi^3 r^2}\frac{k_0{}^2}{(x + x_L)^2} \tag{5.12}$$

It is seen that the leakage flux limits bearing force for small gaps. (As mentioned above, the other limit is set by the condition that the critical field of the bearing materials must not be exceeded.)

An important parameter in bearing operation is the "stiffness," defined as dF/dx. For the bearing under discussion, with shunted coil, Equation 5.12 gives

$$\frac{dF}{dx} = -\frac{Ak_0{}^2}{16\pi^3 r^2}(x + x_L)^{-3}$$

which is seen to be dependent on the gap x.

A closer approach to a practical bearing is shown in Figure 5.16. This consists of a superconducting disk between two embedded coils. If these are both shunted and carry identical trapped currents, then Equation 5.12 shows that for a displacement Δx from the central position, the disk experiences a restoring force

$$F = \frac{Ak_0{}^2}{32\pi^3 r^2}\left[\frac{1}{(x_0 + x_L + \Delta x)^2} - \frac{1}{(x_0 + x_L - \Delta x)^2}\right]$$

This equation is plotted in the figure. The stiffness is again seen to depend on displacement.

By connecting the bearing coils in parallel it is found that the stiffness is independent of displacement. This is shown as follows. Assume that a current $2I_0$ is passed through the coils. With the disk in the central position, the current will divide symmetrically between the two coils. If

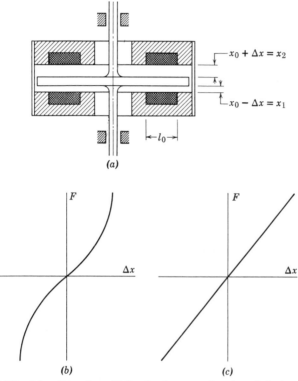

(a)

(b)   (c)

Fig. 5.16 (a) Double coil bearing. (b) Bearing force as a function of displacement with separately shunted coils. (c) Bearing force as a function of displacement with coils shunted together. (Buchhold, 1961.)

the disk is now displaced by a distance Δx, the current will increase by an amount ΔI in coil 1 and decrease by the same amount in coil 2, that is,

$$I_1 = I_0 + \Delta I$$

and

$$I_2 = I_0 - \Delta I$$

Also

$$H_1 = H_0 + \Delta H$$

and

$$H_2 = H_0 - \Delta H$$

Furthermore since the coils are connected in parallel the flux must be the same in both coils,[25] that is,

$$(H_0 + \Delta H)(x_0 + x_L - \Delta x) = (H_0 - \Delta H)(x_0 + x_L + \Delta x)$$

Some reduction gives

$$\frac{\Delta H}{H_0} = \frac{\Delta x}{x_0 + x_L} \tag{5.13}$$

From Equation 5.9 the resultant force on the disk is

$$F = \frac{A}{8\pi} [(H_0 + \Delta H)^2 - (H_0 - \Delta H)^2]$$

$$= \frac{A}{2\pi} H_0 \Delta H$$

which using Equation 5.13 reduces to

$$F = \frac{A H_0^2}{2\pi} \frac{\Delta x}{x_0 + x_L}$$

showing that the stiffness $dF/d(\Delta x)$ is independent of displacement in this configuration.

In the bearing designs shown above, the bearing stiffness is reduced at high pressures because flux can be pushed into the windings. This effect can be reduced by placing a slotted superconducting ring above the windings as shown in Figure 5.17a. The ring must contain a slot to allow the flux generated by the coil to penetrate. Alternatively a continuous ring can be used, a portion of which is temporarily made resistive by means of heated wires as shown in the figure. After the ring has been returned to superconductivity, the coil current can be switched off leaving the bearing flux trapped in the ring.

It is found experimentally that the superconductive bearings illustrated above operate in accordance with theory provided the pressure remains below a critical value. As this value is exceeded, hysteresis appears in the force-displacement characteristic. This is attributed to the surface field exceeding the critical value at some part of the bearing, leading to irreversible flux penetration. Although a bearing whose critical field pressure has been exceeded still exerts pressure, the flux trapped in it can give rise to energy losses on rotation which might lead to an undesirable increase in temperature if the bearing is operated in a vacuum and cooled by radiation only. Bearings for which losses are unimportant can be prepared from

---

[25] The flux in each coil can change with disk movement, since energy can be dissipated in the current source which feeds the coils.

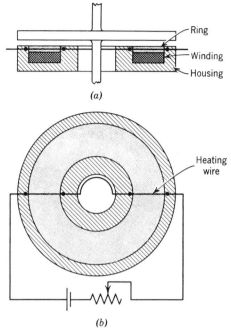

(a)

(b)

Fig. 5.17 The use of a superconducting ring to reduce leakage flux and increase bearing stiffness for small gaps. (a) Cross-section, (b) Top view. (Buchhold, 1961).

cold worked niobium and can sustain surface fields of up to 2500 oersteds at 4.2°K. Bearings designed for minimum loss must be constructed from very pure and annealed niobium and can only sustain surface fields of approximately 1200 oersteds.[26]

23.3 Spherical and Cylindrical Bearings

The problem of supporting a superconducting sphere by magnetic fields was studied by Simon (1953) who achieved success using two circular ring coils energized to produce opposing fields. A sphere made of lead foil supported by this method is shown in Figure 1.6. Field plots of such a system, calculated with a two-dimensional electric potential analog, and therefore not exact for the three-dimensional case, are shown in Figure 5.18. These plots show that it is difficult to achieve lateral stability and vertical stability simultaneously in a two-ring suspension system. Simon was able to support superconducting spheres using circular magnets shaped as shown in Figure 5.19. He found it necessary to construct these of high resistivity ferrite since metallic magnets created an undesirable

---

[26] Buchhold (1961).

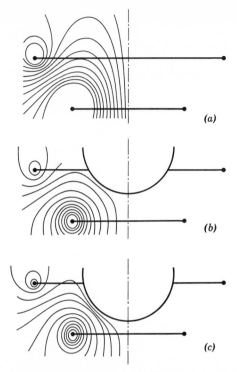

Fig. 5.18 Magnetic field plots for two circular ring coils carrying opposed currents having a ratio 1 : 3. (*a*) In free space; (*b*) and (*c*) with a perfectly diamagnetic sphere in two positions (Simon, 1953).

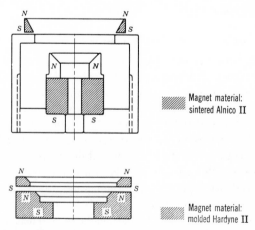

Magnet material: sintered Alnico II

Magnet material: molded Hardyne II

Fig. 5.19 Two successful permanent magnet supports for superconducting spheres (Simon, 1953).

asymmetric drag when the superconducting sphere was rotated, presumably due to the generation of eddy currents in the magnets by flux trapped in the sphere or by shape irregularities.

Using a digital computer, Harding and Tuffias (1960) were able to compute conditions under which a superconducting sphere could be supported by a single ring. They were also able to levitate a sphere in a vacuum of 10^{-6} tor using radiation cooling. A two-coil arrangement was used, the coils being situated in liquid helium external to the vacuum.

A superconducting gyro would require stiff bearing-support in three dimensions. Two schemes that have been suggested for such a purpose are shown in Figure 5.20. One system, more fully described in a patent by Buchhold,[27] uses six coils embedded in a magnetic shell. The other, suggested by Harding and Tuffias (1960) uses eight coils with adjacent coils magnetized in opposite directions.

Both of these techniques can be adapted to the support of super-conducting cylinders as shown in Figure 5.21. The structure in Figure 5.21a represents four coils embedded in iron, and is analogous to the structure shown in Figure 5.20a. The structure in Figure 5.21b shows two coils producing oppositely directed fields which press against the flange on a superconducting cylindrical bearing in such a way that friction-less rotation is possible. Buchhold (1961) points out that the structure in Figure 5.21c, in which a single coil surrounds a shaft, would *not* provide an adequate restoring force in the plane of the coil, since the flux density in the space surrounding the shaft does not change if the shaft is displaced from the coil center.

24. SUPERCONDUCTING MOTORS

The pressure exerted by magnetic fields on superconductors has been used to operate superconducting motors.[28] The principle is illustrated in Figure 5.22, which shows how the passage of current through a conductor can produce a magnetic field that exerts a clockwise torque on the octagonal superconducting rotor. By exciting conductors A, B, and C with sequential current pulses the rotor will turn in a clockwise direction. The direction of rotation can be reversed by changing the order of excitation to ACB.

The torque on a superconducting rotor can be calculated in terms of the inductance L between the stator conductor and the rotor. For a

---

[27] U.S. Patent 3,044,309, "Gyroscope."
[28] Buchhold (1960), Schock (1961).

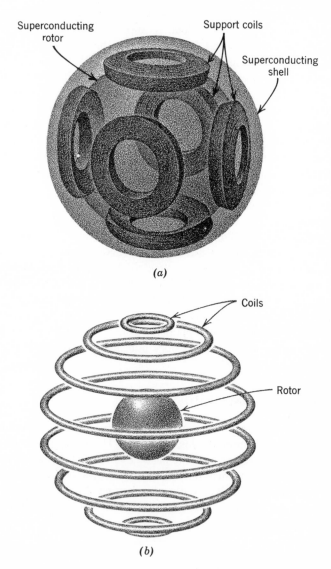

(a)

(b)

Fig. 5.20 Two spherical support systems. (a) Due to Buchhold, 1961; ((b) due to Harding and Tuffias, 1960).

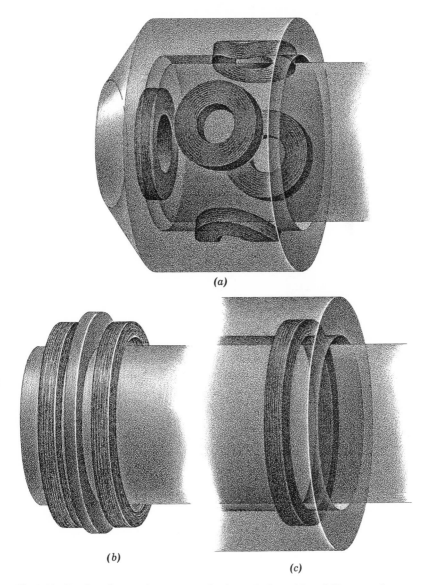

(a)

(b)

(c)

Fig. 5.21 Bearings for rotating superconducting cylinders. (a) and (b) are analogous to the structures of Fig. 5.20a and b respectively; c is not operable since it does not provide sufficient restoring force (Buchhold, 1960, 1961).

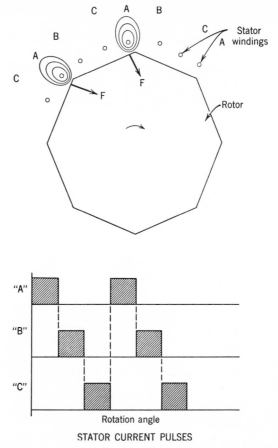

STATOR CURRENT PULSES

Fig. 5.22   A three phase pulsed dc stator with octagonal rotor (Schock, 1961).

current I through the stator, the magnetic field energy is

$$E = \tfrac{1}{2}LI^2$$

As the rotor turns through an angle α, under the influence of torque T, the work done is

$$T d\alpha = dE$$

Hence the torque at a particular rotor position is

$$T(\alpha) = \frac{dE}{d\alpha}$$

$$= \frac{1}{2}\frac{I^2 dL}{d\alpha}$$

This result brings out the fact that the torque for this type of motor is proportional to the square of the exciting current and is independent of speed of rotation. The result also proves that a cylindrical rotor would exhibit no torque since in that case $dL/d\alpha = 0$.

A disassembled cryogenic motor with a slotted rotor and superconductive bearings is shown in Figure 5.23. It is reported[29] that motors of this type have been operated at speeds of up to 1200 rpm in liquid helium and 20,000 rpm in a vacuum of 10^{-6} tor, using radiation cooling.

Fig. 5.23 Parts of a cryogenic motor (Schock, 1961).

Since very small frictional or magnetic losses occur in a superconductive motor with superconductive bearings, very high efficiencies may be obtainable. This may lead to applications in which a superconducting motor drives a room temperature system, perhaps using some form of magnetic field coupling. At present however such motors have been proposed only for low temperature applications such as rotation of superconductive gyroscopes or pumping of liquid helium.

Supplementary References

An exhaustive survey of conventional techniques for generating intense magnetic fields, of superconductive magnets, and of filamentary superconducting

---

[29] Schock (1961).

alloys is contained in the Proceedings of the 1961 International Conference on High Magnetic Fields edited by H. Kolm, B. Lax, F. Bitter, and R. Mills. Many of the references in the body of this chapter are contained in that volume.

A later reference that contains a very detailed design treatment of super-conducting solenoids is by R. W. Boom and R. S. Livingston (1962). Other related references include a proposal to use superconductors for the construction of force-free electromagnet coils[30] and proposals for their use in the generation and distribution of electric power.[31]

---

[30] Furth and Levine (1962).
[31] McFee (1962).

chapter 6

Superconductive Amplifiers and Switching Elements

The first section of this chapter is devoted to the various forms of the wire-wound cryotron. Both its early applications to low noise amplification, as well as later developments as computer switching elements are covered. Requirements for fast and easily fabricated electronic switching devices led to the development of film cryotrons, various forms of which are described and analyzed in Sections 26 and 27. The latter section also includes an analysis of superconducting film transmission lines. Section 28 surveys work on microwave switching devices.

25. WIRE-WOUND CRYOTRONS

25.1 Cryotron Small Signal Amplifiers

A paper by Casimir-Jonker and de Haas (1935) contains what is believed to be the earliest published description of a cryotron, that is, of a device in which the resistance of one superconductive element is varied by means of a magnetic field generated by passing current through another. In this work, a lead (Pb) coil having 40 turns/cm was used to control the resistance of an enclosed Pb-Tl wire 0.35 cm in diameter. The device was used to switch current in an experiment on superconductive alloy systems.

Cryotrons of different form have been used as current switches and modulators,[1] and as small signal amplifiers,[2] in connection with experiments such as the measurement of thermoelectric voltages at low temperatures. Such experiments require sensitivities of the order of 10^{-9} v, and usually employ a room temperature d-c amplifier fed by leads connected

---

[1] Templeton, (1955a, b).
[2] R. W. Schmitt and M. D. Fiske, U.S. Patent 2,935,694.

to the low-temperature source. Unavoidable transient temperature variations that occur in such a system generate thermal voltages in the signal leads coming out of the liquid helium. These thermal emf's can be distinguished from the signal being measured by the use of reversing switches which are operated at the low temperature end of the signal leads

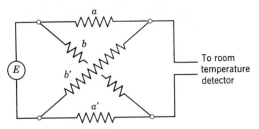

Fig. 6.1 Superconductive reversing switch (schematic).

so that only the measured signal is reversed. A *superconductive reversing switch* that has been used for this purpose by Templeton (1955a) is shown schematically in Figure 6.1. Here E is the signal voltage and a, a', b, and b' are pairs of coils of tantalum wire, which are alternatively driven into the normal state by means of an electromagnet.

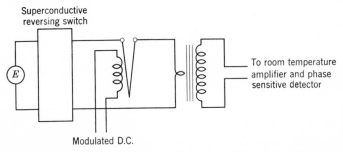

Fig. 6.2 Simplified circuit for a superconductive modulator (Templeton, 1955b).

In a system using a room-temperature amplifier, the noise generated by the room-temperature section of the signal wires is of the order of 10^{-10} volt/cycle. It is possible to measure signals smaller than this by operating a preamplifier or synchronous detector at liquid-helium temperature. Templeton (1955b) developed a superconductive modulator for this purpose, again consisting of a tantalum wire exposed to a magnetic field generated by an electromagnet. The field was at 800 cycles/second superimposed on a steady bias. The device was designed to minimize inductive pickup in the tantalum wire due to the control field variation.

A simplified version of the circuit using the modulator is shown in Figure 6.2. The source voltage, after passing through a superconductive reversing switch, is fed into a screened transformer designed for low leakage inductance, which is in series with the modulator. The purpose of the reversing switch is not to discriminate against thermal voltages, since these are already deleted by the modulator, but to separate the signal from

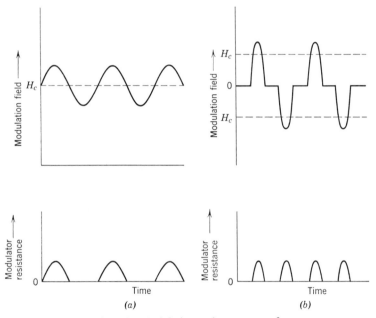

Fig. 6.3   Modulation and output waveforms.

pickup due to the modulator control coil. The modulator resistance variation resulting from Templeton's scheme of a-c superimposed on d-c bias is shown in Figure 6.3a. It is apparent that it produces an output signal which has the same frequency as the chopping signal. This increases the difficulties of separating the output signal from modulation field pickup. De Vrooman and Baarle (1957) have described a modulator using the waveform shown in Figure 6.3b. This gives a modulator output whose fundamental is double the chopping frequency. Since the chopping waveform is symmetrical about zero field, it contains no even harmonics. These two features allow the output signal to be separated from modulation field pickup by means of filters. The systems of Templeton and of de Vrooman and Baarle are reported to give sensitivities of $4 \cdot 10^{-12}$ and 10^{-11} volt respectively. Room-temperature amplifier noise appears to limit the sensitivity, which indicates that further improvement should be obtainable by a higher degree of amplification at low temperatures.

A cryotron biased in the midpoint of its transition can be used as a *high gain amplifier*. Since such a device is very sensitive to small temperature variations, it is usually used in the form of a balanced bridge circuit. An arrangement described by Gygax (1958, 1961) is shown in Figure 6.4. This uses wire-wound cryotrons with Pb-In alloy gates whose critical temperature is 4.08°K. The device was used at 4°K and exhibited a

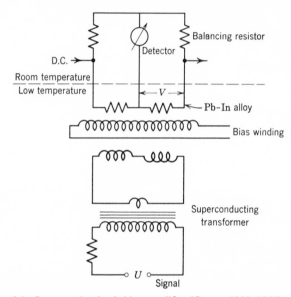

Fig. 6.4   Superconductive bridge amplifier (Gygax, 1958, 1961).

voltage gain dV/dU of 1600 with a time constant of approximately 30 seconds. The noise referred to the input was approximately 10^{-9} volts. A similar system[3] operated with a superconducting reversing switch has been able to detect 10^{-7} A, again "with an impractically high time constant when driven by a low impedance source."[3]

Templeton has pointed out in this connection that since most low temperature sources of interest have very low impedance (usually less than 100 micro-ohms), any method that requires such a source to drive a magnetic field generating coil runs into this problem. For instance, a superconducting galvanometer described by Pippard and Pullan (1952), although attaining a sensitivity of 10^{-12} volt, had a time constant of 12 seconds.

---

[3] Templeton (1960).

25.2 Cryotron Switching Elements

GAIN-BANDWIDTH ANALYSIS. The first published application of super-conductors to digital switching circuits appears to be by the late Dudley A. Buck (1956a), who also introduced the term "cryotron." The cryotron geometry used by Buck (see Fig. 1.7) consisted of a tantalum gate wire wound with an insulated coil of niobium. This device can be operated in liquid helium at atmospheric pressure since the critical temperature of tantalum is only just above 4.2°K. The niobium control coil is designed so that its critical current exceeds the control current required to drive the

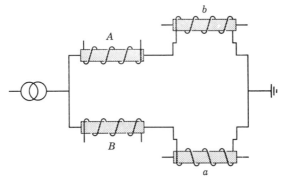

Fig. 6.5 Cryotron switching circuit.

tantalum normal. Hence the control coil remains superconducting during operation.

In computer circuits the cryotron is used to switch current to one of a number of alternative superconducting loads, themselves usually the controls of other cryotrons. An example is shown in Figure 6.5 where, by activating control coils A or B, the source current is directed to loads a or b respectively. It can be seen that the operation of a cryotron as a switching element is somewhat similar to that of a telephone relay. Both devices use current-controlled magnetic fields to control the resistance of another element—relay contacts in the case of the relay, a gate conductor in the case of the cryotron. Furthermore, when used in switching circuits such as in Figure 6.5, where one element drives other similar ones, the maximum current switched by either a relay or a cryotron must be large enough to control another. The maximum current that can be switched by a cryotron is equal to the critical current of the gate, since currents larger than this will drive the gate wire normal, even in the absence of control current. Therefore, cryotrons used in switching circuits are designed so that the control current required to switch the gate is several times smaller than the gate critical current.

By winding two or more controls on top of one another it is possible to obtain various bias and rectification effects. These and other switching circuits and applications are described in references given at the end of this chapter. A discussion of the use of cryotrons in storage circuits is given in Section 31.

A display of cryotron characteristics useful for circuit design is a plot of crytron gate resistance as a function of control current at various steady gate currents. Such a diagram taken for one of Buck's cryotrons is shown in Figure 6.6. The onset of resistance is seen to be a function of

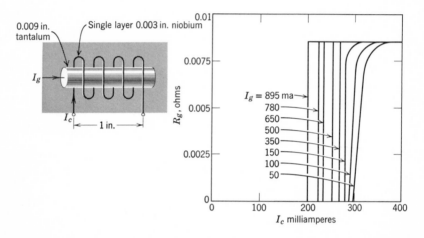

Fig. 6.6 Gate resistance versus control current for a tantalum-niobium wire-wound cryotron at 4.2°K (Buck, 1956a).

both control and gate current. Due to Joule heating the superconducting-to-normal transition is very sharp at the higher gate currents. Another useful display of cryotron characteristics is the dependence of gate critical current on control current. This will be called the *quenching characteristic*.[4] It is ellipsoidal, as shown in Figure 6.7.

To analyze the wire wound cryotron, we will assume a gate wire of diameter W, and critical field H_c surrounded by a control coil wound with $1/\omega$ turns per centimeter.

The field at the surface of the superconducting gate wire due to a gate current I amperes is

$$H_I = \frac{0.4I}{W} \text{ oe} \tag{6.1}$$

---

[4] This usage is different from that of previous authors.

With the gate wire normal, the field due to control coil current C is

$$H_P = \frac{0.4\pi C}{\omega} \qquad (6.2)$$

Since the gate wire can be treated as a bulk superconductor, the superconductivity will be quenched when the total surface field reaches H_c. The fields due to the gate and control current are at right angles to one

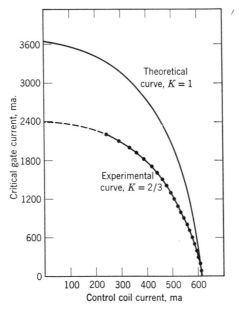

Fig. 6.7 Quenching characteristic for a 0.009 in. diameter tantalum gate cryotron at 4.2°K, compared with Eq. 6.3 (Buck, 1956b).

another and will therefore add in quadrature. Hence the gate will become normal when $H_c{}^2 = H_I{}^2 + H_P{}^2$. Substituting from Equations 6.1 and 6.2 in this equation, we find that the combination of gate and control currents required to quench superconductivity is given by the equation

$$H_c{}^2 = 0.16\left[\left(\frac{I}{W}\right)^2 + \left(\frac{\pi C}{\omega}\right)^2\right]$$

The relation between I and C is seen to be ellipsoidal, in qualitative agreement with Figure 6.7. To obtain exact agreement we must write,

$$H_c{}^2 = 0.16\left[\left(\frac{I}{KW}\right)^2 + \left(\frac{\pi C}{\omega}\right)^2\right] \qquad (6.3)$$

where K is an empirical correction factor, equal to $\frac{2}{3}$ for the cryotron of Figure 6.7. For carefully annealed superconductors which obey Silsbee's rule, K approaches unity.

From Equation 6.3 we find that the critical gate current for zero control current is

$$I_c = \frac{KWH_c}{0.4} \tag{6.4}$$

This is the maximum current that can be controlled by a cryotron since a larger current will cause the gate wire to switch spontaneously. The largest current required to switch the cryotron is the control current, C_{max}, required to drive the gate resistive in the absence of gate current. From Equation 6.3

$$C_{max} = \frac{H_c\,\omega}{0.4\pi} \tag{6.5}$$

The useful current gain G is the ratio of these two currents, that is,

$$G = \frac{I_c}{C_{max}}$$

Substituting from Equations 6.4 and 6.5

$$G = \pi K \frac{W}{\omega} \tag{6.6}$$

For a well-annealed superconducting gate wire that obeys Silsbee's condition, K approaches unity, so that G is independent of temperature below T_c.

In cryotron computer circuits, current is switched between different superconducting controls of inductance L by the action of the gate wire resistance R. Hence the operating speed of a specific design of cryotron can be characterized by the time-constant L/R of one cryotron gate driving one control. Since both L and R are directly proportional to the length of the cryotron, this time-constant is independent of length. With the gate wire normal, the inductance of the control coil surrounding it can be shown to be

$$L = \left(\frac{\pi W}{\omega}\right)^2 \times 10^{-9} \text{ Henry/cm}$$

The resistance of a gate wire of low temperature resistivity ρ ohm-cm is

$$R = \frac{4\rho}{\pi W^2} \text{ ohms/cm}$$

Hence, the characteristic-time constant is

$$\tau = L/R = \frac{\pi^3 W^2}{4\rho}\left(\frac{W}{\omega}\right)^2 \times 10^{-9} \text{ sec}$$

To investigate the relation between time-constant and gain we substitute for W/ω in terms of G, using Equation 6.6. This gives

$$\tau = \frac{\pi}{4K^2\rho} W^2 G^2 \times 10^{-9} \text{ sec} \qquad (6.7)$$

This expression shows that the characteristic time-constant can be reduced by increasing the gate resistivity and reducing its diameter. For a

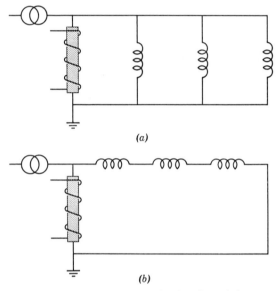

(a)

(b)

Fig. 6.8   Two alternative cryotron circuits of equal time constant.

representative tantalum cryotron for which

$$\rho \sim 10^{-6} \text{ ohm-cm}$$
$$W = 3 \times 10^{-2} \text{ cm}$$
$$K = 0.25$$

and $$G = 2,$$

Equation 6.7 predicts a characteristic circuit time-constant of approximately 50 microseconds. For cryotrons with a very small value of the ratio W^2/ρ the circuit operating speed may be limited by the switching speed of the gate wire itself. This is analyzed below.

An interesting consequence of the fact that τ is proportional to the square of the gain, is that the time-constant of the circuit of Figure 6.8a where one cryotron drives three inductances arranged in parallel, is the same as that of Figure 6.8b, where a lower gain cryotron drives the same inductances arranged in series. To prove this, assume that the gain required for the cryotron driving the series circuit having inductance $3L$ is G. From Equation 6.7 the time-constant of this circuit is

$$\tau_1 = \text{const } 3LG^2$$

The gain required for the cryotron driving the parallel configuration of inductance $L/3$ will be $3G$. Hence, the time-constant of this arrangement will be

$$\tau_2 = \text{const } \frac{L}{3}(3G)^2$$

$$= \tau_1$$

SWITCHING TIME. The process by which a wire-wound cryotron switches from the superconducting to the normal state when a magnetic field is applied, can be understood by considering the switching phenomena of a superconducting cylinder subjected to a parallel supercritical magnetic field. This will be analyzed by an approximate treatment due to Pippard (1950).[5] The cross-section of the cylinder during a transition induced by an applied field $H_e > H_c$ is assumed to consist of a contracting super-conducting core surrounded by a normal region. As the normal region expands inward, circulating eddy currents are generated in it. The velocity of the core boundary adjusts itself so that the field at the boundary due to the eddy currents is just equal to H_c. The field in the normal region varies from H_c at the superconducting boundary to H_e at the surface.

The switching time for the superconducting to normal transition can be calculated as follows. Consider a circle of radius r concentric with the cylinder. At an instant at which the superconducting core has a radius r_0, the total magnetic flux contained inside the circle of radius r is

$$\phi = \pi(r^2 - r_0^2)H(r)$$

The emf generated around the circle r as the superconducting core shrinks is

$$E(r) = -\frac{1}{2\pi r}\frac{d\phi}{dt}$$

$$= H_c \frac{r_0}{r}\frac{dr_0}{dt} \tag{6.8}$$

In differentiating Equation 6.8 the simplifying assumption has been made that $H(r) = H_c$ everywhere in the normal region.

---

[5] A more exact calculation has been performed by Swihart (1963).

The induced eddy currents are

$$J(r) = \frac{E(r)}{\rho}$$

$$= \frac{H_c r_0}{\rho r} \frac{dr_0}{dt} \tag{6.9}$$

where ρ is the resistivity of the normal region. Maxwell's equation

$$\text{curl } \mathbf{H} = 0.4\pi \mathbf{J}$$

reduces to

$$\frac{dH}{dr} = 0.4\pi J(r)$$

for this geometry. Hence integrating along a cylinder radius, we find

$$H_e - H_c = -0.4\pi \int_{r_0}^{a} J(r)\, dr \tag{6.10}$$

where a is the radius of the cylinder.

Substituting for $J(r)$ from Equation 6.9 and integrating Equation 6.10 we obtain

$$r_0 \ln\left(\frac{a}{r_0}\right) \times \frac{dr_0}{dt} = -\frac{(H_e - H_c)\rho}{0.4\pi H_c}$$

Integrating with respect to time and putting $r_0 = a$ at $t = 0$, we obtain,

$$\frac{t}{t_0} = 1 - f^2(1 - 2\ln f)$$

$$f = \frac{r_0}{a} \quad \text{and} \quad t_0 = \frac{\pi a^2}{10\rho} \frac{H_c}{H_e - H_c} \text{ sec.} \tag{6.11}$$

where ρ is in ohm-cm. It is readily shown that $t = t_0$ when $f = 0$. Hence, t_0 is the time required for the superconducting-to-normal transition.[6]

Pippard (1950b) has also calculated the switching time due to the magnetic field of a current flowing in a superconducting cylinder and finds that this is equal to

$$t_0 = \frac{\pi a^2}{5\rho}\left(\frac{3}{2} + p + p(2 + p)\log\frac{p}{1 + p}\right)$$

where $p = (H_e - H_c)/H_c$, H_e being the field at the surface of the wire due

---

[6] The same result has been obtained by Lifschitz (1950).

to the applied current. It is interesting to note that whereas the switching time due to an applied field only slightly larger than H_c approaches infinity, the switching time due to a current slightly larger than the critical does not. This happens because the current tends to be compressed into the vanishing superconducting regions thus increasing the field at their surface.

As the phase boundary moves inwards during a superconducting-to-normal transition, the normal material cools slightly owing to the latent heat of transition. This tends to retard the boundary movement. This effect is counteracted by the Joule heat produced by eddy currents. The effect of heat production and absorption on boundary velocity is small compared to that of eddy currents. The problem has been analyzed by Sim (1961), who discusses earlier experimental results obtained by Ittner (1958).

The expression (Eq. 6.11) derived for the superconducting-to-normal transition of a superconductor has been verified experimentally for tin cylinders by Faber (1953). By measuring the variation of resistance with time, Buck (1956b) has obtained field-induced transition times shown in Figure 6.9 for different cryotrons in the presence of various gate currents. It can be seen that the presence of gate current reduces the switching time and that the dependence of this time on radius, resistivity, and applied field is roughly that predicted by Equation 6.11. The curves of Figure 6.9 are seen to depart from the predicted linear form at the longer switching times, particularly in the case of the larger gate currents. Buck attributed this to Joule heating effects.

The transition from the normal to the superconducting state that takes place when the applied field is removed is far more complex than that for the inverse transition. It is under these conditions that the magnetic propagation effects described in Section 7.3 occur. As mentioned there, Faber (1954), working with carefully annealed specimens, found that a superconducting nucleus forms at the surface of a normal cylinder when the applied field is removed. This originates a narrow superconducting filament that travels along the whole length of the cylinder at a velocity limited not by eddy currents but by interphase boundary effects. The filament then spreads into a superconducting sheath around the cylinder. Finally, the superconducting sheath penetrates through the cylinder. This has to take place in an irregular manner because flux trapped within the sheath has to escape by breaking through it. In the large annealed specimens studied by Faber, this process could take as long as 10 seconds, whereas the initial filament propagation velocity was of the order of 20 cm/sec.

For all the specimens described in Figure 6.9, Buck found that resistance

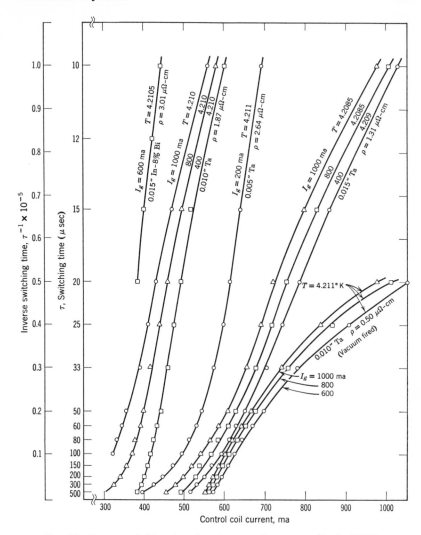

Fig. 6.9 Inverse switching time for wire-wound cryotrons (Buck, 1956b).

disappeared in less than one microsecond after an applied field was removed, even in the presence of gate current equal to an appreciable fraction of the initial value. However the time required for the last trace of the normal state to disappear was found to be of the order of hundreds of microseconds. These results suggest a relatively slow phase transition, initiated by superconducting filaments propagating at high speed along the surface of the gate wire.

26. CROSSED FILM CRYOTRONS

As described in Section 25.2, the operating speed of wire-cryotron circuits is limited either by the high control-inductance to gate-resistance ratio, or by the long switching time of the gate wire itself. Both these limitations can be ameliorated by reducing the gate wire diameter. An alternative, simpler approach is to replace the gate wire by a cylinder of superconductive film deposited on an insulator. This greatly increases the resistance of the gate in the normal state since its cross-section is reduced, and this decreases the L/R ratio of cryotron circuits. Furthermore, the superconducting-to-normal switching time is much less for a cylindrical film than for a conducting cylinder of the same radius. Provided that the cylindrical superconductive film is thicker than the penetration depth, the critical current and field of the hollow cylinder should be identical to those for a solid cylinder of the same radius.

That improvements in cryotron switching speed can be obtained by the use of a hollow gate cylinder has been established by a number of workers. For instance, J. W. Bremer reports switching speeds of approximately 10 microseconds for wire-wound cryotrons whose gates consist of tin film deposited on quartz fiber.[7] Lead wire was used for the control coils of these cryotrons.

The appearance of cylindrical film cryotrons was soon followed by the arrival of the various "two-dimensional" film cryotrons that are described in the remainder of this section and in Section 27. These flat-film cryotrons, which retain the high switching speed of cylindrical-film cryotrons are much easier to fabricate in quantity. This is particularly advantageous for digital computers, of which large portions can be constructed solely from cryotrons. For such an application, large arrays of flat-film cryotrons can be deposited at one and the same time, together with their interconnections. (See Frontispiece.)

The remainder of this section describes and analyzes the various forms of crossed-film cryotron, beginning with the unshielded type. This is followed by a description of the shielded cross-film cryotron; the section concludes with an account of crossed-film structures with superimposed controls.

26.1 The Unshielded Crossed-Film Cryotron

As mentioned in Chapter 1, the electrical properties of the wire-wound cryotron can be duplicated by the two-dimensional crossed-film cryotron structure consisting of a gate-film superconductor such as tin, crossed by

---

[7] J. W. Bremer, *Superconductive Devices*. New York: McGraw-Hill, 1962, p. 55.

a much narrower control of lead. As in the case of the wire-wound cryotron, the crossed-film cryotron (CFC) is operated at a temperature just below the critical temperature of the gate and far below that of the control. The structure and dimensions of an early vacuum deposited CFC are shown in Figure 6.10. It should be noted that the ends of the tin film were made wider than the center to avoid any possible limitation of the critical gate current due to oxide formation between the tin gate and the lead connector films. If the lead, insulator, and tin films are

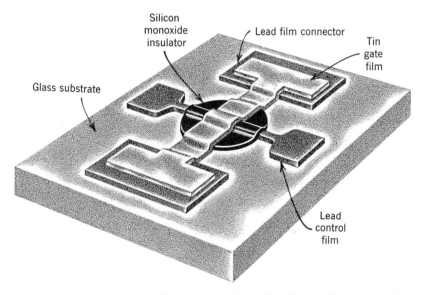

Fig. 6.10 Unshielded crossed film cryotron (schematic). Tin gate film cross section: 3 mm × 0.3 μ; lead control film cross section: 1 × 15 μ; insulating film thickness: 0.4 μ (Newhouse and Bremer, 1959).

deposited in the same vacuum, that is, without admitting air between the separate depositions, this precaution is unnecessary.

The dependence of the critical gate current on control current is shown in the broken curve of Figure 6.11. The extended "tail" of this curve indicates the presence in the gate film of a portion having a small critical current and a very large critical field. Delano (1960) identified this region with the thin edges of the gate film, which tend to become 'smeared out' during conventional vacuum deposition. Several methods for producing films with sharp edges are described in Section 15.

The variation of gate resistance with control current, at constant gate current, is shown as solid lines in Figure 6.11. As the control current exceeds a critical value (calculated below), the gate film becomes normal in the vicinity of the control, and gate resistance appears. Further increase of the control current causes regions of the gate film not adjacent to the control to become normal. If the control current could be increased sufficiently, the resistance would eventually reach a limiting value determined by the length of the gate film. In practice, the length of the gate film is always much greater than the width of the control, so that this limit on the gate resistance is not approached.

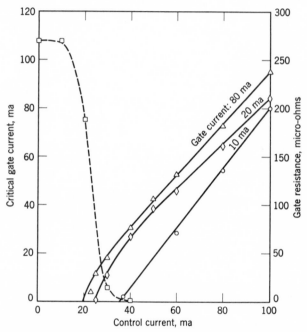

Fig. 6.11 Electrical characteristics of the unshielded CFC of Fig. 6.10 at 3.617°K. Broken curve: quenching characteristic. Solid curves: gate resistance versus control current. (Newhouse and Bremer, 1959.)

The electrical characteristics of the CFC are so similar to those of the wire-wound cryotron that the same circuit design considerations apply to both. Since a superconducting film is very sensitive to the presence of magnetic fields normal to its surface, unshielded film-cryotron circuits should be operated in magnetically screened enclosures. These can be produced by means of Helmholtz coils or by means of a superconducting cap of spun lead that strongly attenuates external fields, due to the Meissner effect.

Just as for the wire-wound cryotron, the current gain of the CFC is defined as the ratio of the gate critical current to the minimum control current required to quench superconductivity in the gate. The gate critical current is proportional to the gate width W (see Sec. 16), and the field produced by a given control current is inversely proportional to the control width ω. Hence, for high current gain, the ratio W/ω between the gate and control widths must be kept large.

The gate-film switching time of crossed-film cryotrons is less than 10^{-8} sec so that their circuit operating speed in practice depends on the L/R ratio of circuit inductance and gate resistance. A typical CFC circuit is laid out as shown in Figure 7.4 of the next chapter, with broad lead films connecting the gate of one CFC to the much narrower controls of the next. Since the inductance of a flat film is roughly inversely proportional to its width, the broad interconnections between the gate of the first CFC and the control of the second can be neglected when calculating circuit inductance. Therefore, the ratio of control inductance to gate resistance provides a good figure of merit for the circuit operating speed of a particular CFC. Used in a circuit of this type and operated at a current gain of 2, the CFC shown in Figure 6.10 gave a circuit time-constant of approximately 25 microseconds. Expressions for CFC gain and time-constant in terms of the material parameters, cryotron dimensions and temperature are derived below.

26.2 Electromagnetic Analysis of the Crossed-Film Cryotron Structure

No exact analysis of the unshielded CFC has been published, but it is possible to account for the intercepts and slopes of the curves of Figure 6.11 approximately.

In the presence of very small control currents that are not sufficient to drive any part of the gate film normal, the field distribution near the control is similar to that between a superconducting film and ground plane as analyzed in connection with Figure 3.13.[8] Resistance will appear in the gate film in the absence of gate current when the control current reaches a value of C_c amperes such that the gate film surface field exceeds the critical value H_F. From Equation 3.60

$$0.4\pi C_c \sim H_F \omega$$

where ω is the width of the control. This equation should be exact if the gate and control penetration depths are much smaller than the gate and control film thickness. Newhouse, Bremer and Edwards (1960) have verified experimentally that it holds approximately even when the penetration depths are comparable to the film thicknesses.

---

[8] The two cases are not completely identical because the gate film is not infinitely wide and is not necessarily much thicker than its penetration depth.

Once the control current exceeds C_c the portion of the gate film covered by the control becomes normal. This destroys the imaging effect of that region of the gate film. Consequently the field in the vicinity of the control can now grow with any further increase of control current, as shown in Figure 6.12. Very approximately, it may be assumed that the control field in the normal gate region adjacent to the control is doubled in value due to image currents flowing in those parts of the gate film that are in the intermediate and superconducting state. To calculate the length of this normal region we will assume that the gate film resumes its full resistance in the region where the control field exceeds $\frac{1}{2}H_F$.[9]

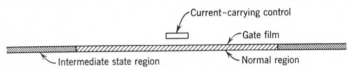

Fig. 6.12   Cross-section of an energized unshielded CFC.

The field due to a control current C amperes at a distance r large compared to the control width is

$$H = \frac{0.2C}{r} \text{ oe}$$

Assuming that this field is doubled in magnitude due to image currents, we find that the length m of the region in which the net field is equal or larger than $\frac{1}{2}H_F$ is

$$m = \frac{1.6C}{H_F}$$

If k is defined as the resistance per unit length of the gate film, the resistance of the normal portion is

$$R = \frac{1.6Ck}{H_F}$$

hence,

$$\left(\frac{\partial R}{\partial C}\right)_I = \frac{1.6k}{H_F}$$

This expression is in approximate agreement with the slope of the experimental resistance curves of Figure 6.11.

26.3   The Shielded Crossed-Film Cryotron

One way of increasing the operating speed of CFC circuits is to reduce the inductance of the connecting elements and controls. This can be

---

[9] This assumption is based on measurements of the transition in a tin film due to a field normal to the film surface, by J. M. Corsan (1961).

accomplished by depositing the whole CFC circuit on an insulated super-conducting "shield" or "ground plane." The cross section of such a shielded CFC is shown in Figure 6.13. It can be seen that the permanently superconducting ground plane will produce the effect of a control image (shown dashed in the figure), even when the gate film is normal. Consequently, the field due to current in the control or any other conductor will now be zero everywhere except in the region between the conductor

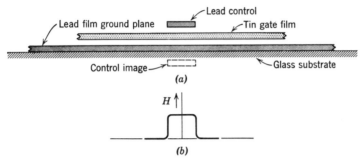

Fig. 6.13 (a) Cross section of a shielded CFC (schematic). (b) Field between control and ground plane in the presence of control current.

and the shield plane. This effect drastically reduces the self inductance of all conductors situated close to the shield plane, since every line has now been replaced by the equivalent of "twisted pair." The quenching characteristic of a shielded CFC is compared with that of an unshielded CFC in Figure 6.14.

It can be seen that the gate critical current I_c is increased in the shielded configuration. As explained in Section 16 above, this is due to the cancellation of the normal field component of the gate current by the shield. The control current at which resistance appears is approximately the same in the shielded as in the unshielded configuration. The dependence of gate resistance on control current for a shielded CFC is shown schematically in Figure 6.15. The gently rising portion of the curve corresponding to the initial onset of resistance is known as the "toe." This resistance is at least partially due to control fields *normal* to the gate film which exists in regions several microns in length, near each edge of the control. The steep rise in the resistance curve is due to that portion of the gate film situated between the control and the shield which becomes normal when the field in this region reaches H_F. Once the gate film between the control and shield has become normal, gate resistance only increases very slowly with increasing control current. This can be understood from Figure 6.13b, which shows that in a shielded CFC the control field drops off very sharply outside the edges of the control.

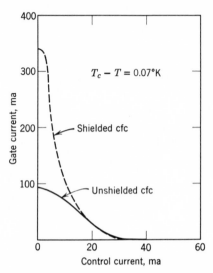

Fig. 6.14 Quenching characteristic for identical shielded and unshielded crossed-film cryotrons (Newhouse, Bremer and Edwards, 1960). Dimensions: Gate cross section $\sim$ 0.2 cm $\times$ 0.3 μ; Control cross section $\sim 1\ \mu \times 30\ \mu$; Inter-element insulation thickness $\sim 0.4\ \mu$.

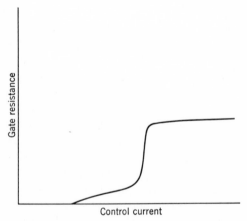

Fig. 6.15 The effect of control current on gate resistance for the shielded CFC (schematic).

26.4   Gain-Bandwidth Analysis

It is convenient to define the gain of the shielded CFC at a given temperature as

$$G = \frac{I_c}{C_c} \qquad (6.12)$$

where I_c is the critical gate current at zero control current, and C_c is defined as the control current sufficient to restore half the maximum gate resistance at vanishingly small gate current.

It will be found convenient to replace I_c by the surface field H_I produced by this current flowing in the gate film. This field will exist between the gate film and the ground plane and from Equation 3.60 is given by

$$H_I = \frac{0.4\pi I_c}{W} \text{ oe} \qquad (6.13)$$

where W is the width of the gate film and I_c is in amperes. Since I_c is uniformly distributed in the shielded gate film, H_I is a function of the film properties only, independent of its width.

Since C_c is defined as the control current that produces half of the maximum gate resistance, the field generated by this current between the control and the shield must equal the film critical field H_F, that is, the field corresponding to the midpoint of the field-induced transition.

Again using Equation 3.60, we find

$$H_F = 0.4\pi C_c/\omega \qquad (6.14)$$

where ω is the width of the control. H_F is, of course, a parameter of the gate film only, independent of the widths of the gate and control film.

Substituting for I_c and C_c from Equations 6.13 and 6.14 in Equation 6.12, we have for the current gain

$$G = \frac{H_I}{H_F} \frac{W}{\omega} \qquad (6.15)$$

Related expressions for voltage and power gain have been derived by Smallman et al. (1960).

For a film thick compared to the penetration depth $H_I/H_F \sim 1$. However, for high speed operation it is desirable to use thinner film so as to achieve a higher gate resistance. Under these conditions $H_I/H_F < 1$ and the "crossing ratio" W/ω has to be made large to achieve a gain larger than unity.

To determine the dependence of the gain on gate film thickness and temperature we combine Equations 4.10 and 4.11 to give[10]

$$\frac{H_I}{H_F} \sim \frac{1}{9}\left(\frac{d}{\lambda}\right)^2 \tag{6.16}$$

which holds, provided $d \ll \lambda$.

Substituting for H_I/H_F in Equation 6.15

$$G = \frac{1}{9}\frac{W}{\omega}\left(\frac{d}{\lambda}\right)^2$$

By considering the variation of λ with temperature (see Eq. 2.4) it becomes apparent that G increases rapidly as the temperature decreases

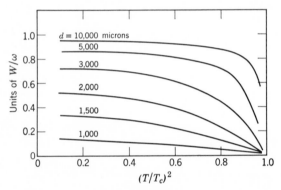

Fig. 6.16 Crossing ratio for unit gain of the tin-lead CFC as a function of reduced temperature; d is the gate film thickness (Young, 1961).

below T_c and approaches a constant value as T/T_c becomes much smaller than unity. This is illustrated by the experimental data of Figure 6.16. Furthermore, since λ is a function of the electron mean free path that determines the resistivity in the normal state, the gain is dependent on the gate film resistivity. If gate resistance is increased either by reducing the gate film thickness, or by adding impurities to increase the gate film resistivity, the gain is decreased.

The time constant of one shielded CFC driving another can be defined in a similar manner to that for the unshielded CFC, that is, as

$$\tau = L/R$$

where L is the inductance of a (shielded) control and R is half of the

---

[10] Eq. 6.16 is only approximate, since H_I in Eq. 4.6 is defined as the surface field corresponding to the *midpoint* of the current induced transition, whereas in Eq. 6.13 it is defined as the surface field corresponding to the *onset* of the transition.

resistance of that part of the gate film covered by the control. The inductance of a shielded control can be calculated very simply since the field due to the control is zero everywhere except between the control and the shield.

For a control field H oersted, the magnetic-field energy per unit length of control is

$$E_H = \frac{1}{8\pi} H^2 \omega t' \times 10^{-7} \text{ joules} \tag{6.17}$$

where t' is the effective distance between control and shield. When the gate film underlying the control is normal so that its presence can be ignored,

$$t' = t + \lambda(\text{control}) + \lambda(\text{shield})$$

where t is the distance between the control and the shield plane, and where the penetration depths of the control and shield are assumed to be respectively much smaller than the control and shield thickness. (This result is proved in Section 27.)

Substituting for H in Equation 6.17, using the relation

$$H = \frac{0.4\pi I}{\omega} \quad \text{(see Eq. 3.60)}$$

and using the equivalence

$$E_H = \tfrac{1}{2}MI^2$$

where M is the inductance per unit length, we obtain

$$M = \frac{4\pi t'}{\omega} \times 10^{-9} \text{ henry} \tag{6.18}$$

Hence, the inductance of a control crossing a gate film of width W is

$$L = \frac{4\pi t' W}{\omega} \times 10^{-9}$$

The resistance of half of the gate film lying under the control is

$$R = \tfrac{1}{2}\rho \, \frac{\omega}{Wd}$$

where ρ is the effective gate resistivity in ohm-cm.

Combining these two expressions gives the time constant of the shielded CFC as

$$\tau = \frac{L}{R}$$

$$= \frac{8\pi \, dt'}{\rho} \left(\frac{W}{\omega}\right)^2 \times 10^{-9} \text{ sec} \tag{6.19}$$

To obtain the time constant as a function of gain we substitute for W/ω from Equation 6.15 and obtain

$$\tau = \frac{8\pi \, dt'}{\rho} \, G^2 \left(\frac{H_F}{H_I}\right)^2 \times 10^{-9} \tag{6.20}$$

This equation shows that just as in the case of the wire-wound cryotron, τ is proportional to G^2. The dependence of τ on d and ρ is complex since these parameters affect H_F/H_I. Ittner (1960) has calculated that τ/G^2 goes through a minimum of the order of 10^{-8} sec for values of d ranging from 0.3 to 0.5 microns, depending on the resistivity.

Equation 6.19 shows that τ does not depend directly on temperature. However, Equation 6.20 and Figure 6.16 show that when designing for a given gain, τ can be minimized by operating as far below T_c as possible.

26.5 Multi-Control Cryotrons

It is of interest to inquire whether one control of a CFC can be used to cancel the effect of another. With this aim, Fruin and Newhouse (1963) have studied several CFC structures having superimposed controls. It was found that current in one control cannot completely cancel the effect on the gate film of current in a superimposed control of equal width, unless the two controls are precisely aligned. This effect is due to the existence of areas of incomplete field cancellation, which are illustrated in Figure 6.17a. A structure in which current in one control *can* effectively cancel the effect of current in another, and in which precise alignment is not required, is shown in Figure 6.17b. This represents a cross section of a narrow superconducting control of width ω superimposed on a wider control of width W, which in turn is superimposed on a tin gate film and a superconducting ground plane. The controls are assumed to be much thicker than the penetration depth, and their vertical separations are assumed to be small compared to their widths. The tin gate is assumed to be thin compared to the penetration depth, so that its presence can be ignored in the argument that follows.

Current passed through these controls will flow near the surface and will distribute itself so that the surface field, H_s, is parallel to the superconductor surface.[11] Furthermore

$$|H_s| = 0.4\pi |j|$$

where j is the current surface density in amperes cm^{-1}. Current passed through the narrow control will produce screening currents j_2, j_3, and j_4. These will ensure that the magnetic field is vanishingly small everywhere

---

[11] See Sec. 12.4 for a more detailed analysis of a simpler related structure.

except in the regions a and b between the control surfaces. The field in these regions will be parallel to the control surfaces and will thus be uniform in direction. Since div $\mathbf{H} = 0$ in free space, $\mathbf{H}$ will be uniform in magnitude also.

Assume that current I is passed through the top control. This will flow on the bottom surface as shown, with surface density $j_1 = I/\omega$. Screening current of surface density j_2 will be induced underneath the

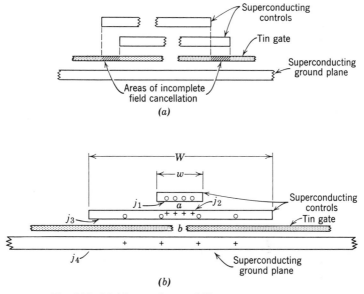

(a)

(b)

Fig. 6.17 Multi-control crossed-film cryotron structures.

narrow control on part of the top surface of the wide control as shown in the figure.

$$j_2 = j_1$$

Hence, the total screening current on the top surface of the wide control equals I. Since the net flow of screening current in the wide control is zero, the top surface screening current will return on the bottom surface as shown. Since it must be uniformly distributed,

$$j_3 W = j_2 \omega = I$$

The field in the region b will therefore equal

$$H = 0.4\pi j_3$$
$$= \frac{0.4\pi I}{W}$$

Notice that ω does not appear in this equation even though I is the current through the *narrow* control. From Equation 3.60 we see that the same field is produced if current I is passed through the wide control. If current is passed through both controls simultaneously, the field in region b is given by the expression

$$H = \frac{0.4\pi \Sigma I}{W}$$

where ΣI represents the algebraic sum of the currents. Fruin and the author were able to verify this equation experimentally, and to establish that it also applies to a structure consisting of two narrow controls, placed *side by side* upon a broader one.

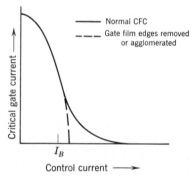

Fig. 6.18   The effect of the gate edges on the CFC quenching characteristic.

One application of this multi-control cryotron to switching circuits arises from the property that current through one control can be used to "inhibit" the effect of current through another. This inhibit function cannot be mechanized with a single conventional CFC. Again, by passing a steady bias current through one control sufficient to keep the gate resistive, the device becomes a "logical inverter," since current of the correct polarity through the second control makes the gate superconducting, a result that is the inverse of the usual control action. Other applications, including a negative impedance circuit, and logic circuits whose switching function can be changed by adjusting the bias current through one control, are described in the original paper.

R. Delano (1960) reports that the quenching characteristic of the CFC can be sharpened, as shown schematically in Figure 6.18, by forming the gate film in such a manner that the thin edges are broken up. With a broken-edge gate film, the small signal gain of one control of a multi-control cryotron can clearly be considerably increased by passing a bias current such as I_B through the other. Alternatively, this type of bias makes it possible to achieve a gain greater than unity with a smaller gate-to-control width ratio, thus reducing the CFC loop-circuit time constant (see Eq. 6.19). By operating in this way, the gate-to-control width ratio can be reduced to approximately 2, bringing the L/R time constant of simple loops into the millimicrosecond region.[12]

27. PARALLEL FILM STRUCTURES

27.1 In-line Cryotrons

Because of the shape of the quenching characteristic of the crossed-film cryotron, the use of bias to increase operating speed strongly reduces the

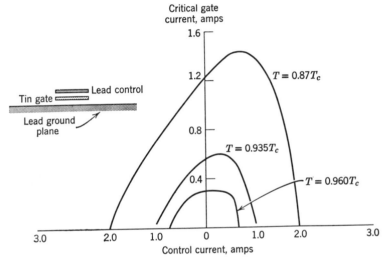

Fig. 6.19 Structure and quenching characteristic of a tin in-line cryotron at several temperatures. Gate and control width $\sim 9 \cdot 10^{-3}$ in, gate thickness ~ 9000 Å, $T_c = 3.84°$K (Brenneman, 1963).

amplitude of the effective critical current and thus of the gain. A control current characteristic more suitable for bias application is obtained if the control is arranged parallel to the gate and made of equal width. The control field is now parallel to that produced by the gate current. This device is known as an in-line cryotron. The structure and the control characteristics at several temperatures are shown in Figure 6.19. It is to be noticed that a strong asymmetry in the gate-film critical current develops at the lower temperatures, where the penetration depth falls below the

---

[12] D. R. Young (1961).

gate film thickness. By biasing the in-line cryotron to the steepest part of the asymmetrical characteristic it is possible to obtain high-speed operation with a gain above unity.

The reasons for the asymmetrical quenching characteristic can be understood by examining the field distribution near a singly shielded, superconducting film of width w, much thicker than the penetration depth, carrying a current I emu. This structure was analyzed in Section 12.4 where it was shown that all the current will flow on the bottom of the film, and that the field below the film is given by the expression

$$H_i = \frac{4\pi I}{w}$$

The field generated above the film is zero to first order. If the current through the film is increased, it will enter the intermediate state and exhibit

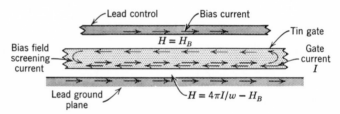

Fig. 6.20   Distribution of screening currents in an in-line cryotron (schematic).

resistance when the field on its lower surface reaches the (bulk) critical value H_c. It is possible to increase the current I_c at which resistance appears, by applying an external bias field H_B in a direction such that the net field underneath the film is decreased.

This bias field must be in the plane of the film and normal to the direction of current flow. It can be conveniently generated by current through a control above and parallel to the gate film. The resultant field H underneath the gate film is given by

$$H = \frac{4\pi I}{w} - H_B \qquad (6.21)$$

The field between the gate film and the control is always equal to H_B. The distribution of screening currents is shown schematically in Figure 6.20.

The current I_c corresponding to the onset of the intermediate state and the appearance of resistance is that current at which $H = H_c$, that is, from Equation (6.21)

$$4\pi I_c = (H_c + H_B)w \qquad (6.22)$$

I_c/w is plotted against H_B in the broken line of Figure 6.21. The maximum film critical current is determined by the condition that the field H_B above the film must not exceed H_c. Therefore, from Equation 6.22,

$$I_c \not> \frac{H_c w}{2\pi}$$

The maximum value of I_c occurs when the surface current density on the top and bottom surfaces of the film are equal. Under these conditions,

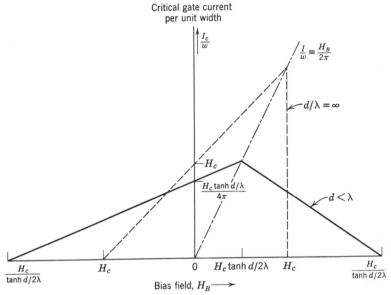

Fig. 6.21 In-line cryotron quenching characteristics calculated from the London theory.

the screening current density due to H_B is just half the current density due to the injected current I.

The effect of a bias field on a film of thickness comparable to the penetration depth has been treated by Young (1961), using the London theory and assuming that the onset of the intermediate state occurs when the net film surface current density reaches a critical value j_c. The calculation is repeated in Appendix 35.3 and the results are illustrated in the solid line of Figure 6.21. Again it is found that for maximum critical current, the current density is the same on the top and bottom surface of the gate film, and that

$$\frac{4\pi I}{w} = 2H_B$$

Both these results are independent of d/λ. The bias field for maximum critical current is shown to be

$$H_{BM} = H_c \tanh \frac{d}{2\lambda}$$

where H_c is the bulk critical field. It is found that for values of bias field less than H_{BM}, entry into the intermediate state is initiated on the bottom surface of the gate film. For $H_B > H_{BM}$, the current density reaches the critical value first on the top surface. The critical current curve intersects the horizontal axis at the same value of the film critical field H_F, as that derived in Section 14.3 that is, $H_F = H_c \coth d/2\lambda$. As d/λ becomes large, both H_F, the bias field for zero critical current, and H_{BM} the field for maximum critical current, approach H_c. Hence the section of quenching characteristic between them approaches infinite slope.

Comparison of Figures. 6.19 and 6.21 reveals that the experimental quenching curve is convex downward in the region of zero control current, whereas the theoretical curve is not. This is probably due to the effect, not considered in Young's model, that the presence of the wide control produces some current flow on the top surface of the gate film even at zero bias field. Other discrepancies between the theoretical and experimental curves are probably due to the fact that the London theory used in the analysis breaks down at fields approaching the critical.

Although the overall current gain of the in-line cryotron must always be less than unity, it can be operated as an amplifier by biasing the gate film to the steep portion of the quenching characteristic. The bias can be provided by passing a steady bias current through the control, by passing current through a second control deposited on top of the first, or by an external field. Experimental curves of maximum incremental gain for indium and tin in-line cryotrons are shown in Figure 6.22. Since a varying control current introduces a voltage into the underlying gate due to transformer coupling, most in-line cryotron circuits require some type of noise cancellation arrangement.

The speed of circuits involving in-line cryotrons or crossed-film cryotrons with low cross-over ratio need not be limited by the inductance of controls or interconnections, since by extending the gate length to several centimeters it is possible to match the transmission line impedance of these elements. The in-line cryotron dimensions required to match such a transmission line can be calculated as follows. The characteristic impedance Z of a distributed transmission line consisting of a film of width ω separated by an effective distance t' from a ground plane is given by

$$Z = \frac{120\pi t'}{\omega} (\varepsilon)^{-\frac{1}{2}} \text{ ohms}$$

where ε is the dielectric constant of the insulator separating film and ground plane.

If an in-line cryotron of length l, width ω and gate film impedance r ohms per square is to match this impedance, then

$$\frac{lr}{\omega} = 120\pi \frac{t'}{\omega} \varepsilon^{-\frac{1}{2}}$$

that is,

$$l = \frac{120\pi t'}{r} (\varepsilon)^{-\frac{1}{2}}$$

which is independent of the width. Assuming realistic values for t', r and

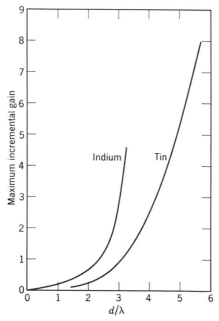

Fig. 6.22 Maximum incremental gain for indium and tin in-line cryotrons (Brenneman, 1963).

ε of 0.5 microns, 2 milli-ohms per square, and 2 respectively, gives the value for the required gate length l as 6.6 cm.

The pulse switching process of the "thick" in-line cryotron gate film is complex and is found to be of the order of 10^{-8} sec. This is much slower than the switching time of crossed-film cryotrons using gate films thinner than the penetration depth. For both devices the repetition rate for random pulses appears to be limited to approximately $200 Mc/s$ by thermal time constants.[13]

27.2 A Film Rectifier

Another parallel film structure is shown in Figure 6.23. This consists of an unshielded tin film flanked by two narrow lead "bias" lines lying parallel to the edges in the plane of the film. It is shown in Section 16.1 that the critical current of such an unshielded film is much smaller than

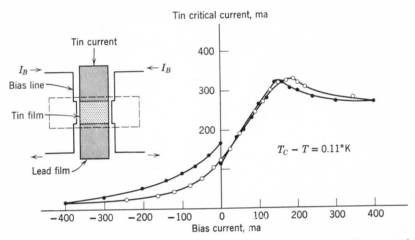

Fig. 6.23 A film structure with asymmetrical quenching characteristic. The exposed portion of the tin film is 1.6 mm long, 2 mm wide and 0.3 microns thick. The bias lines are lead films, 0.05 mm wide and 1 micron thick, located directly over the (insulated) edges of the tin film (Edwards and Newhouse, 1962).

that of a shielded film, because the current in the former cannot be uniformly distributed without generating fields perpendicular to the film surface. It was discovered[14] that current passed through the bias lines would increase the film critical current in one direction and decrease it strongly in the other.

The maximum critical current in this unshielded structure is nearly equal to the critical current of an equivalent shielded film. This suggests that the field created by the optimum bias currents enables the film current to become uniformly distributed without creating any perpendicular field. That is, the bias field just cancels out the field normal to the film, generated by a uniformly distributed film current.

The field normal to a line joining two bias conductors carrying a

---

[13] Brenneman et al. (1963).
[14] Edwards and Newhouse (1962).

current I_B emu is plotted in Figure 6.24 and is given by the expression

$$H_B(x) = 2I_B\left(\frac{1}{w - x} - \frac{1}{w + x}\right) \text{ oe}$$

Here x is the distance from the point midway between the conductors whose separation is $2w$, and the diameter of the conductors is neglected. H_B is, of course, normal to the line joining the conductors.

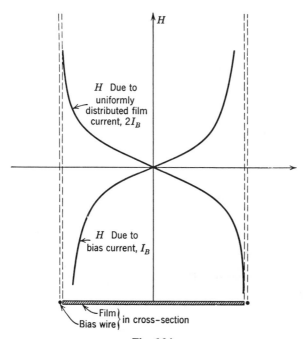

Fig. 6.24

To calculate the normal field at any point x on a film of width $2w$ due to a uniformly distributed current I, we consider first the effect of a section of width δz at a distance from the origin. The current density at all points of the film is $I/2w$. Hence, the field normal to the film surface at x due to the segment at z is

$$\delta H_N(x) = \frac{I}{w}\frac{1}{z - x}\delta z$$

The field at x due to the whole width of the film is

$$H_N(x) = \frac{I}{w}\int_{-w}^{w}\frac{dz}{z - x}$$

$$= \frac{I}{w}\ln\frac{w - x}{w + x} \qquad (6.23)$$

This expression is plotted in Figure 6.24 for $I = 2I_B$. It is seen that except near the film edges where the calculated fields approach infinity, the field due to current I_B in the two bias conductors approximately cancels the normal component of the field due to a current $2I_B$ uniformly distributed in the film. It can be calculated that better field cancellation occurs if the current density in the film is assumed to fall off gradually near each edge. Since this cancellation is not perfect, hysteresis occurs when the bias currents are varied cyclically. This can be observed in Figure 6.23.

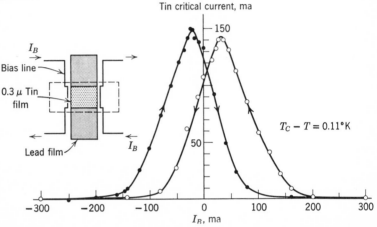

Fig. 6.25 Quenching characteristic for anti-parallel bias currents cycled through high negative and positive values. Dimensions as in Fig. 6.23.

The optimum calculated field canceling action should occur when the bias lines are spaced 28 per cent further apart than the film width. Experiment confirms this prediction since the hysteresis in the bias current-critical gate current characteristic disappears at this spacing. The ratio of bias current to film current for maximum film critical current can be calculated as a function of the ratio of bias line spacing l, to film width. Good agreement with experiment is obtained.

The highly asymmetrical dependence of film critical current on bias current suggests that the structure of Figure 6.23 can be made the basis of a superconductive rectifier. For instance, for a constant bias current of 300 ma, the tin critical current is approximately 280 ma in one direction and only 50 ma in the other.

If the bias currents are anti-parallel, a quenching characteristic exhibiting strong hysteresis is obtained, as shown in Figure 6.25. This indicates that considerable amounts of magnetic flux can be trapped in the tin film, and suggests the possible use of the device for information storage.

27.3 Slow Wave Transmission Lines

Transmission or delay lines are widely used in electronic circuits to introduce a signal delay. The coaxial line, and the strip line are the most commonly used forms. Propagation in lines of this type, as contrasted with that in wave guides, is in the TEM mode, characterized by electric and magnetic fields transverse to the direction of propagation.

The phase velocity in a transmission line is well known to be

$$v = 1/\sqrt{MC} \tag{6.24}$$

where M and C are respectively the inductance and capacitance per unit length. For a line consisting of a strip of width w separated by a dielectric of thickness t from a conducting ground plane, M and C are given by the expressions, in esu,

$$M = \frac{4\pi\mu t}{c^2 w} \quad \text{and} \quad C = \frac{\varepsilon w}{4\pi t} \tag{6.25}$$

ε is the dielectric constant of the insulator and μ is the magnetic permeability.

Substituting these expressions into that for the phase velocity, gives

$$v = \frac{c}{(\mu\varepsilon)^{1/2}} \tag{6.26}$$

The velocity is seen to be the same as that in an unbounded medium of the same dielectric as that used in the line.

The above derivation has assumed ideal conductors having zero surface impedance. In practice the surface impedance of real metals is finite and has both reactive and resistive components. The reactive component increases M and thus decreases the phase velocity. The resistive component causes dispersion and attenuation. These last two factors limit the amount of useful delay that can be obtained with transmission lines bounded by normal metals.

At frequencies up to at least 1 kilomegacycle, the surface impedance of superconductors is much smaller than that of normal metals. Hence, in this frequency range superconducting delay lines can provide longer delays than is possible with conventional lines. By using lines made of thin superconducting films, the penetration effects that vary with temperature can be made relatively large, so that the phase velocity is strongly decreased below the value for the unbounded dielectric. This is beneficial, since it increases the delay per unit length of line.

The inductance of a superconducting transmission line has been calculated by Pippard (1947b) and by Swihart (1961), taking penetration effects into account. The inductance cannot be calculated by the simple energy-density method used in Section 26.4, because under conditions where penetration effects become important, the component of electric field parallel to the direction of propagation can no longer be neglected. Meyers (1962) has pointed out, however, that the energy-density method gives the correct result provided that the kinetic energy of the super-electrons is taken into account.

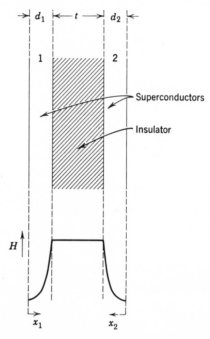

Fig. 6.26 Low frequency magnetic field distribution in a thin film transmission line.

The calculation proceeds as follows. Assume a superconducting line of width w and thickness d_1, carrying current I, separated from a super-conducting ground plane of thickness d_2 by an insulator of thickness t, dielectric constant ε, and unit permeability. The cross-section of the line, showing the field distribution, is shown in Figure 6.26. Following the analysis of Section 12.4, the field in the insulator region is

$$H = \frac{4\pi I}{cw}$$

Solving the London equation $\nabla^2 H = H/\lambda^2$, which in this geometry reduces to $d^2 H/dx^2 = H/\lambda^2$, for superconductor 1, and using the boundary conditions $H = 0$ at $x_1 = 0$, $H = 4\pi I/wc$ at $x_1 = d_1$, gives

$$H_1 = \frac{4\pi I}{cw} \frac{\sinh x_1/\lambda_1}{\sinh d_1/\lambda_1}$$

An identical solution with different subscripts is obtained for super-conductor 2. In this geometry Maxwell's equation curl $\mathbf{H} = \frac{4\pi \mathbf{J}}{c}$ reduces to $dH/dx = 4\pi J/c$. Hence, the superconductive screening current volume density in medium 1 is given by

$$J(x_1) = \frac{I}{\lambda_1 w} \cosh \frac{x_1}{\lambda_1} \sinh \frac{d_1}{\lambda_1}$$

and similarly for medium 2. In the intervening insulator the screening currents are of course zero and displacement currents can be neglected.

The electromagnetic energy in the superconductors is composed of a magnetostatic term, and a term corresponding to the kinetic energy of the super-electrons (see sec. 10.3); that is,

$$\delta E = \frac{H^2}{8\pi} + \frac{2\pi J^2 \lambda^2}{c^2}$$

where E is the energy per unit volume. In the dielectric the electron kinetic energy term drops out.

Hence, the total energy per unit length of the line is

$$E = w \int_0^{d_1} \left[\frac{H^2(x_1)}{8\pi} + \frac{2\pi \lambda_1^2}{c^2} J^2(x_1) \right] dx_1 + 2\pi \left(\frac{I}{cw} \right)^2 tw$$

$$+ w \int_0^{d_2} \left[\frac{H^2(x_2)}{8\pi} + \frac{2\pi \lambda_2^2}{c^2} J^2(x_2) \right] dx_2$$

Substituting for H_1, H_2, J_1 and J_2, and integrating, gives finally

$$E = \frac{2\pi}{w} \left(\frac{I}{c} \right)^2 \left[t + \lambda_1 \coth \frac{d_1}{\lambda_1} + \lambda_2 \coth \frac{d_2}{\lambda_2} \right]$$

By definition

$$E = \tfrac{1}{2} M I^2$$

where M is the inductance per unit length. Hence,

$$M = \frac{4\pi}{c^2 w} \left[t + \lambda_1 \coth \frac{d_1}{\lambda_1} + \lambda_2 \coth \frac{d_2}{\lambda_2} \right] \tag{6.27}$$

For $d/\lambda \to \infty$ this expression reduces to

$$M = \frac{4\pi}{c^2 w} [t + \lambda_1 + \lambda_2]$$

Substituting Equation 6.27 into Equation 6.24 for the phase velocity. and using Equation 6.25 for C,[15] we obtain

$$\frac{c^2}{v} = \frac{\varepsilon}{t}\left[t + \lambda_1 \coth \frac{d_1}{\lambda_1} + \lambda_2 \coth \frac{d_2}{\lambda_2}\right]$$

Since $\coth d/\lambda$ approaches infinity as d/λ becomes small, this expression shows that penetration effects *lower* the phase velocity in superconducting transmission lines. The variation of phase velocity with temperature has been verified experimentally by Young et al. (1960) and is shown schematically in Figure 6.27. By using a 400 Å indium film deposited on

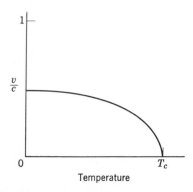

Fig. 6.27 Dependence of phase velocity on temperature for a superconducting film transmission line (schematic).

electropolished tantalum which had been anodized to a thickness of 300 Å, values of v/c as low as 2 per cent have been demonstrated by Mason (1961).

28. MICROWAVE MIXERS AND DEMODULATORS

The extreme non-linearity of superconductors suggests their use for devices such as microwave mixers and demodulators. Andrews and Clark (1946) found that a superconducting bolometer of niobium nitride could absorb, rectify, and demodulate A.M. radio broadcasts at frequencies ranging from 3 to 16 megacycles. Galkin and Lazarev (1948) have reported the detecting qualities of superconductors and Feucht and Woodford (1961) have used a superconductive mixer to investigate high frequency properties of superconductors. In their device, a tin film,

---

[15] Penetration effects need not be considered in calculating C, since charge does not penetrate into a superconductor.

switched at frequencies up to 900 Mc/s by means of a magnetic field, was used to control the transmission of an R.F. signal separated by 40 Mc/s from the switching frequency. Successful mixer action with an output at 40 Mc/s was obtained. More recently Sherrill and Rose (1964) demonstrated the generation of third harmonics at 30 KMc in 100 Å tin and lead films exposed to 10 KMc.

References

For further information on the bulk superconductive devices described in Section 25, reference to the original papers is recommended. Cryotron switching circuits are discussed at length in the book by Bremer (1962), in the paper by Buck (1956a), and in the reviews by Young (1959) and Newhouse (1961). References to cryotron storage circuits and systems are given at the end of the next chapter.

Much of the source material for Section 26 is contained in the ONR Symposium Report ACR-50 "Superconductive Techniques for Computing Systems." Most of these papers have been reprinted in *Solid-State Electronics*, Vol. 1, No. 4 (1960).

Very recently Meyerhoff et al. (1964) have described a cryogenic film switching element whose action depends on the inductance variation of a superconducting lead (Pb) film. This variation is produced by driving an adjacent tin film in or out of the superconducting state.

chapter 7

Superconductive Storage Devices and Resonant Cavities

Much of the hardware of electronic computers is devoted to the function of temporary or semi-permanent data storage. This can be performed by punching holes in cards, by varying the remanent magnetization in magnetic tape or ferrite cores, or by arranging tubes or transistors in bistable positive-feedback circuits such as the well-known Eccles-Jordan flip-flop. Other storage devices, such as neon lamps and tunnel diodes, possess voltage-current characteristics that contain a negative-impedance portion.

These storage devices and circuits can be divided into "non-destructive readout" elements, such as flip-flops and tunnel diodes that emit a steady output signal capable of controlling other similar devices, and "destructive readout" elements such as magnetic cores whose output signal in general requires filtering and amplification before it can be used. The operation of ferrite core memories is described in Section 29, which also explains the distinction between location addressed and content addressed systems.

The properties of superconductors have suggested a variety of attractive storage devices of both the non-destructive and destructive readout type. Non-destructive readout cells consisting of cryotron controlled persistent current loops are described in Section 30. Destructive readout cells are treated in Section 31.

Section 32 is devoted to superconducting resonant cavities. These cavities play the same role in microwave systems as do tuned circuits at lower frequencies. Their sharpness of resonance is strongly dependent on the high frequency surface resistance of the cavity walls. The surface resistance of superconductors becomes vanishingly small under certain conditions, hence superconducting cavities can have much higher quality factors than those made of metals in the normal state.

218

29. DIGITAL STORAGE SYSTEMS

Electronic digital computers are usually divided into separate sections—the "logic" section, for organizing information transfer; the "memory," for temporary or permanent data storage; and the "arithmetic unit." A part of the memory usually consists of magnetic tape or a magnetic drum. These devices can store a very large amount of information, but since they move relatively slowly, a period of time equivalent to many computation

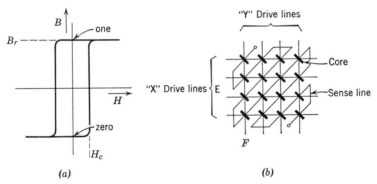

(a)   (b)

Fig. 7.1 (a) Idealized hysteresis loop of a digital storage core. (b) Simplified two-dimensional core array.

periods may elapse before a specific item of information stored on the moving surface becomes available for computation. In order to make full use of the high-speed computing abilities of the arithmetic and control section, computers are provided with a relatively small higher-speed store, the so-called random access memory, containing many thousands of storage locations each capable of storing a binary number of perhaps thirty digits.

A much smaller number of temporary storage registers are associated with the rest of the computer. These usually consist of some type of flip-flop circuit capable of controlling other circuits without intermediate amplification. Storage functions in the random access memory are usually performed by means of tiny ferrite rings or "cores," since the use of flip-flop circuits would be completely uneconomic. These cores exhibit a rectangular hysteresis loop of the type shown in Figure 7.1a. Each core is used to store a binary digit of information, with the positive and negative remanent magnetization states representing binary "one" and "zero" respectively. The cores are typically arranged in an array such as the one shown in the figure, with each core threaded by two or more "drive" lines and one "sense" line. At the outset all cores in the array may be assumed to store zero and are thus at negative remanence. To store binary "one" in a core such as that threaded by lines E and F, the core is switched to positive remanence by sending currents through these two lines whose sum exceeds the coercive force H_c of the hysteresis loop. Each current is small enough so that none of the other cores threaded by lines E and F suffer a permanent change of magnetization. This arrangement provides a great economy in the number of selection circuits, since $2N$ switching circuits ($N = 4$ in Fig. 7.1b) can control N^2 cores.

To "interrogate" a particular core, current pulses sufficient to produce a negative-sense saturating magnetic field are passed through the drive lines that intersect it. If the interrogated core is at positive remanence, the current pulses will switch it to negative remanence, inducing a relatively strong voltage pulse on the sense line in the process. If the core was already at negative remanence before the interrogating pulses, no permanent magnetization change takes place, so that only a relatively small signal is induced on the sense line. This interrogation process is known as "destructive readout," since by resetting the core to negative remanence its information content is destroyed. (An interrogated core can of course be reset to positive remanence if interrogation shows it to have been in this state.)

It is apparent that in contrast to the slower, large capacity, magnetic tape or drum stores, any specified location of a random access memory can be interrogated instantaneously. However, even this type of memory has one fundamental limitation. If it is desired to check whether the memory contains within it a specific binary number or part of a number, every location of the store must be interrogated, an extremely time consuming operation. Such requirements can occur during various sorting, searching and decoding operations.

The development of inexpensive vacuum-deposited cryotrons has encouraged the construction of so-called content addressed memories. These overcome the above-mentioned limitations of more conventional memories by incorporating switching circuits into each storage location so that it is possible to simultaneously compare a specific item with the contents of every location. In one such system proposed by Seeber (1960) the contents of every location are ordered with respect to their magnitude and are automatically shifted when a new item is inserted so as to maintain the ordered arrangement. In another system constructed by Newhouse and Fruin (1962), access is automatically provided to the storage location nearest the output circuit whose contents match the item with which the memory is being interrogated.

These two systems both use the cryotron controlled loops of the type described in Section 30 as storage elements, since these loops can control other cryotrons directly. Superconductive random-access memories analogous to magnetic core systems have also been developed. These use destructive readout persistent current cells which are described in Section 31.

30. CRYOTRON-CONTROLLED PERSISTENT CURRENT CIRCUITS

This section describes two cryotron storage circuits that can control others without the use of additional intermediate amplification. The first of these, called a latching circuit, is analogous to the well-known Eccles-Jordan "flip-flop." It exhibits two stable states that are established by means of two cryotrons interconnected with positive feedback.

The second circuit is based on the persistent current properties of superconductors and has no direct room temperature analog. It makes use of the fact that any current distribution established in a superconducting network is stable and thus has an infinite number of stable states. This circuit forms the basis of most proposed cryotron memory systems, and a simplified version of it is reported to have been used in adiabatic demagnetization refrigerators for the liquid helium range.[1]

30.1 A Latching Circuit[2]

A schematic of this bistable circuit using wire-wound cryotrons is shown in Figure 7.2. If current flows through branch 1, the gate of cryotron A becomes resistive, thus maintaining the current flow in this branch. By activating the control of the transfer cryotron C, the current is forced over to branch 2 where it is held through the action of cryotron B. The circuit is seen to be analogous to the well-known Eccles-Jordan flip-flop in which either of two tubes can hold the other in a cut-off state.

Further insight into circuit operation is obtained from Figure 7.3, which shows I_1/I_c plotted against I_2/I_c.[3] I_1 and I_2 are the currents in branches 1 and 2 respectively and I_c is the critical gate current of each cryotron. The cryotrons are assumed to have a current gain of 2 and their elliptical control characteristics are shown superimposed on the diagram. With a supply current of 1.5 I_c the circuit operating points lie on the straight line having intercepts of 1.5 on the two axes. These intercepts correspond to the two stable end-states in each of which one cryotron is superconducting and the other normal. In switching from one of these stable states to the other, it is seen that the circuit operating point must pass through a region in which both cryotrons are superconducting. Every operating point in this region is stable, hence if the circuit is left in

[1] Garwin (1957).
[2] Buck (1956a).
[3] This method of analysis is due to D. R. Young (1959).

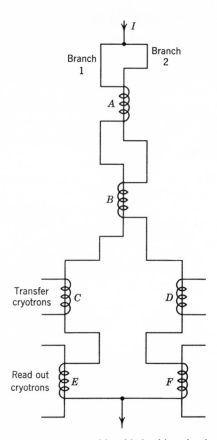

Fig. 7.2 Cryotron bi-stable latching circuit.

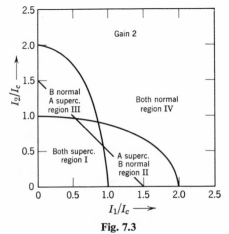

Fig. 7.3

this region it will remain there. Once the circuit has been driven across the boundary of region I into regions II or III, it will switch spontaneously to the nearest end-state in which all the supply current passes through one or the other of cryotrons A and B.

Since the gate resistance of the transfer cryotrons can be made arbitrarily large, the switching speed of the latching circuit can be increased until it is limited by the switching speed of the transfer cryotron itself, or possibly by factors such as distributed capacitance.

30.2 Persistent Current Loop

The unique properties of superconductors make storage circuits possible which, unlike the latching circuit described above, do not depend on positive feedback. A storage circuit of this type using crossed-film cryotrons[4] is shown in Figure 7.4, together with its equivalent circuit.

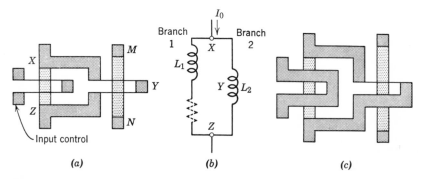

(a)   (b)   (c)

Fig. 7.4 (a) CFC storage cell. (b) Equivalent circuit of (a). (c) High speed version of (a).

One branch of the storage portion of the circuit consists of the tin gate film XZ and the other consists of the permanently superconducting lead film XYZ. This includes the control Y of CFC MN, which is used as a sensing or output element. In the equivalent circuit, the inductance L_2 refers to the control branch XYZ of the storage loop. L_1 refers to the gate branch XZ. In practice $L_1 \ll L_2$ since the gate XZ is much wider than the control in branch XYZ.

If a current I_0 is injected into the storage loop which is assumed to be superconducting, it must divide itself between the two branches in inverse ratio to their inductances, that is,

$$L_1 I_1 = L_2 I_2$$

---

[4] Newhouse, Bremer, and Edwards (1960).

where I_1 and I_2 are the currents in branches 1 and 2 of Figure 7.4b respectively. Since

$$I_1 + I_2 = I_0 \tag{7.1}$$

$$I_1 = \frac{L_2}{L_1 + L_2} I_0 \tag{7.2}$$

The act of switching off the injected current can be simulated mathematically by injecting a current $-I_0$. This divides into currents $-I_1$ and $-I_2$. Hence no stored current is produced as the result of injecting a pulse of current into a loop that remains superconducting throughout. This result is true for circuits of more than two components.

To store current, CFC XZ is made resistive by activating its control in the presence of an injected current I_0. This resistance is shown as a broken line in the equivalent circuit and may be assumed to be of magnitude R. While it is present current is diverted from branch 1 to branch 2. Clearly

$$L_1 \dot{I}_1(t) + R I_1(t) = L_2 \dot{I}_2(t)$$

Substituting for $I_2(t)$ from Equation 7.1 and integrating, we obtain

$$I_1(t) = I_1(0) e^{-t/\tau} \tag{7.3}$$

where

$$\tau = \frac{(L_1 + L_2)}{R} \tag{7.4}$$

and $I_1(0)$ is defined as the value of I_1 at $t = 0$. If R is now reduced to zero, Equations 7.3 and 7.4 indicate that the rate of change of I_1 and I_2 vanishes. I_1 and I_2 will thus remain constant after R reaches zero.

If the injected current I_0 is now switched off, a permanent circular current will appear in the storage loop. The magnitude of this current can be calculated as follows. Let the currents in branches 1 and 2 before the injected current I_0 is switched off be equal to $I_1(t)$ and $I_0 - I_1(t)$ respectively, as shown in Figure 7.5a. Simulating the effect of reducing I_0 to zero by injecting a current $-I_0$ gives rise to the additional currents $-I_1(0)$ and $-[I_0 - I_1(0)]$ in legs 1 and 2 respectively, shown as upward flowing currents in Figure 7.5b. It can be seen that the net currents in branches 1 and 2 are equal and opposite. Hence a circulating current has been created of magnitude

$$|C| = I_1(0) - I_1(t)$$

$$\equiv \frac{L_2}{L_1 + L_2} I_0 - I_1(t) \tag{7.5}$$

where we have substituted for I_1 from Equation 7.2. This circulating current is a maximum when $I_1(t) = 0$, that is, when all current has been diverted from branch 1 to branch 2 before the injected current is turned off.

The fact that any distribution of currents between arms 1 and 2 of the storage loop of Figure 7.5 is stable provided that both branches remain superconducting, is true in general; that is, any current distribution that has been established in a macroscopic superconducting network is stable.

A convincing experimental demonstration of this rule is obtained by applying a series of single-current pulses, each much shorter than the circuit time constant, to the control of CFC XZ in the presence of a steady

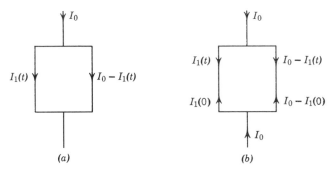

Fig. 7.5

injected current I_0. Each pulse increases I_2 to a new value that can be estimated by measuring the resistance of the previously calibrated CFC MN with a d-c instrument. A typical set of experimental values plotted against the number of pulses applied is shown in Figure 7.6. It is found that these points lie on the exponential calculated from Equations 7.3 and 7.4 just as if the control of CFC XZ had been activated continuously. The solid points in the figure show the piecewise destruction of a stored current that has been produced by switching off the injected current after completely diverting it to branch XYZ of the storage loop.

The time constant of the storage loop can be reduced to a few nano-seconds[5] at the expense of increased drive requirements and decreased output, by widening the input control and shortening the output control as shown in Figure 7.4c.

31. PERSISTENT CURRENT CELLS

31.1 Introduction

Random-access memory storage elements which need not control other circuits directly, do not require the relatively elaborate cryotron circuits

---

[5] V. L. Newhouse (1961).

described above. For these systems it is possible to use persistent-current cells such as the Crowe-type cell described in Section 2.4. Such cells are deposited in rectangular arrays and are switched and interrogated selectively by passing current along two or more lines that intersect in the selected element. Cells of three different geometries will be described below, all of which employ persistent currents circulating in a superconducting loop.

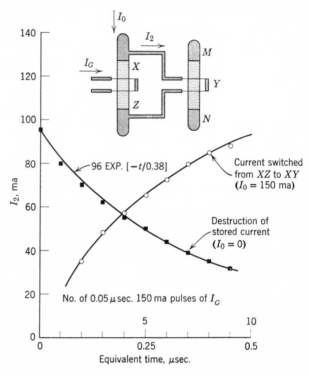

Fig. 7.6 Pulsed operation of a cryotron storage cell (Newhouse, Bremer and Edwards, 1960).

As in the cryotron-controlled loop described above, changes in the persistent current require that part of the loop be temporarily made resistive. In the cells described, this is achieved by inducing in the cell a current large enough to exceed the critical current of a portion of it.

Persistent-current cells appear to be able to operate in either of two modes. In the so-called isothermal mode, described in Chapter 1 in connection with the Crowe cell, the effect of the joule heat on the cell temperature is small enough to be neglected. It is found, however, that if a persistent-current cell is operated far below the critical temperature of its quenching element, thermal runaway occurs once the critical current is exceeded. This mode of operation will be referred to as adiabatic and is described in Section 31.2, again in connection with the Crowe cell. The isothermal mode is described in Section 31.3 in connection with the "Persistor," a cell of somewhat different geometry from the Crowe type. The so-called continuous sheet memory is described in Section 31.4. This utilizes flux trapped in a continuous sheet of tin, and is the furthest developed of the existing superconductive random access storage systems.

To selectively write into a persistent current storage cell, the combined current induced by several selection currents, added to the current stored in the selected cell, must exceed the critical current of its quenching element, while leaving all the other cells of the array undisturbed. These factors place very high demands on the uniformity of superconductive storage cells operated in multi-dimensional arrays. These tolerance requirements are analyzed in Section 31.5.

31.2 Adiabatic Operation (Crowe Cell)

The so-called Crowe cell, using tin as the quenching element and operating in the isothermal mode, has been described in Section 2.4. A schematic representation of the cell, showing the two persistent current states used for binary storage, is repeated in Figure 7.7.

As described by Crowe (1957) this cell used a lead film cross-bar less than 0.1 micron thick deposited across a 1 mm diameter hole in a sheet

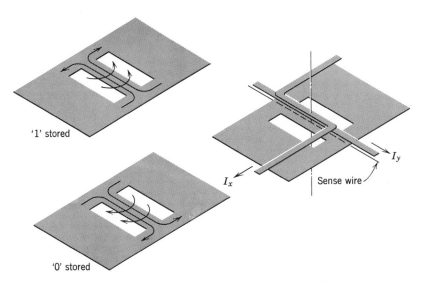

Fig. 7.7 The "Crowe" type persistent current cell.

of lead that remained superconducting throughout the operation. The device was deposited on glass, a relatively bad conductor of heat, and was operated at 4.2°K, far below the critical temperature of lead. Under these conditions, joule heating effects play an important role unless all current changes in the cell take place very slowly. Crowe found that if the current through one of the drive lines of Figure 7.7 is increased very slowly, the

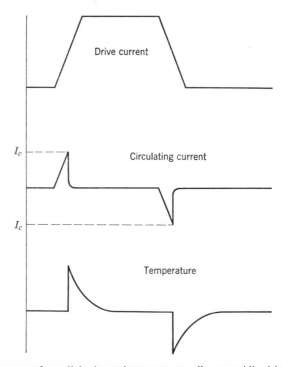

Fig. 7.8 Response of an adiabatic persistent current cell to a rapidly rising drive pulse.

cell behaves in the isothermal mode described in Chapter 1; that is the induced current in the cross-bar increases to a value very slightly above that at which resistance begins to appear and remains constant at this value as long as the drive line current continues to increase.

With a drive-current pulse having a rise-time less than approximately 1000 microseconds, it is found that the current in the lead cross-bar reaches a value high enough for the film to heat up in runaway fashion. This is illustrated schematically in Figure 7.8 and occurs under conditions where the rise in film temperature is so rapid that the decrease of film critical current with time is faster than the decay of current in the persistent current loop. Crowe (1957) reports that the cross-bar temperature rises to a value above the critical temperature of lead in a period of less than 10 nanoseconds, and that the cross-bar current falls to zero in a period of approximately 50 nanoseconds, determined by the L/R time-constant of the loop. The cross-bar temperature then falls with an exponential decay constant of the order of 0.1 microsecond, whose exact value is dependent on the substrate and on whatever films are deposited on top of the lead cross-bar. No persistent current is established.

It is possible to establish a persistent current by using a "priming" pulse as shown in Figure 7.9. After causing the cross-bar to become normal, this pulse is reduced to a sub-critical value ($0.6I_c$ in the figure), which is held until the cross-bar temperature has returned to 4.2°K. The drive current is then turned off, inducing a permanent circulating current of $+0.6I_c$. It is possible to sense the presence and polarity of this circulating current by destructive readout that simultaneously inverts its polarity. This is performed by applying a "read" pulse of $-0.6I_c$ as shown in the figure. This increases the circulating current above I_c, again causing it to decay to zero, and generating a signal on the sense line. By maintaining the "read" pulse long enough for the cross-bar to cool, a circulating current of $-0.6I_c$ is induced when the pulse is turned off. A second application of this pulse would not cause the circulating current to exceed I_c and would therefore produce no permanent change in it, and no signal on the sense line. Application of the "read" pulse can therefore be used for sensing the content of the cell, with the appearance of a sense line signal indicating the inversion of a previously present circulating current. This can be restored by applying a positive "write" pulse of $+0.6I_c$ as shown in the figure.

The amplitude of the stored current has been chosen so that half-amplitude selection pulses do not permanently affect it. This is designed to allow the cell to be used in a two-dimensional array analogous to that shown in Figure 7.1b.

With the operating mode of Figure 7.9, the drive pulse must be longer than the time required for the cross-bar to cool after quenching. Broom and Simpson (1959) have measured minimum write-pulse widths for a number of Crowe cells utilizing a 600 Å × 0.1 mm × 2 mm lead cross-bar deposited on various substrates. The results are given in Table 7.1 and show the expected dependence on thermal conductivity and also considerable scatter from cell to cell. The electrical time constants of all their cells were found to be between 10 and 20 nanoseconds.

It is apparent that the maximum operating speed of Crowe cells operating in the adiabatic mode is determined by joule heating effects, and could therefore be improved by operating closer to the critical temperature.

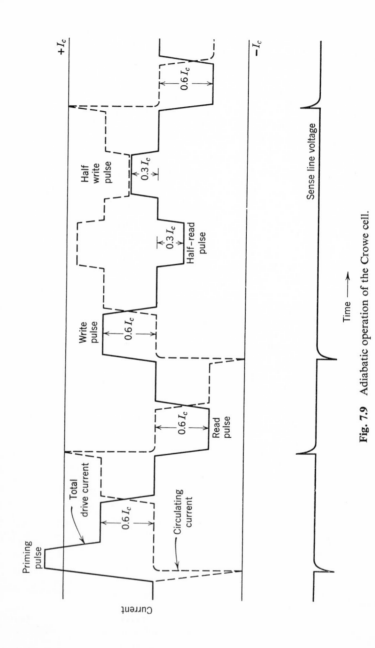

Fig. 7.9 Adiabatic operation of the Crowe cell.

TABLE 7.1

Experimental Minimum Write-pulse Lengths for 600 Å × 0.1 mm × 2 mm
Pb Cross-bar Crowe Cells (Broom and Simpson, 1959)

Substrate	Glass	Mica	Single Crystal Sapphire
Minimum write pulse time in nanosecs	200–500	50–150	70–100
Thermal conductivity in cals/sec deg. cm at 5°K	2.4×10^{-4}		0.44

Under these conditions an isothermal mode of operation is obtained and regenerative heating does not occur.

31.3 Isothermal Operation (Persistor)

It was pointed out by Crittenden (1957) that a persistent current loop consisting of a permanently superconducting inductance connected in parallel with a film of tin or indium could be used as a digital storage element. He suggested the name "persistor" for this device. At about the same time a somewhat similar structure was suggested for use as a switching element by Buckingham (1957) who proposed the name "persistatron." The same type of loop was also mentioned in the earlier paper by Casimir-Jonker and de Haas (1935).

The behavior of the persistor as a storage element has been studied by Crittenden et al. (1960) at temperatures close to the critical where regenerative heating effects of the current quenching element are absent. Waveforms for an idealized persistor operating under isothermal conditions are shown in Figure 7.10. They are calculated under the assumption that the inductance of the quenching element is negligible compared to the remainder of the loop and that heating effects can be neglected. At the outset a "write" pulse $P = 1.3I_c$ is injected into the loop. The pulse attempts to flow through the low inductance-quenching element until this exhibits resistance after which an amount $P - I_c$ is diverted through the loop inductor. By using the analysis of Section 31.2, it can be seen that when this injected current has been turned off, a persistent current of magnitude $P - I_c = 0.3I_c$ remains. By injecting a "read" pulse P as shown in the figure, this persistent current can be inverted in polarity. At the same time a large voltage pulse appears across the loop.

Although the magnitude of P has been chosen such that the sum of the stored current M and a half-select current $\frac{1}{2}P$ is less than I_c, inspection of Figure 7.10 shows that the second of two successive "read" pulses, temporarily brings the stored current to I_c. This indicates that a series of successive "read" pulses will cause a slight decrement in the stored current.

Tolerances are apparently improved if the persistor is operated quasi-isothermally, that is in such a way that the stored current is slightly

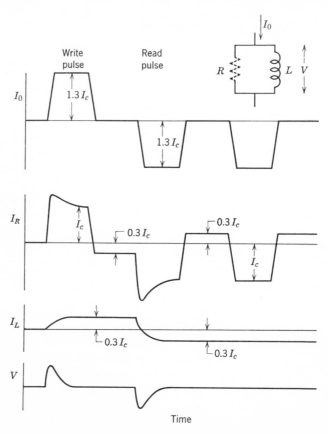

Fig. 7.10 A "persistor" circuit with idealized operating waveforms. R represents a superconductive film of negligible inductance. L represents a permanently superconducting inductance.

quenched during successive "write" and "read" pulses. This is illustrated in Figure 7.11 where $P = 1.2I_c$ and where the induced cell current during the "write" pulse is assumed to fall to $0.9I_c$. This leads to a stored current of $M = 0.3I_c$. Once again a half-select pulse will not disturb a stored current, since $M + \frac{1}{2}P = 0.9I_c$. Furthermore, as illustrated, the second of two successive "read" pulses now only raises the stored current to $0.9I_c$

and can thus no longer degrade stored information. The disadvantage of this operating mode is that the thermal and electrical time constants must be interrelated.

Crittenden, Cooper, and Schmidlin (1960) suggest that transformer-coupled persistors could be arranged in a two-dimensional random access memory array. They find, however, that difficulties arise due to the

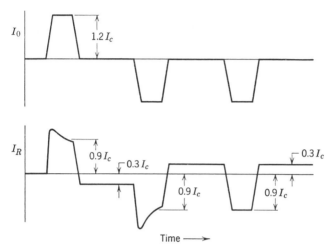

Fig. 7.11 Waveforms illustrating the operation of the persistor circuit in a quasi-isothermal mode.

breadth of the current-induced transitions of the unshielded tin or indium films used as quenching elements.

The maximum operating frequency of circulating current cells operating in the isothermal mode is much higher than that in the adiabatic mode, since the evolved heat is so much less. For example, Crittenden and co-workers have operated persistors deposited on glass with 15 nanosecond pulses. This is to be compared with the minimum pulse width of 200 nanoseconds required for adiabatically operated Crowe cells deposited on glass (see Table 7.1).

31.4 Continuous Sheet Memory

It is shown in Section 31.5 that the permissible tolerances on the critical current of storage cells operated as a multi-dimensional array are quite narrow. Unfortunately, it has been found that the critical currents of an array of Crowe cells are quite non-uniform, even though they have all been deposited at one and the same time. Burns, Alphonse, and Leck (1961) have attributed this non-uniformity of the critical current to accidental variations in the widths of the cross-bars, resulting from diffusion of the metal being evaporated under the edges of the mask. They have been able to show that these edge effects can be eliminated by using a continuous tin film for storage.

An individual storage location is shown in simplified form in Figure 7.12, and consists of two drive lines intersecting at right angles above a 0.2 to 0.3-micron film of tin. A sense conductor is located on the other side of this film and is shown dotted in the figure. With the current directions

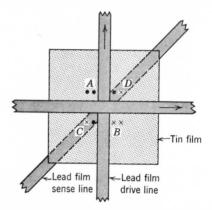

Fig. 7.12 Continuous-sheet memory cell showing flux penetration in the presence of drive currents.

shown, magnetic fields normal to the tin, due to current in the drive lines, reinforce at A and B. By applying currents above an empirically determined critical value I_c it is found that permanent flux penetration occurs in the vicinity of the cross-over (presumably at points A and B) when both drive currents are applied simultaneously with the correct polarity.[6] The flux can be permanently reversed by applying reversed drive currents simultaneously, but with proper choice of drive current amplitude, remains undisturbed in the presence of a single drive current. Output signals appear on the sense line during the leading edge of pulses that cause flux reversal. The electrical behavior of the continuous sheet cell appears similar to that of the tin film Crowe cell operating in the isothermal mode (see Chap. 1).

The complete structure of the continuous sheet array described by Burns, Alphonse, and Leck (1961) is shown in exploded form in Figure 7.13. It should be noticed that a *tin* ground plane is used, and that the

---

[6] If one current were reversed flux reinforcement would occur at points C and D. Flux penetrating there would not be able to link the sense conductor effectively.

sense line only approaches the xy lines at their intercepts. Hence any flux trapped under x or y conductors elsewhere than at their intercepts will not be detected by the sense line. The two superconducting tin films act as effective electromagnetic shields for the sense line, and are seen to be extended on either side of the sense line to a considerable distance from the array. A 100-cell array one square inch in area whose conductors had a nominal width of 10^{-3} inch, is reported to have operated with currents of 30 ma to 80 ma depending on the temperature. Pulse rise times were varied between 200 and 20 nanosecs, giving sense line switching voltages between 0.8 mv and 8 mv respectively.

Memory operation is reported to have been obtained with 4 nanosec and half-sine wave pulses. Since the writing process occurs within a fraction of the rise time of the drive pulse, this result indicates that it must take place in less than 1 nanosecond. The fact that a pulse width of 4 nanosecs is sufficient for switching, proves that the thermal recovery time required is less than this period. It is likely therefore that the upper operating speed of this cell will be limited by relaxation effects of non-thermal origin.

The spread in critical current values for different cells of one array is found to be very narrow and to depend little on the width of the drive lines. It is reported that with conventional deposition techniques the continuous-sheet cells could be made reproducible to within 10 per cent with respect to the drive currents required, and that with special care in the fabrication of the storage plane this figure could be reduced to $\frac{1}{4}$ per cent. The small dependence of cell critical current on drive line width suggests that the drive line current is carried mainly by the edges of these lines, as though the lines were unshielded. This indicates that the tin ground plane allows significant field penetration.

Most recently Burns et al. (1963) have reported the operation of a continuous sheet memory, in which the sense winding (see Fig. 7.13) is replaced by a single continuous film of silver. It is found that the eddy currents generated in the silver film by destructive read-out of the tin film storage locations, produce voltages which are large enough to be detected at the edges of the silver film. This technique greatly reduces delays associated with propagation along the sense line, simplifies memory fabrication, and allows both diagonals of each x-y cross-over to be used independently for storing flux.

31.5 Tolerance Analysis

The drive current tolerances that are permissible in persistent current cells depend strongly on the type of array and on the mode of operation. The adiabatic and isothermal modes of operation will be analyzed in turn.

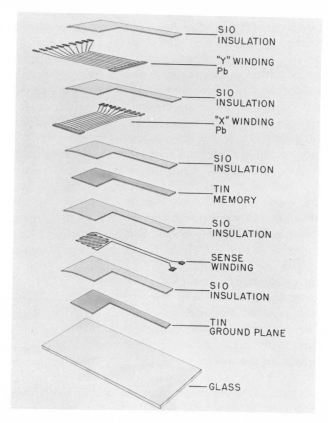

Fig. 7.13 Exploded and condensed views of a continuous sheet memory array (Burns, Alphonse and Leck, 1961).

The following symbols will be used.

M Persistent current stored in cell.

P Switch current used on each of two selection lines.

I_c Current corresponding to onset of resistance in quenching element.

I_t Current corresponding to onset of thermal propagation.

$I_{\frac{1}{2}}$ Current corresponding to midpoint of current-induced transition.

$\bar{I}$ Mean value averaged over the cells of an array.

The tolerance analysis of the adiabatic operating mode for a two-dimensional array proceeds as follows. From Figure 7.9 it can be seen that during normal operation,

$$M = 2P \qquad (7.6)$$

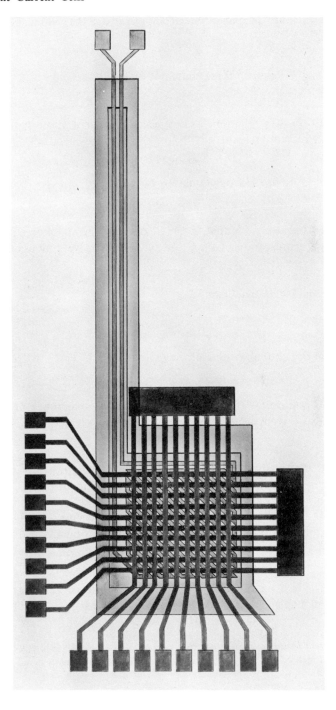

During switching, the maximum current induced in the cell must exceed I_t, that is,

$$M + 2P > I_t \qquad (7.7)$$

Eliminating M between these equations gives

$$P > \tfrac{1}{4}I_t \qquad (7.8)$$

In the case of a two-dimensional selection matrix whose half-selected cells must remain undisturbed,

$$M + P < I_c$$

or, substituting for M from Equation 7.6

$$P < \tfrac{1}{3}I_c \qquad (7.9)$$

In the adiabatic mode that occurs at operating temperatures far below the critical temperature of the quenching element, we may assume[7] that

$$I_c \sim I_t$$

Hence from Equations 7.8 and 7.9

$$\frac{1}{4} < \frac{P}{I_t} < \frac{1}{3}$$

Therefore the optimum value of the drive current is

$$P = \tfrac{1}{2}(\tfrac{1}{3} + \tfrac{1}{4})\bar{I}_t = \tfrac{7}{24}\bar{I}_t$$

With this value of P it can be shown that the maximum permissible variation of I_t from the mean is determined by the relation

$$\tfrac{7}{8}\bar{I}_t < I_t < \tfrac{7}{6}\bar{I}_t$$

We will now analyze the case of a two-dimensional array operated in the isothermal mode following the treatment of Crittenden et al. (1960).[8] These workers find that to obtain rapid switching, the maximum induced current $M + 2P$ should equal or exceed $I_{1/2}$, since at currents only slightly above I_c the transition takes place by the relatively slow thermal propagation process. Hence

$$M + 2P > I_{1/2}$$

Since a single drive pulse superimposed on the stored current must not cause switching

$$M + P < I_c$$

---

[7] A treatment assuming a more complex relation is given by Peacock (1961).

[8] A similar method has been applied to magnetic memories by Kaufman and Newhouse (1958).

Finally two drive pulses applied in opposition to the stored current must not cause switching, that is,

$$2P - M < I_c$$

Dividing throughout by $I_{\frac{1}{2}}$ these equations can be rewritten as

$$m + 2p > 1$$
$$m + p < \alpha \qquad (7.10)$$
$$2p - m < \alpha$$

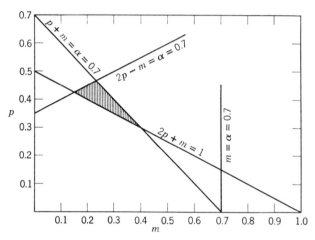

Fig. 7.14 Diagram illustrating the operating range of an isothermal mode persistor array (Crittenden et al., 1960).

where we use the definitions,

$$m = \frac{M}{I_{\frac{1}{2}}}, \quad p = \frac{P}{I_{\frac{1}{2}}} \quad \text{and} \quad \alpha = \frac{I_c}{I_{\frac{1}{2}}}$$

These inequalities are plotted in Figure 7.14 for $\alpha = 0.7$, with the region of operation shown shaded. By solving Equations 7.10 for α, it can be shown that the region of operation vanishes for $\alpha = 3/5$. Inspection shows that for a value of $m = 0.23$, p can vary from approximately 0.38 to 0.46. By setting $P = 0.42\bar{I}_{\frac{1}{2}}$, it can be seen that the permissible variation of $I_{\frac{1}{2}}$ over the cells of an array is determined by the relation

$$0.38I_{\frac{1}{2}} < 0.42\bar{I}_{\frac{1}{2}} < 0.46I_{\frac{1}{2}}$$

that is

$$0.9\bar{I}_{\frac{1}{2}} < I_{\frac{1}{2}} < 1.1\bar{I}_{\frac{1}{2}}$$

It is clear from the above calculation that broad operating margins require values of α that approach unity which corresponds to a sharp transition. Experimental values of α for 0.1 micron thick unshielded tin and indium films are shown in Figure 7.15. These indicate that persistor array operation using such films is only possible at temperatures con-

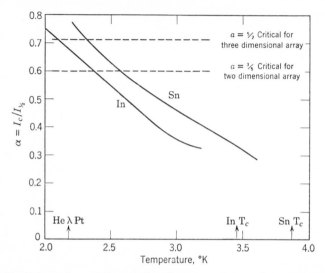

Fig. 7.15 Values of α = $I_c/I_{1/2}$ as a function of temperature for unshielded 0.1μ thick tin and indium films (Crittenden et al., 1960).

siderably below T_c. Shielded films are known to have a narrower transition than unshielded ones. Hence shielded structures should be operable closer to the critical temperature than persistor arrays that use unshielded quenching elements.

32. RESONANT CAVITIES

32.1 Introduction

Tuned circuits consisting of an inductor-capacitor combination play an important role in oscillators and filters at frequencies up to several hundred megacycles. At higher frequencies, the inductors required for a tuned circuit become impractically small hence resonant cavities take over the role played by tuned circuits at lower frequencies.

Microwave cavities are customarily cylindrical, spherical or pill-box shaped, and like an organ pipe, can resonate in an infinite number of modes with wavelengths related to the cavity dimensions.[9]

---

[9] For a description of resonant cavities see for instance the books by Moreno (1958) or Ramo and Whinnery (1956).

The performance of a cavity, just as that of a lower frequency resonant circuit, is determined by the resistive losses which accompany oscillation. For each mode n we can define a dimensionless quality factor

$$Q_n = 2\pi \frac{\text{energy stored}}{\text{energy lost per cycle}} \tag{7.11}$$

It can be shown that the energy W in a resonator excited in mode n will decay with time according to the relation $W = W_0 e^{-\omega t/Q_n}$. Furthermore, the band of frequencies of width Δf to which the cavity responds is given by the relation

$$\frac{\Delta f}{f_n} = \frac{1}{Q_n}$$

where f_n is the resonant frequency of the nth mode.[10] Hence Q is also a measure of the sharpness of resonance.

To calculate Q explicitly we proceed from the definition in Equation 7.11. If dielectric and radiation losses are neglected, and only losses from conduction currents in the resonator walls are considered, it can be shown that[11]

$$\text{Energy lost per cycle} = \frac{\delta}{8} \int H^2 \, dA$$

where δ is the skin depth, H is the magnetic field intensity at the cavity wall and dA is an element of wall area. The integral is carried out over the inner surface of the cavity. The energy stored in the cavity is

$$\text{Energy stored} = \frac{1}{8\pi} \int H^2 \, dv$$

where the integral is carried out over the cavity volume. Combining these two expressions as in Equation 7.11 we find

$$Q = \frac{2}{\delta} \frac{\int H^2 \, dv}{\int H^2 \, dA}$$

By introducing the wavelength λ of the resonant mode, the expression for Q can be rewritten as

$$Q \frac{\delta}{\lambda} = \frac{2}{\lambda} \frac{\int H^2 \, dv}{\int H^2 \, dA} = G \tag{7.12}$$

---

[10] Δf is defined so that the impedance of the cavity for frequencies $f_n \pm \Delta f$ is 70.7 per cent of that for the resonant frequency f_n.
[11] See for instance Moreno (1958).

G is known as the "form factor" of the cavity, it is independent of the wavelength, and depends only on cavity shape and on the mode.

32.2   Surface Impedance

Using Equation 7.18, and 7.20 which are proved below, we may write

$$\frac{\delta}{\lambda} = \frac{Rc}{4\pi^2\mu} \tag{7.13}$$

Here R is the real part of the so-called surface impedance Z. Z can be defined as the ratio of the tangential surface electric field $\mathbf{E}$, to the tangential magnetic field, or alternatively, by the expression

$$Z = \frac{E}{\displaystyle\int_0^\infty \mathbf{J}(x, y, z) \times d\mathbf{n}} \tag{7.14}$$

where $\mathbf{J}$ is the current volume density in the cavity wall and $\mathbf{n}$ is the unit vector normal to the cavity surface. Hence the integral represents the induced surface current density.

Substituting Equation 7.13 into 7.12 we obtain

$$Q = G\frac{4\pi^2\mu}{Rc} \tag{7.15}$$

To demonstrate the physical significance of the surface impedance, we will derive it first for a normal metal and then for a superconductor at very low frequencies.

For a normal metal we start from Maxwell's equations

$$\text{curl } \mathbf{H} = \frac{4\pi}{c}\,\mathbf{J}$$

therefore

$$\text{curl } \dot{\mathbf{B}} = \frac{4\pi}{c}\,\mu\dot{\mathbf{J}}$$

Also

$$\text{curl } \mathbf{E} = -\frac{1}{c}\,\dot{\mathbf{B}}$$

Combining these two equations we have

$$\text{curl curl } \mathbf{E} = -\frac{4\pi}{c^2}\,\mu\dot{\mathbf{J}}$$

$$\text{grad div } \mathbf{E} - \nabla^2\mathbf{E} \equiv$$

Since $\mathbf{E}$ is the field outside the cavity surface, we may write

$$\text{div } \mathbf{E} = 0$$

Hence,

$$\nabla^2 \mathbf{E} = \frac{4\pi}{c^2} \mu \mathbf{j} \tag{7.16}$$

$\mathbf{J}$ is the volume density of the induced cavity wall current. Assuming rectangular coordinates with the z axis normal to the surface, and assuming a solution for $\mathbf{J}$ of the form

$$\mathbf{J} = \mathbf{J}_0 \, e^{i\omega t}$$

we may rewrite Equation 7.16 as

$$\frac{d^2 E}{dz^2} = \frac{4\pi}{c^2} \mu i \omega J \tag{7.17}$$

For a normal metal $J = \sigma E$ where σ is the conductivity. This falls off at very high frequency due to the anomalous skin effect.

Substituting this relation into Equation 7.17 we find

$$\frac{d^2 E}{dz^2} = \frac{i4\pi\mu\omega\sigma}{c^2} E$$

$$\equiv \frac{2i}{\delta^2} E$$

where

$$\delta^{-1} = (2\pi\mu\omega\sigma/c^2)^{\frac{1}{2}} \tag{7.18}$$

This has the solution

$$E = Ae^{-z\sqrt{2i}/\delta} + Be^{z\sqrt{2i}/\delta}$$

where A and B are constants of integration. Since E disappears at $z = \infty$, $B = 0$, and A equals the surface field $E(0)$ at $z = 0$. Furthermore,

$$\sqrt{2i} \equiv (1 + i) \tag{7.19}$$

Therefore

$$E = E(0) \exp \left\{ -\frac{z}{\delta}(1 + i) \right\}$$

δ is known as the *skin depth*.

Substituting this result into Equation 7.14 and using the relation $J = \sigma E$, we obtain

$$Z = \frac{E(0)}{\sigma E(0) \int_0^\infty \exp \left\{ -\frac{z}{\delta}(1 + i) \right\} dz}$$

$$= \frac{1 + i}{\alpha\delta}$$

Substituting for δ in terms of σ from Equation 7.18 we finally obtain

$$Z = (1 + i)\left(\frac{2\pi\omega\mu}{c^2\sigma}\right)^{\frac{1}{2}} \tag{7.20}$$

This indicates that in a classical normal metal at frequencies below those at which the anomalous skin effect becomes important, the real and imaginary parts of the surface impedance are equal, and proportional to $(\omega/\sigma)^{\frac{1}{2}}$.

It will be shown that for a superconductor at low frequencies and low temperatures Z is purely imaginary and is dependent on the penetration depth λ. Z will be derived by calculating the conductivity from the London equation and substituting it into Equation 7.20.

By combining the London equation

$$-\frac{4\pi}{c}\lambda^2 \operatorname{curl} \mathbf{J} = \mathbf{H}$$

with Maxwell's equation

$$-c \operatorname{curl} \mathbf{E} = \mu\dot{\mathbf{H}}$$

we obtain

$$\mathbf{E} = \frac{4\pi\mu\lambda^2}{c^2}\dot{\mathbf{J}}$$

Again assuming a solution of the form

$$\mathbf{J} = \mathbf{J}_0\,e^{i\omega t}$$

we obtain

$$\mathbf{E} = \frac{4\pi\mu\lambda^2 i\omega}{c^2}\,\mathbf{J}$$

Therefore for the superconductor at low frequencies the equivalent conductance becomes

$$\sigma = \frac{c^2}{i4\pi\mu\lambda^2\omega}$$

Substituting this into Equation 7.20 and using Equation 7.19 we obtain

$$Z = i\,\frac{4\pi\omega\mu\lambda}{c^2} \tag{7.21}$$

Hence for a London type superconductor the surface impedance is purely imaginary and proportional to the penetration depth. Real superconductors approximate this prediction at low temperatures and frequencies. This is illustrated by Figure 7.16, which shows the dependence of R_s, the real part of the surface impedance, on temperature and frequency for a typical superconductor. R_s is expressed in terms of its ratio to R_n, the surface impedance in the normal state, and is plotted against the quantum energy of incident radiation. The figure shows that, at temperatures close to absolute zero, R_s/R_n is negligibly small, unless the incident quantum energy $h\nu$ exceeds the width of the energy gap, equal to approximately $3.5kT_c$.[12]

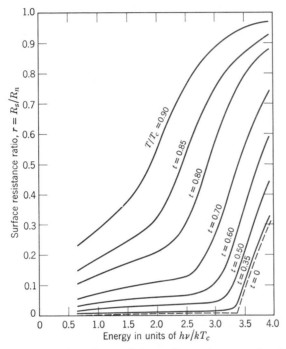

Fig. 7.16 Frequency dependence of the surface resistance ratio of aluminum as a function of reduced temperature. (Biondi and Garfunkel, 1959.)

At higher temperatures R_s/R_n is seen to be larger than zero even at low frequencies. This happens because an alternating electric field can penetrate a superconductor, and act on the "normal" electrons that are always present at finite temperatures. In terms of the BCS model, these electrons are formed by Cooper pairs that have been thermally excited across the energy gap and split up in the process. In the older theoretical formulations these "normal" electrons were introduced by means of the two-fluid model described in Chapter 3.

32.3 Superconductive Resonant Cavities

The dependence of R_s on temperature and frequency shown in Figure 7.16 indicates that practical superconducting resonators should be operated

---

[12] k is Boltzman's constant and h is Planck's constant.

at temperatures as far below T_c as possible and at frequencies considerably less than the gap frequency $v = 3.5kT_c/h$. With such precautions it is possible to reduce the cavity-wall losses so that they become negligible compared to dielectric and radiation losses.

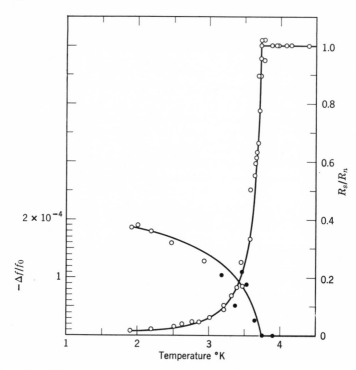

Fig. 7.17   Shift in resonant frequency with temperature for a tin cavity (Simon, 1949).

The surface resistance of a superconductor is found to be strongly dependent on surface strains. Hence the Q of a superconducting cavity depends on the fabrication process used. In a review of superconducting resonators Maxwell (1961) states that casting followed by electropolishing is the construction technique that yields the lowest surface resistance. Since a cavity whose inside surfaces are to be electropolished has to be made in two separable halves, it must be designed so that the split does not interrupt current lines existing in the resonant mode.

Using a machined lead cavity that is expected to have a relatively high surface resistance, Grebenkamper and Hagen (1952) report a Q of 8.3 × 10^6 at 9200 Mc/s. Using electroplated lead, Maxwell (1961) reports a Q of 400,000 at 425 Mc/s with a rather unfavorable geometry.

At temperatures close to T_c the penetration depth of a superconductor is large enough to alter the effective size of a cavity and thus affect the resonant frequency. It can be shown[13] that the fractional perturbation of the resonant frequency is given by

$$\frac{\Delta f}{f} = \frac{X}{2RQ}$$

where X is the imaginary component of the surface impedance. The shift in the resonant frequency with temperature of a tin cavity is shown in Figure 7.17.

References

An excellent description of magnetic-core memories is contained in Quartly (1962), and a well-organized bibliography of digital magnetic circuits and materials has been compiled by W. L. Morgan (1959).

A survey of cryotron random-access memory systems and circuits is given by M. K. Haynes (1960) and in Bremer (1962). A description of a cryotron associative memory system is given by Newhouse and Fruin (1962).

Microwave cavities are discussed in books by Moreno (1948), Ramo and Whinnery (1956), and Slater (1950).

---

[13] See for instance Maxwell, Marcus, and Slater (1949).

chapter 8

Superconductive Bolometers and Heat Flow Valves

The devices described in previous chapters are operated isothermally, except for brief rises in temperature associated with switching transients. This chapter deals with those superconductive devices that are designed to respond to temperature changes, and also with magnetically-controlled devices that control the flow of heat at low temperatures.

Section 33, which follows, describes and analyzes superconductive bolometers and the systems in which they are used. Superconductive bolometers employ a superconducting foil or film connected by loose thermal coupling to a sink held at the midpoint of its temperature transition. Impinging electromagnetic or atomic radiation produces a temperature rise accompanied by a detectable resistance change in the bolometer sensing element. Superconductive bolometers are among the most sensitive detectors of electromagnetic radiation known, and promise to be of importance in infrared spectrometry and imaging.

Section 34 describes magnetic field controlled heat valves and the adiabatic demagnetization refrigerators in which they are used. The section also includes references to temperature-controlled electrical current switches, to a refrigeration scheme dependent on the superconductive heat of magnetization, and to a suggestion for using the Meissner effect to convert heat into electrical energy.

33. SUPERCONDUCTIVE BOLOMETERS

33.1 Bolometers as Infrared Detectors

Bolometers measure the change in resistance of some kind of detector element due to the temperature rise produced by absorption of incident radiation. They are particularly valuable for the wavelength range lying

248

between 50 and 1000 microns, known as the "far infrared," since other types of radiation detector become ineffective in this region of the spectrum.

Superconductive bolometers derive two advantages from their low operating temperature. In the first place the minimum signal detectable by room-temperature bolometers is limited by thermal fluctuations. In the second place the sensitivity of a bolometer is inversely proportional to its specific heat, which decreases as the temperature is lowered. For these two reasons, and because of the extremely strong dependence of resistance on temperature, superconductive bolometers appear to be capable of greater ultimate sensitivity than any other electromagnetic radiation detector operating at the same temperature or above.

Bolometers are used in infrared spectrometers, radiometers, and imaging devices. IR spectrometers are of great importance in routine chemical analysis as well as in research because the presence in a molecule of a specific chemical group such as the —COOH group leads to characteristic lines in the IR spectrum; lines that are relatively unaffected by the structure of the remainder of the molecule.

The importance of IR imaging devices and radiometers is based on the fact that bodies at or near room temperature emit their maximum radiant power at a wavelength in the infrared (approximately 10 microns), and that this wavelength varies appreciably with temperature according to the relation $\lambda T = \text{const.}$[1] For this reason IR devices can detect relatively small temperature differences. This leads to many military and industrial applications. For instance, troops or vehicles can be detected in total darkness by infrared imaging devices if silhouetted against a colder background, and an infrared radiometer can detect overheated 'journals' on trains moving at speeds up to 70 mph. IR image devices have also been proposed for certain medical diagnoses in which it is necessary to estimate the skin temperature distribution.[2]

33.2 Description of Bolometer Systems

We will continue our account of superconductive bolometers with a description of two published systems, followed in succeeding sections by an analysis of their performance and limitations.

The first superconducting bolometer was constructed by Andrews and co-workers,[3] using tantalum, whose critical temperature lies in the liquid-helium range. Later work[4] was carried on with niobium nitride. This

---

[1] This can be deduced from Wien's radiation law.

[2] A review of industrial, technical, and medical applications of IR detectors and imaging devices is given by Ovrebo et al. (1959).

[3] Andrews et al. (1942).

[4] Andrews et al. (1946).

material has a critical temperature of 14.3°K and could therefore be operated in liquid hydrogen, which, at the time, was considered a more practical cooling medium. The nitride, which is exceedingly brittle, was prepared by heating a thin niobium ribbon (a typical ribbon was 25 microns thick and 0.4 mm wide), in ammonia. The nitrided ribbon was glued to a copper post, so as to produce a thermal time constant in the region of 1 millisecond. Many of these bolometers could detect a steady flux of 5×10^{-10} watt or an individual flash of light having an energy of 2×10^{-13} joule. In a later experiment[5] a similar bolometer was able to detect individual α particles possessing a calculated energy of 5.2×10^{-13} joule. As mentioned in Section 28, Andrews and Clark[6] found that the niobium nitride bolometer was capable of detecting and demodulating radio waves of frequencies up to 16 Mc/s. Using a redesigned bolometer mount M. Bodmer was able to detect frequencies as high as 10,000 Mc/s.[7] It was possible to show that the mechanism of detection did not involve heating effects but was based on the rectification (due to the non-linear dependence of resistance on current) of radio frequency currents induced in the bolometer.

Because of the narrow superconducting transition, the operating temperature of a superconducting bolometer must be controlled to within 10^{-4}°K. In the niobium nitride system this control was achieved by maintaining the bolometer heat reservoir at the hydrogen triple point[8] temperature of 14°K, while heating the bolometer to its critical temperature of approximately 14.4°K by means of an electrically-operated heating coil.

Martin and Bloor (1961) have shown that by energizing the heating coil from the bolometer output circuits, it is possible for a bolometer to control its own average temperature.

Their bolometer, which operates at liquid helium temperatures, is shown in Figure 8.1. The sensitive element consists of a tin film, vacuum-deposited on a 3 micron × 3 mm × 2 mm disk of mica, which is suspended from nylon threads attached to a split brass ring C. When in use, the space containing the detector is evacuated. The ring C constitutes a heat sink whose thermal time constant is deliberately extended to a period of several seconds by connecting it to the liquid helium reservoir with a

---

[5] Andrews, Fowler, and Williams (1949).
[6] Andrews and Clark (1946). See also Lebacqz, Clark, Williams, and Andrews (1949).
[7] Bodmer (1950).
[8] The triple point of a material is that temperature and pressure at which solid, liquid, and vapor coexist in equilibrium. If such a system is held at constant volume, small heat increments lead to changes in the relative quantities of the three phases, but to no change in pressure or temperature.

nylon washer W of low thermal conductivity. Coarse temperature control to $10^{-3}\,^\circ$K is provided by this reservoir whose pressure is held constant by a manostat. Fine temperature control of the detector is provided by an electrical heating coil H, driven from the bolometer output circuits as mentioned above. This negative feedback arrangement holds the temperature of the detector constant to within $10^{-5}\,^\circ$K, in the

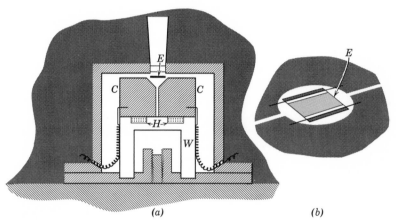

(a)   (b)

Fig. 8.1 A superconducting film bolometer (Martin and Bloor, 1961). (a) Bolometer housing. (b) The film detector and its suspension.

face of the marked variations in incident power that occur as an IR spectrum is being scanned.

Electrical contact to the tin film is provided by lead films that, because of their higher transition temperature, stay superconducting during bolometer operation. The lead films are evaporated over the ends of the tin film, the nylon supporting threads, and the faces of the split ring.

The amplifying and control circuits are shown in Figure 8.2. The sensing element B, which has a resistance of about ten ohms, forms part of a bridge network. A constantan resistor of similar value forms arm D, which is also at liquid helium temperature. Resistors E and F are at room temperature and are used to balance the bridge. The bridge is fed with 800 c/s rather than direct current to lessen the noise and drift problems of signal amplification. The incident radiation is interrupted at 10 c/s with a rotating shutter. The resulting off-balance bridge signal therefore consists of an 800 c/s carrier modulated at 10 c/s. This signal is amplified by transformer T whose secondary is tuned to 800 c/s. The transformer is operated in liquid helium and is made from a 50 micron thick mu-metal of special composition having an initial susceptibility of about 7000 at

4°K. The transformer output signal is amplified by a tuned vacuum-tube amplifier and then rectified and demodulated in phase with a square wave reference signal from the shutter unit. The output is smoothed by a circuit having a time constant adjustable between 1 and 40 seconds and is fed to a pen-recorder. The output of the tuned amplifier is also used to

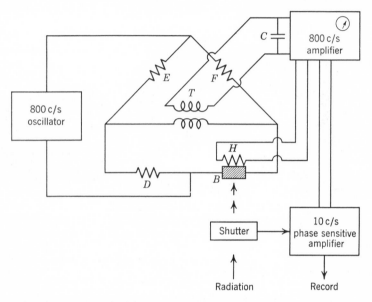

Fig. 8.2   Amplifier and control circuits for the bolometer of Fig. 8.1.

control the heater current in such a way as to hold the mean bolometer temperature steady.

Room temperature objects emit considerable radiation at wavelengths of up to 50 microns. Since the sources available for far-IF spectrometry are relatively weak, as much as possible of this room temperature radiation must be prevented from reaching the bolometer. This is usually accomplished by quartz filters cooled to helium temperatures. These filters cut down the near-infrared while being relatively transparent to the far-infrared.

The noise mechanisms that contribute to the noise of low temperature bolometers include Johnson noise, photon noise, and possibly noise associated with the superconducting transition.[9] Martin and Bloor have calculated the noise due to the first two of these processes and derive a noise power for their bolometer of 3×10^{-14}w. Experimentally they

---

[9] These mechanisms are discussed in Sec. 33.3.

find a noise power equal to an incident signal of 10^{-12}w at a system time constant of 1.25 secs. The difference between the experimental and theoretical estimates is considered to be largely due to noise from the room-temperature amplifier. An analysis given in Section 33.5 indicates that an ideal thermal detector with a time constant of one second, operating at 4°K may be able to detect a signal as low as 6×10^{-16}w.

33.3 Bolometer Responsivity

A bolometer that produces the largest output signal in response to a given input is not necessarily able to detect the smallest input signal. The size of the response to a given input is measured by the "responsivity" r, which may be loosely defined as the change in the voltage across the detector element per unit of incident radiant power. The minimum detectable power on the other hand is measured by a parameter called the "Noise Equivalent Signal" which is defined and calculated in Section 33.5.

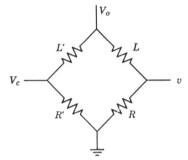

Fig. 8.3

In calculating the responsivity, it will be assumed that the bolometer sensing element is connected in a bridge circuit driven by an a-c voltage source as shown in Figure 8.2. Since the output transformer is tuned to the voltage-source frequency, the current drawn by it can be neglected. The bolometer bridge network can thus be represented by the simplified circuit of Figure 8.3 in which R represents the bolometer resistance, and L a much larger resistor held at room temperature. R' and L' are similar in magnitude to R and L respectively. The circuit is driven by an a-c voltage source of peak value V_0. The bridge output signal is $v - V_c$. V_c is clearly independent of bolometer resistance and can thus be treated as constant.

$$v = iR \qquad (8.1)$$

where i is the bolometer current. Since L is much larger than R, i can be regarded as constant also.

In the absence of incident radiation the equilibrium temperature of the bolometer will be determined by Joule heat generated by the current through it, and by heat flow to the heat sink connected to the bath. If the bolometer is at temperature T_1 slightly above the sink temperature T_0, and if the heat flow from the bolometer takes place mostly by conduction, we may write

$$K(T_1 - T_0) = i^2 R \qquad (8.2)$$

where K is a constant. We will assume that the radiation incident on the bolometer is chopped at a frequency $\omega/2\pi$ so as to produce a time varying component of power $P = P_0 \sin \omega t$. If the heat capacity and absorptivity of the bolometer are C and a respectively, the sinusoidal component of the incident radiation will produce a bolometer temperature fluctuation ΔT so that

$$C\frac{d(\Delta T)}{dt} + K\,\Delta T = \frac{d(i^2 R)}{dT}\Delta T + aP_0 \sin \omega t$$

where t is the time. This equation may be written as

$$C\frac{d(\Delta T)}{dt} + K_e\,\Delta T = aP_0 \sin \omega t \tag{8.3}$$

where

$$K_e = K - i^2\frac{dR}{dT} \tag{8.4}$$

Equation 8.3 is a first order differential equation whose solution is

$$\Delta T = \text{const. exp}\left(-\frac{K_e}{C}t\right) - \frac{aP_0}{\sqrt{\omega^2 C^2 + K_e^{\,2}}}\sin\left(\omega t + \tan^{-1}\frac{\omega C}{K_e}\right)$$

If K_e is positive, the first term of this solution decays to zero with a time constant

$$\tau = C/K_e \tag{8.5}$$

τ is the thermal time constant of the bolometer. Following this transient, the bolometer exhibits sinusoidal temperature variations of peak amplitude

$$\Delta T_p = \frac{aP_0}{\sqrt{\omega^2 C^2 + K_e^{\,2}}} \tag{8.6}$$

If K_e is zero or negative the exponential term in the expression for the bolometer temperature grows with time, and the bolometer heats up either to destruction or to the high temperature end of the superconducting-to-normal transition where dR/dT is low enough to again drive K_e positive. From Equation 8.4 we see that the critical current i_c for "thermal runaway" is given by the expression

$$i_c^{\,2} = \frac{K}{dR/dT} \tag{8.7}$$

This equation is derived graphically in Section 17.1. To avoid this instability the bolometer current is maintained at a fraction of the critical value i_c. If we define a parameter b by the expression

$$b = \frac{i}{i_c} \tag{8.8}$$

then from Equation 8.7

$$i = b\left(\frac{K}{dR/dT}\right)^{\frac{1}{2}} \qquad (8.9)$$

Hence from Equation 8.4 K_e may be written as

$$K_e = K(1 - b^2) \qquad (8.10)$$

In proper operation, the bolometer will execute sinusoidal temperature swings of peak amplitude ΔT_p, given by Equation 8.6, and will exhibit corresponding voltage fluctuations of peak amplitude

$$v = i\frac{dR}{dT}\Delta T_p$$

$$= \frac{ia(dR/dT)P_0}{\sqrt{\omega^2 C^2 + K_e{}^2}}$$

Hence substituting for K_e from Equation 8.4 the responsivity may be written as

$$r = \frac{v}{P_0} = \frac{ia(dR/dT)}{\sqrt{\omega^2 C^2 + [K - i^2(dR/dT)]^2}} \qquad (8.11)$$

This shows that for maximum responsivity the chopper frequency ω should be made as low as possible. Comparison of Equation 8.11 with 8.4 shows that just those changes in i, dR/dT, or K, which increase the responsivity, also decrease K_e and thus encourage thermal instability. Substituting for i from Equation 8.9, the responsivity can be written as

$$r = ab\left[\frac{K(dR/dT)}{\omega^2 C^2 + K^2(1 - b^2)^2}\right]^{\frac{1}{2}} \qquad (8.12)$$

With r written in this form it becomes clear that for a given chopper frequency ω, r can be maximized by choosing an optimum value of K, the thermal impedance between the bolometer and the heat sink. By equating dr/dK to zero and solving for K, this optimum value of K is found to satisfy the equation

$$\omega C = K(1 - b^2) \qquad (8.13)$$

Using Equations 8.5 and 8.10, this equation can be rewritten as $\omega = 1/\tau$, which brings out the fact that the responsivity is a maximum when the ratio of the chopper frequency to the thermal response frequency of the system is $(2\pi)^{-1}$. It will be shown below that the condition for maximum signal-noise ratio is slightly different.

33.4 Noise Mechanisms

It is well known that the maximum sensitivity of electronic amplifiers is set by random electrical fluctuations or "noise" originating in one or more of the input stages. If further stages of amplification are added to the output of a noise-limited amplifier, no useful increase in gain results since the random noise voltage is amplified by the same amount as any signal. The maximum sensitivity of any amplifier system can therefore be specified by calculating the input signal that would produce an output equal to that of the noise output. In the case of bolometer systems this signal is called the *noise equivalent signal* and is approximately equal to the smallest radiant power detectable by that system. The limit to the sensitivity of the superconducting film bolometer described above was set by noise in the room temperature vacuum tube amplifier. By incorporating some type of low-temperature amplifier, it should be possible to reduce the amplifier noise to the point where the system sensitivity is limited by the noise equivalent signal of the bolometer sensing element itself. The processes that contribute to noise present in the bolometer output voltage, include electrical and thermal fluctuations of the bolometer-sensing element, and photon noise present in the incident radiation. It is the purpose of this section to discuss these various noise mechanisms and to state the equations which govern their magnitude. These equations are used in the next section to calculate the noise equivalent signal and its dependence on temperature, frequency, and the properties of the sensing element.[11]

JOHNSON NOISE. The dynamic behavior of an electrical or mechanical system has to be described in terms of a minimum number of independently variable parameters, defined as the degrees of freedom of the system. In the electrical case these roughly correspond to the number of possible resonant electrical modes. According to the equipartition-of-energy theorem,[12] a system in thermal equilibrium at temperature T resonates in each possible mode with an average kinetic energy $\frac{1}{2}kT$, where k is Boltzmann's constant.

In an electrical circuit containing resistance, capacitance, and inductance connected in a loop, the random electrical excursions lead to the appearance across the resistor of an alternating voltage containing components at all frequencies. In a small frequency band Δf, the average value of the square of this noise voltage is found to be given by the expression

$$v^2(f) = \frac{4kTR\,\Delta f}{(1 - \omega^2 LC)^2 + R^2 C^2 \omega^2}$$

---

[11] For a fuller discussion and derivation of the various noise equations stated in this section see Smith, Jones, and Chasmar (1957); or Kruse, McGlauchlin, and McQuistan (1962).

[12] See R. C. Tolman, *The Principles of Statistical Mechanics*, New York: Oxford University Press, 1938, p. 93.

where $f = 2\pi\omega$. This is known as "Johnson" noise. In most practical cases C is so small that for all frequencies that can be amplified the Johnson noise may be written as

$$v_J{}^2 = 4kTR\,\Delta f \tag{8.14}$$

It should be noted that Johnson noise varies directly with temperature and is present even in the absence of applied current.

THERMAL FLUCTUATIONS. In analogy with electrical fluctuations that give rise to noise voltage across a resistive bolometer, fluctuations in the mechanical modes and in incident radiation lead to random temperature excursions. It can be shown that for a body at temperature T that has thermal capacity C and is connected to its surroundings by a thermal impedance R_T, the random temperature variation ΔT has a time averaged square value of

$$\Delta T^2 = \frac{4kT^2 R_T{}^{-1}\,\Delta f}{R_T{}^{-2} + \omega^2 C}$$

where $f = 2\pi\omega$.

At frequencies low compared to the thermal resonant frequency of the system, this reduces to

$$\Delta T^2 = 4kT^2 R_T\,\Delta f$$

The thermal impedance between two objects whose temperature differs by ΔT is related to the power transfer by the equation

$$\Delta P = \frac{\Delta T}{R_T} \tag{8.15}$$

Hence the available noise power due to thermal fluctuations becomes

$$\Delta P_T{}^2 = 4kT^2 \frac{\Delta f}{R_T} \tag{8.16}$$

If heat transfer takes place mainly by conduction, $R_T = K^{-1}$ defined in Equation 8.2, and is approximately independent of temperature. If heat transfer due to radiation predominates, R_T can be calculated by using a form of Stefan's law which states that a body at temperature T_1 exchanges radiant heat with an environment at temperature T_2 according to the expression

$$P = \varepsilon \sigma A (T_1{}^4 - T_2{}^4)$$

where ε is the emissivity, equal to unity for a "black" body, σ is Stefan's constant[13] and A is the radiating area. If $T_1 - T_2 = \Delta T$, then by

---

[13] $\sigma = 5.6686 \times 10^{-10}$ watts cm^{-2} °K^{-4}.

differentiating the above equation we find that

$$\Delta P = 4\varepsilon\sigma A T^3 \Delta T$$

Hence using Equation 8.15 we find that the thermal impedance for radiation exchange is

$$R_T = [4\varepsilon\sigma A T^3]^{-1} \tag{8.17}$$

By substituting for R_T in Equation 8.16, we find that the thermal fluctuation noise in a body which is coupled to its environment predominantly by radiation coupling is

$$\Delta P_T{}^2 = 16kT^5\varepsilon\sigma A \, \Delta f \tag{8.18}$$

PHOTON NOISE. The radiation emitted from a hot body is incoherent in phase (as opposed to that emitted by a laser for instance), and can therefore be regarded as a stream of photons or quanta of radiation, with each photon emitted in a manner uncorrelated with the rest. By using the appropriate statistics it is possible to show that the random variation from the mean in the power emitted from a radiator of area A, emissivity ε and temperature T_1 is

$$\Delta P_1{}^2 = 8kT_1{}^5\varepsilon\sigma A \, \Delta f$$

Furthermore if the body is in an environment at temperature T_2, it can be shown that the radiation it absorbs exhibits power variations from the mean value, given by

$$\Delta P_2{}^2 = 8kT_2{}^5\varepsilon\sigma A \, \Delta f$$

If a body at temperature T_1 is exchanging radiation with an environment at temperature T_2 then the temperature fluctuations of the body correspond to a variation in received power of

$$\Delta P_1{}^2 + \Delta P_2{}^2 = 8k\varepsilon\sigma A \, \Delta f(T_1{}^5 + T_2{}^5) \tag{8.19}$$

If $T_1 = T_2$, that is if the body is in equilibrium with its surroundings

$$\Delta P_1{}^2 + \Delta P_2{}^2 = 16k\varepsilon\sigma A T^5 \Delta f \tag{8.20}$$

Comparison of this result with Equation 8.18 shows that the thermal fluctuation noise in a body that is connected to its environment purely by radiation is completely accounted for by photon noise. This indicates that the effect of thermal-fluctuation noise in a bolometer can be minimized by reducing the proportion of the energy exchange with the environment which takes place by heat conduction. It is shown in the following section that the Johnson noise of a bolometer can be made negligible with respect to thermal fluctuation noise by increasing the responsivity sufficiently. Hence Equation 8.20 gives the ultimate possible sensitivity of a low temperature bolometer.

OTHER MECHANISMS. It is possible that in addition to the Johnson and thermal fluctuation noise, superconductive bolometers may be found to exhibit noise due to mechanisms specifically associated with the super-conducting-to-normal transition. One such mechanism that is current-dependent is thermal propagation, which may take place over small regions of unusually high resistivity at currents below that at which thermal propagation takes place over the specimen as a whole.

The fact that the inter-phase boundaries that occur in the intermediate state of a superconductor have a positive surface energy and therefore possess surface tension, may lead to noise when the temperature of a superconductor maintained in the intermediate state is varied. Noise of this type is known to occur in magnetic materials, presumably due to domain wall movement, when their temperature is varied.[14] For reasons given in Section 7.1, it is likely that during the superconducting-to-normal transition a thin superconductive film exhibits a "mixed" state in which no inter-phase boundaries of positive surface energy exist. Such a film may show 'flux jumping' phenomena similar to those exhibited by filamentary superconductors.

33.5 Minimum Detectable Power

As mentioned above, the minimum power detectable by a bolometer is approximately equal to the so-called "noise equivalent signal power" that produces a bolometer output signal equal to the bolometer noise output. The noise-equivalent signal is calculated below, using the results of Section 33.4, which may be summarized as follows:

A bolometer of resistance R operated at temperature T produces a Johnson noise voltage of average value

$$v_J{}^2 = 4kTR \, \Delta f \tag{8.14}$$

If the thermal conductance between the sensing element of the bolometer and its heat sink is K, the sensing element will experience temperature fluctuations corresponding to a received power

$$\Delta P_T{}^2 = 4kT^2K \, \Delta f \tag{8.16}$$

Finally, radiation exchanged between the sensing element of temperature T_1 and the environment of temperature T_2 leads to a temperature fluctuation equivalent to a received power of

$$\Delta P_1{}^2 + \Delta P_2{}^2 = 8k(T_1{}^5 + T_2{}^5)\varepsilon\sigma A \, \Delta f \tag{8.19}$$

---

[14] Newhouse (1952).

The Johnson noise voltage v_J must be equivalent to a received power

$$P_J = \frac{v_J}{r}$$

where r is the responsivity (calculated in Section 33.3).
A well-known theorem due to Rayleigh states that

$$\overline{A + B}^2 = \overline{A^2} + \overline{B^2} \tag{8.21}$$

where A and B vary sinusoidally. This theorem can be applied to summing the separate contributions to the noise equivalent power P_s. That is,

$$P_s^{\,2} = \frac{v_J^{\,2}}{r^2} + \overline{\Delta P_T^{\,2}} + \overline{\Delta P_1^{\,2}} + \overline{\Delta P_2^{\,2}} \tag{8.22}$$

This expression shows that the contribution of Johnson noise to the total bolometer noise can be made negligibly small by increasing the responsivity sufficiently. Also if the thermal conductivity K between the sensing element and the temperature sink is made sufficiently small, the thermal fluctuation noise contribution $\Delta P_T^{\,2}$ vanishes. Hence the minimum noise equivalent signal power for a bolometer coupled to its surroundings by radiation alone is given by Equation 8.20 provided that the bolometer and its surroundings are at the same temperature. Assuming that the bolometer approximates a black body, so that $\varepsilon \sim 1$, that $A = 0.01$ cm², that $\Delta f = 1$ c/s and that $T = 4°$K, we find that Equation 8.20 predicts a noise equivalent signal power of approximately 10^{-16} watt. This appears to be the ultimate sensitivity possible using a bolometer at 4°K.

In practice, the possible increase in sensitivity produced by reducing K is limited because a strong reduction in K may increase the thermal time constant of the bolometer and thus decrease the frequency response to an intolerable extent. For this reason the heat coupling of the two types of bolometers described above used conduction rather than radiation. Using Equations 8.16 and 8.22 we find that for such a bolometer the noise equivalent signal is

$$P_s^{\,2} = \frac{v_J^{\,2}}{r^2} + 4kT^2K\,\Delta f$$

Substituting for r from Equation 8.12 and for $v_J^{\,2}$ from Equation 8.14, we obtain after some rearrangement

$$P_s^{\,2} = 4kT^2K\,\Delta f\left[\frac{R}{T}\frac{\omega^2C^2 + K^2(1 - b^2)^2}{a^2b^2K^2\,dR/dT} + 1\right]$$

For a given chopper frequency ω, we can find that value of K which gives the minimum noise equivalent signal by solving the equation

$$\frac{dP_s^{\,2}}{dK} = 0$$

This gives

$$\frac{\omega^2 C^2}{K^2} = (1 - b^2)^2 + a^2 b^2 \frac{T}{R}\frac{dR}{dT} \qquad (8.23)$$

This is to be compared with Equation 8.13, which describes the value of K giving maximum responsivity. For a superconductive bolometer $\dfrac{T}{R}\dfrac{dR}{dT} \sim 200$, $b \sim \frac{1}{2}$, and for an unblackened sensing element the absorptivity may be taken as $a = \frac{1}{4}$. Substituting these values into Equation 8.23 gives $\omega C/K \sim 1.9$ for minimum noise equivalent signal. This is close to the result $\omega C/K \sim 1$ calculated from Equation 8.13 for the value of K giving maximum *responsivity*.

34. HEAT SWITCHES AND CONVERTERS

34.1 The Magnetic Field Controlled Heat Valve

At present, temperatures down to $1°K$ are obtained by pumping on the common isotope of helium, and temperatures down to $0.3°K$ can be reached by pumping on the somewhat rarer isotope He^3. Still lower temperatures require the use of the adiabatic demagnetization technique that is described in the following paragraphs. This is a cyclic procedure that requires the use of some type of thermal valve. Thermal valves are also used for experiments at other temperatures that require a controlled flow of heat.

One of the most successful and widely used thermal valves employs a superconductor and depends upon the strong difference in thermal conductivity between the normal and superconducting state, which occurs at temperatures far below T_c. This behavior is illustrated in Figure 8.4, which shows that in lead the ratio between the normal and superconducting thermal conductivity rises above $200:1$ at temperatures below $1°K$. As mentioned in Section 4.2 the decrease of thermal conductivity associated with the superconducting state is due to the fact that the conduction electrons, which play an important role in heat conduction in the normal state, cannot contribute in the superconducting state since they can no longer interact with the lattice.

The strong change in thermal conductivity associated with the magnetically-induced superconducting-to-normal transition at temperatures far below T_c led to a number of independent proposals for a superconductive

thermal valve.[15]   Such a valve consists of a wire or ribbon of superconductor held at a temperature far below T_c.   To "open" the valve, it is
switched into the normal state by means of an external super-critical
magnetic field, thus causing a sharp increase in thermal conductivity.
The operation of such a valve was first demonstrated by Heer and Daunt
(1949), who used a tantalum wire 56 cm long and 0.017 cm in diameter.

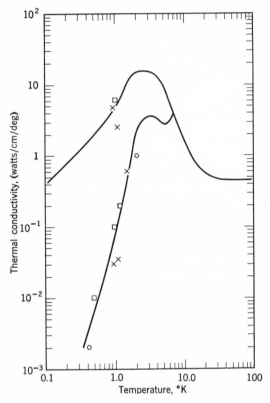

Fig. 8.4   Thermal conductivity of normal and superconducting lead.   For references,
see Heer, Barnes, and Daunt (1954).

At 0.7°K the heat leak through this valve could be increased from 7 to
approximately 7500 ergs per minute by applying a magnetic field above
the critical value.

Thermal valves are designed to maximize the ratio of the normal to the
superconducting thermal conductivity.   They are usually constructed of a
cold-worked superconductor.   The cold work produces phonon scattering.

---

[15] Gorter (1948); Heer and Daunt (1949); Mendelssohn and Olsen (1950).

This reduces the superconducting heat conductivity while leaving the normal state conductivity, which is mainly due to electrons, relatively unaffected. The thermal valve material is usually highly purified, to minimize flux trapping. This is desirable because the abrupt destruction of trapped flux that may occur during the normal-to-superconducting transition generates unnecessarily large eddy currents in the superconductor which in turn produce undesirable heating.[16] For this reason, lead, a "soft" and easily purified superconductor, is now used in preference to tantalum as valve material. For polycrystalline lead sheets, subjected to a transverse magnetic field, it is found[16] that between 0.1°K and 0.5°K the ratio between the normal and superconducting thermal conductivity is given by the relation

$$\frac{K_n}{K_s} = 45T^{-2.3}$$

For different field orientations the multiplying factor on the right hand side of this expression may vary from 20 to 70 due to variations of the normal state thermal conductivity.

34.2 Applications of Thermal Valves

Superconductive thermal valves play an important role in refrigeration systems using adiabatic demagnetization. These systems are used to obtain temperatures below 0.3°K and depend on the fact that a paramagnetic salt such as iron-ammonium-alum possesses a latent heat of magnetization. This causes specimens of such a salt to heat up when magnetized and to cool when demagnetized, thus absorbing heat from their surroundings.

The use of thermal valves in a cyclic refrigerator suggested by Daunt and Heer (1949), is illustrated in Figure 8.5. This figure shows an evacuated chamber immersed in a liquid helium reservoir, containing the object to be cooled R, two thermal valves V_1 and V_2, and the paramagnetic salt P. The operating cycle is as follows. First with V_1 open (i.e., conducting) and V_2 closed, P is magnetized isothermally. The heat produced by this process is absorbed by the helium reservoir through the contact B. As soon as P has assumed the reservoir temperature, V_1 is closed and V_2 is opened (made conductive). This isolates P thermally from the reservoir and connects it to the sample. P is now demagnetized, causing it to cool and thus extract heat from the sample R. As soon as P and R are in temperature equilibrium V_2 is closed, V_1 is opened and the cycle is repeated. Temperatures down to 0.2°K have been obtained with this system.

A cascade system using two salt "pills" A and B connected by a thermal

---

[16] Reese and Stegert (1962).

valve V is shown in Figure 8.6. The cooling process proceeds as follows. A and B are first magnetized, using a solenoid that surrounds the dewar, and cooled to the temperature of the external helium bath by admitting helium "exchange" gas to the enclosure containing them. As soon as A and B are in thermal equilibrium with the helium bath, the exchange gas is pumped out of the enclosure, thus leaving A and B thermally isolated.

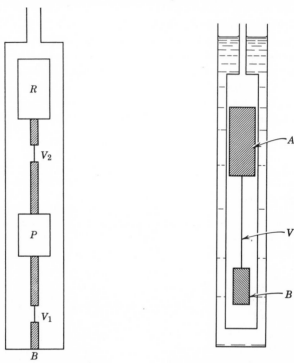

Fig. 8.5 Schematic diagram of a cyclic magnetic refrigerator (Daunt and Heer, 1949).

Fig. 8.6 Schematic diagram of a two-stage magnetic refrigerator (After de Klerk, 1956).

The dewar is now partly raised out of the solenoid thus reducing the magnetic field applied to A. This causes A and B to drop in temperature. As soon as A and B are in thermal equilibrium the dewar is raised further, reducing the magnetic field on the thermal valve. This therefore becomes superconducting, thus thermally isolating B from A. Finally the dewar is raised out of the magnetic field altogether, causing the salt pill B to cool even further. With this type of system temperatures as low as $0.003°K$ have been obtained starting with an external field of 4200 oe.[17]

---

[17] Darby, Hatton, and Rollin (1950). Darby, Hatton, Rollin, Seymour, and Silsbee (1951).

34.3   Temperature Controlled Current Switches

Current flow in a superconducting network can be controlled by making portions of the circuit resistive. This is usually performed by applying a supercritical magnetic field, as described in Chapter 6. Occasionally, particularly when it is necessary to control currents in the presence of large magnetic fields, it is found more convenient to use a superconducting switch whose state is controlled by varying its temperature. One such application arose in connection with the control of a "superconducting galvanometer" developed by Pippard and Pullan (1952). This circuit used a temperature-controlled superconducting switch consisting of a lead film evaporated on a strip of German silver. This film could be heated above its critical temperature by means of a heating coil. Another application in which a heat-controlled superconducting switch is used as a shunt for a high field solenoid, is described in Section 21.2.

34.4   Energy Converters

An as yet untested method for using a superconductor to convert heat to electrical energy has been suggested by Chester (1962) who predicts an efficiency of 44%. In this process, a superconductor wrapped in a coil, and exposed to a magnetic field, is repeatedly temperature-cycled through the phase transition. This causes flux to alternately penetrate and be expelled from the superconductor, thus generating an a-c voltage in the coil.

Attempts to use the latent heat of transition of a superconductor for refrigeration are reported by Yaqub (1960). He found that a massive block of tin alloy if cooled to $0.8°K$ and then driven normal with a magnetic field would drop to a temperature of $0.18°K$. This temperature drop was less than that calculated theoretically, apparently because of eddy current heating in the superconductor.

Bibliography

Further information on superconducting and other infrared bolometers is contained in the following books:

P. W. Kruse, L. D. McGlauchlin, and R. B. McQuistan, *Elements of Infrared Technology*. New York: Wiley, 1962.

R. A. Smith, F. E. Jones, and R. P. Chasmar, *The Detection and Measurement of Infrared Radiation*. New York: Oxford University Press, 1957.

Further details on the use of superconducting thermal valves in adiabatic demagnetization refrigerators is given in D. de Klerk, "Adiabatic Demagnetization," *Encyclopedia of Physics*, Vol. XV, ed. S. Flügge. Berlin: Springer, 1956.

Appendixes

35.1 Solution of the Non-local Integral

The solution of the integral

$$I(R) = \int \frac{(\mathbf{a}_1 \cdot \mathbf{r}_1)\mathbf{r}_1}{r^2} \, e^{-r/\xi} \, dv$$

integrated over a sphere of radius R is carried out as follows.

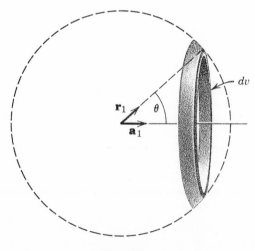

Fig. 35.1

266

From Figure 35.1 it can be seen that

$$dv = 2\pi r^2 \sin \theta \, dr \, d\theta$$

also

$$(\mathbf{a}_1 \cdot \mathbf{r}_1) = \cos \theta$$

Hence

$$I(R) = 2\pi \int_0^R e^{-r/\xi} \left[\int_0^\pi \mathbf{r}_1 \cos \theta \sin \theta \, d\theta \right] dr$$

When integrating the unit vector $\mathbf{r}_1$ over a sphere we need only consider the component along the line $\theta = 0$ since all other components cancel out due to the symmetry of the problem. Hence

$$I(R) = 2\pi \int_0^R e^{-r/\xi} \left[\mathbf{a}_1 \int_0^\pi \cos^2 \theta \sin \theta \, d\theta \right] dr$$

$$= 2\pi \mathbf{a}_1 \int_0^R e^{-R/\xi} \tfrac{1}{3} [\cos^3 \theta]_0^\pi \, dr$$

$$= -\frac{4\pi}{3} \mathbf{a}_1 \int_0^R e^{-R/\xi} \, dr$$

$$= -\frac{4\pi}{3} \mathbf{a}_1 \xi (1 - e^{-R/\xi})$$

For $R = \infty$,

$$I = \frac{4\pi}{3} \mathbf{a}_1 \xi$$

35.2 Surface Current Density on a Flat Superconducting Sheet[1]

The problem is solved by carrying out a conformal transformation of the magnetic field around a superconducting cylinder. The magnetic potential lines, ψ, for the cylinder (see Fig. 35.2) are defined so that $\nabla \psi = -H = -2I/cr$.

$$\frac{1}{r} \frac{d\psi}{d\theta} = \nabla \psi$$

Hence

$$\psi = \frac{2I\theta}{c}$$

where I esu is the current carried by the cylinder. If the potential near the cylinder is represented by the equation $z = re^{i\theta}$, we may transform the

---

[1] This derivation is due to H. H. Edwards.

cylinder to an ellipse by using the transformation

$$W = \frac{1}{2}\left(z + \frac{\alpha^2}{z}\right) = u + iv$$

$$= \frac{1}{2}\left(r + \frac{\alpha^2}{r}\right)\cos\theta + i\frac{1}{2}\left(r - \frac{\alpha^2}{r}\right)\sin\theta$$

For $r = $ const, W is an ellipse which reduces to a line for $\alpha \rightarrow r$. For the straight line, the surface field is $H = d\psi/du = d\psi/d\theta \; d\theta/du|_{\alpha=r=w}$. Now

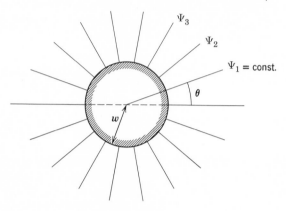

Fig. 35.2

if $\alpha = r, u = w\cos\theta$ where w is the cylinder radius. Hence

$$\frac{du}{d\theta} = -w\sin\theta$$

$$= -(w^2 - u^2)^{\frac{1}{2}}$$

Hence at a distance u from the center of a flat superconductor of width $2w$, carrying a current I, the surface field is

$$H(u) = \frac{2I/c}{(w^2 - u^2)^{\frac{1}{2}}}$$

Hence the surface current density on *each* surface of the film is

$$J = \frac{H(u)}{4\pi}$$

$$= \frac{I}{2\pi(w^2 - u^2)^{\frac{1}{2}}}$$

35.3 Analysis of the In-Line Cryotron

The structure analyzed is that shown in Figure 6.20, consisting of a singly-shielded film of width w and thickness d, carrying a current I emu. Taking the top of the film as the origin of coordinates, with the z axis directed downwards, and solving London's equation which in this geometry reduces to $\lambda^2 \, d^2 H/dz^2 = H$, we find that the field parallel to the film surface is

$$H(z) = Me^{z/\lambda} + Ne^{-z/\lambda}$$

Above the film $H(0) = -H_B$. Below the film,

$$H(d) = 4\pi I/w - H_B$$

From these two boundary conditions, we find that

$$M = \frac{B + \dfrac{4\pi I}{w} - H_B + H_B e^{-d/\lambda}}{2 \sinh d/\lambda}$$

$$N = \frac{H_B - H_B e^{d/\lambda} - \dfrac{4\pi I}{w}}{2 \sinh d/\lambda}$$

Since curl $\mathbf{H} = 4\pi\mathbf{J}$ the surface current density is given by

$$4\pi j(z) = \frac{dH}{dz} = \frac{M}{\lambda} e^{z/\lambda} - \frac{N}{\lambda} e^{-z/\lambda}$$

Therefore, on the top film surface where $z = 0$,

$$4\pi j(0) = \frac{M - N}{\lambda} \tag{35.1}$$

and on the bottom surface where $z = d$,

$$4\pi j(d) = \frac{M}{\lambda} e^{d/\lambda} - \frac{N}{\lambda} e^{-d/\lambda} \tag{35.2}$$

The critical (bias) field H_F is obtained by setting $j(d) = \pm j_c$ in Equation 35.2 and solving for H_B with $I = 0$. This gives

$$H_F = \pm 4\pi j_c \lambda \coth d/2\lambda$$
$$\rightarrow \pm 4\pi j_c \lambda$$

as $d/\lambda \rightarrow \infty$

This shows that we may identify $4\pi j_c \lambda$ with the bulk critical field H_c. Hence

$$H_F = H_c \coth d/2\lambda \tag{35.3}$$

The critical current at zero bias field is obtained by solving Equation 35.2 for I with $H_B = 0$, and $j(d) = j_c$. This gives

$$I_c = \frac{H_c w}{4\pi} \tanh d/\lambda \tag{35.4}$$

The maximum critical current occurs when the current densities on both surfaces of the film become critical simultaneously, that is, when

$$j(0) = j(d) = j_c$$

Using Equations 35.1 and 35.2, it can be shown that when this condition occurs

$$\frac{I}{w} - \frac{H_B}{4\pi} = j_c = \frac{H_B}{4\pi}$$

and

$$\frac{4\pi I}{w} = 2H_B \tag{35.5}$$

a result which is independent of d/λ. To calculate the bias for maximum critical current explicitly, we again put $j = j_c$ in Equations 35.1 and solve for H_B, using Equation 35.5. This gives the bias value for maximum critical current as

$$H_{BM} = H_c \tanh d/2\lambda \tag{35.6}$$

The points calculated in the above equations are plotted in Figure 6.21.

Selected Bibliography

Chapters 2 to 4

1. Bardeen, J., and Schrieffer, J. R., "Recent Developments in Super-conductivity," *Progress in Low Temperature Physics*, Vol. III, ed. C. J. Gorter. New York: Interscience, 1961.
2. London, F., *Superfluids*, Vol. I, 2nd ed, with epilogue by M. J. Buckingham. New York: Dover, 1961.
3. Lynton, E. A., *Superconductivity*. New York: Wiley, 1962.
4. Matthias, B. T., "Superconductivity in the Periodic System," *Progress in Low Temperature Physics*, Vol. II, ed. C. J. Gorter. New York: Interscience, 1957.
5. Mayer, H., Physik Dünner Schichten Vol. I, 1950; Vol. II, 1955. Stuttgart (German): Wissenschaftliche Verlagsgesellschaft.
6. Serin, B., "Superconductivity—Experimental Part," *Handbuch der Physic*, Vol. XV, ed. S. Flügge. Berlin: Springer, 1956.
7. Shoenberg, D., *Superconductivity*, 2nd ed. reprinted with additional appendix. New York: Cambridge University Press, 1960.

Chapter 5

8. Kolm, H. et al., eds., *High Magnetic Fields*. New York: Wiley, 1962.
9. Kropshot, R. H., and Arp, V. D., "Superconducting Magnets," *Cryogenics*, Vol. 2, 1961.
10. Timmerhaus, K. D., ed., *Advances in Cryogenic Engineering*, Vol. 6. New York: Plenum Press, 1961.

Chapters 6 and 7

11. Bremer, J. W., *Superconductive Devices*. New York: McGraw-Hill, 1962.

12. Quartly, C. J., *Square Loop Ferrite Circuitry*, Englewood Cliffs: Prentice-Hall, 1962.
13. Newhouse, V. L., "Superconductive Circuits for Computing Machines," *Electro-Technol.* Vol. 67, p. 78, (1961).
14. Young, D. R., "Superconducting Circuits," *Progress in Cryogenics* Vol. I, ed. K. Mendelssohn. London: Heywood and Co., 1959.
15. *Proc. Symp. Superconductive Tech. Computing Systems*, Washington, May 1960; ONR symposium report ACR-50, Office of Naval Research, Washington, 1960; partly reprinted in *Solid State Electron.*, Vol. 1, No. 4, 1960.

Chapter 8

16. De Klerk, D., "Adiabatic Demagnetization," *Handbuch der Physik*, Vol. XV, ed. S. Flügge. Berlin: Springer, 1956.
17. Smith, R. A., Jones, F. E., and Chasmar, R. P., *The Detection and Measurement of Infrared Radiation.* New York: Oxford University Press, 1957.

References

Abrikosov, A. A. (1952), *Dokl. Akad. Nauk SSSR*, **86**, 43 (Russian).
Abrikosov, A. A. (1957), *J. Exp. Theor. Phys. USSR*, **32**, 1442; *Soviet Phys. JETP*, **5**, 1174; *J. Phys. Chem. Solids*, **2**, 199.
Alers, P. B. (1957), *Phys. Rev.*, **105**, 104.
Anderson, P. W. (1959), *J. Phys. Chem. Solids*, **11**, 26.
Anderson, P. W., and Rowell, J. M. (1963), *Phys. Rev. Letters*, **10**, 230.
Andrew, E. R. (1948a), *Proc. Roy. Soc. (London)*, **A194**, 80.
Andrew, E. R. (1948b), *Proc. Roy. Soc. (London)*, **A194**, 98.
Andrews, D. H., Bruksch, W. F., Jr., Ziegler, W. T., and Blanchard, E. R. (1942), *Rev. Sci. Instr.*, **13**, 281.
Andrews, D. H., and Clark, C. W. (1946), *Nature*, **158**, 945.
Andrews, D. H., Milton, R. M., and DeSorbo, W. (1946), *J. Opt. Soc.*, **36**, 518.
Andrews, D. H., Fowler, R. D., and Williams, M. C. (1949), *Phys. Rev.*, **76**, 154.
Appleyard, E. T. S., Bristow, J. R., London, H., and Misener, A. D. (1939), *Proc. Roy. Soc. (London)*, **A172**, 540.
Arkadiev, V. (1945), *J. Phys. U.S.S.R.*, **9**, 148.
Arkadiev, V. (1947), *Nature*, **160**, 330.
Autler, S. H. (1960), *Rev. Sci. Instr.*, **31**, 369.
Autler, S. H. (1962), in Kolm, H., et al., eds., *High Magnetic Fields*. New York: Wiley, 1962, p. 324.
Baloshova, B. M., and Sharvin, I. W. (1957), *Soviet Phys. JETP*, **4**, 54.
Bardeen, J. (1956), "Theory of Superconductivity," *Encyclopedia of Physics*. Vol. XV, Part II, ed. S. Flügge. Berlin: Springer.
Bardeen, J. (1958), *Phys. Rev. Letters*, **1**, 399.
Bardeen, J. (1961a), *Phys. Rev. Letters*, **6**, 57.
Bardeen, J. (1961b), *Phys. Rev. Letters*, **7**, 162.
Bardeen, J. (1962), *Rev. Mod. Phys.*, **34**, 667.
Bardeen, J., Cooper, L. N., and Schrieffer, J. R. (1957), *Phys. Rev.*, **108**, 1175.
Bardeen, J., and Schrieffer, J. R. (1961), "Recent Developments in Superconductivity," *Progress in Low Temperature Physics*, Vol. III, ed. C. J. Gorter. New York: Interscience.
Bean, C. P. (1962), *Phys. Rev. Letters*, **8**, 250.
Bean, C. P., and Doyle, M. (1962), *J. Appl. Phys.*, **33**, 3334.
Bean, C. P., Doyle, M., and Pincus, A. G. (1962), *Phys. Rev. Letters*, **9**, 93.

Becker, R., Heller, G., and Sauter, F. (1933), *Z. Physik*, **85**, 772.

Behrndt, M. E., Blumberg, R. H., and Giedd, G. R. (1960), *IBM J. Res. Develop.*, **4**, 184.

Benjamin, P., and Weaver, C. (1960), *Proc. Roy. Soc. (London)*, **A254**, 163.

Berlincourt, T. G., Hake, R. R., and Leslie, D. H. (1961), *Phys. Rev. Letters*, **6**, 671.

Biondi, M. A., and Garfunkel, M. P. (1959), *Phys. Rev.*, **116**, 853, 862.

Bitter, F. (1939), *Rev. Sci. Instr.*, **10**, 373.

Blumberg, R. H., and Seraphim, D. P. (1962), *J. Appl. Phys.*, **33**, 163.

Bobeck, A. H. (1957), *Bell System Tech. J.*, **36**, 1319.

Bodmer, M. (1950), thesis, Johns Hopkins University.

Bogoliubov, N. N., Tolmachev, V. V., and Skirkov, D. V. (1948), *A New Method in the Theory of Superconductivity*, Sec. 6.3 (Acad. Sci. USSR Press, Moscow; Translation: Consultants Bureau, Inc., New York 1959); see also Tolmachev, V. V., *Dokl. Akad. Nauk SSSR*, **140**, 563 (1961); *Soviet Phys. Doklady* (Engl. Trans.), **6**, 800 (1962).

Bömmel, H. E. (1954), *Phys. Rev.*, **96**, 220.

Boom, R. W., and Livingston, R. S. (1962), *Proc. IRE*, **50**, 274.

Bozorth, R. W. (1951), *Ferromagnetism*. New York: Van Nostrand.

Bremer, J. W. (1958), *Elec. Mfg.*, **61**, 78.

Bremer, J. W. (1962), *Superconductive Devices*. New York: McGraw-Hill.

Bremer, J. W., and V. L. Newhouse (1958), *Phys. Rev. Letters*, **1**, 282.

Bremer, J. W., and V. L. Newhouse (1959), *Phys. Rev.*, **116**, 309.

Brenneman, A. E., McNichol, J. J., Seraphim, D. P. (1963), *Proc. IEEE*, **51**, 1009.

Broom, R. F., and Rhoderick, E. H. (1960), *Brit. J. Appl. Phys.*, **11**, 292.

Broom, R. F., and Rhoderick, E. H. (1962), *Proc. Phys. Soc. (London)*, **79**, 586.

Broom, R. F., and Simpson, O. (1960), *Brit. J. Appl. Phys.*, **11**, 78.

Buchold, T. A. (1960), *Scientific American*, **202**, No. 3, 74.

Buchold, T. A. (1961), *Cryogenics*, **1**, 203.

Buck, D. A. (1956a), *Proc. I.R.E.*, **44**, 482.

Buck, D. A. (1956b), *Proc. Eastern Joint Computer Conf.*, p. 47.

Buckingham, M. J. (1958), *Proc. 5th Intern. Conf. Low Temp. Phys. Chem.*, ed. J. R. Dillinger. Madison: University of Wisconsin Press, p. 229.

Budnick, J. I. (1960), *Phys. Rev.*, **119**, 1578.

Budnick, J. I., Lynton, E. A., and Serin, B. (1956), *Phys. Rev.*, **103**, 286.

Burns, L. L., Jr., Alphonse, G. A., and Leck, G. W. (1961), *IRE Trans.*, EC-**10**, 438.

Burns, L. L., Christiansen, D. A., and Gange, R. A., (1963), *Proc. Fall Joint Compt. Conf.*, p. 91.

Byers, N., and Yang, C. N. (1961), *Phys. Rev. Letters*, **7**, 46.

Calverley, A., and Rose-Innes, A. C. (1960), *Proc. Roy. Soc. (London)*, **A255**, 267.

Casimir-Jonker, J. M., and De Haas, W. J. (1935), *Physica*, **2**, 935.

Caswell, H. L. (1961a), *J. Appl. Phys.*, **32**, 105.

Caswell, H. L. (1961b), *J. Appl. Phys.*, **32**, 2641.

Chanin, G., Lynton. E. A., and Serin, B. (1959), *Phys. Rev.*, **114**, 719.

Cherry, W. H., and Gittleman, J. I. (1960), *Proc. Symp. Superconductive Tech. Computing Systems*, Washington, May 1960; ONR Symposium report ACR-50, p. 75.

Chester, M. (1962), *J. Appl. Phys.*, **33**, 643.

Christy, R. W. (1962), *J. Appl. Phys.*, **31**, 1680.

Cioffi, P. P. (1962), *J. Appl. Phys.*, **33**, 875.

Cohen, M. L. (1961), *Proc. I.R.E.*, **49**, 371.

Collins, S. C., and Zimmerman, F. J. (1953), *Phys. Rev.*, **90**, 991.

Condon, E. U., and Maxwell, E. (1949), *Phys. Rev.* **76**, 578.

Cooper, L. N. (1956), *Phys. Rev.*, **104**, 1189.

Cooper, L. N. (1961), *Phys. Rev. Letters*, **6**, 689; *IBM J. Res. Develop.*, **6**, 75 (1962).

Cornish, F. H. J., and Olsen, J. L. (1953), *Helv. Phys. Acta*, **26**, 369.

Corsan, J. M. (1961), *Cryogenics*, **1**, 180.

Crittenden, Jr., E. C. (1958), *Proc. 5th Int. Conf. Low Temp. Phys. Chem.*, ed. J. R. Dillinger. Madison: University of Wisconsin Press, p. 232.

Crittenden, Jr., E. C., Cooper, J. N., Schmidlin, F. W. (1960), *Proc. I.R.E.*, **48**, 1233.

Crowe, J. W. (1957), *IBM J. Res. Develop.*, **1**, 295.

Darby, J., Hatton, J., and Rollin, B. V. (1950), *Proc. Phys. Soc. (London)*, **A63**, 1179.

Darby, J., Hatton, J., Rollin, B. V., Seymour, E. F. W., and Silsbee, H. B. (1951), *Proc. Phys. Soc. (London)*, **A64**, 861.

Daunt, J. G., and Heer, C. V. (1949), *Phys. Rev.*, **76**, 985.

Davies, E. A. (1960), *Proc. Roy. Soc. (London)*, **A255**, 407.

Deaver, B. S., Jr., and Fairbank, W. M. (1961), *Phys. Rev. Letters*, **7**, 43.

Delano, R. B., Jr. (1960), *Proc. Symp. Superconductive Tech. Computing Systems* Washington; ONR Symposium report ACR-50, Office of Naval Reaserch, Washington, 1960; partly reprinted in *Solid State Electron*, 1, No. 4, 1960, p. 381

Desirant, M., and Shoenberg, D. (1948a), *Proc. Roy. Soc. (London)*, **A194**, 63.

Desirant, M., and Shoenberg, D. (1948b), *Proc. Phys. Soc. (London)*, **60**, 413.

DeSorbo, W. (1960), *Phys. Rev. Letters*, **4**, 406;

DeSorbo, W., and Healey, W. A. (1961), *G. E. Research Lab Report* 2743M.

DeSorbo, W., and Newhouse, V. L. (1962), *J. Appl. Phys.*, **33**, 1004.

Doll, R., and Näbauer, M. (1961), *Phys. Rev. Letters*, **7**, 51.

Donadieu, L. J., and Rose, D. J. (1962), in Kolm et al., eds. *High Magnetic Fields*. New York: Wiley, 1962, p. 358.

Douglass, D. H. Jr. (1961), *Phys. Rev.*, **124**, 735.

Douglass, D. H. Jr. (1962), *IBM J. Res. Develop.*, **6**, 44.

Drangeid, K. E., and Sommerhalder, R. (1962), *Phys. Rev. Letters*, **8**, 467.

Edwards, H. H., and Newhouse, V. L. (1962), *J. Appl. Phys.*, **33**, 868.

Faber, T. E. (1952), *Proc. Roy. Soc. (London)*, **A214**, 392.

Faber, T. E. (1953), *Proc. Roy. Soc. (London)*, **A219**, 75.

Faber, T. E. (1954), *Proc. Roy. Soc. (London)*, **A223**, 174.

Faber, T. E. (1955), *Proc. Roy. Soc.*, **A231**, 353.

Faber, T. E. (1958), *Proc. Roy. Soc. (London)*, **A248**, 460.

Faber, T. E., and Pippard, A. B. (1955), *Proc. Roy. Soc. (London)*, **A231**, 336.

Feigin, L. A., and Shalnikov, A. I. (1956), *Soviet Phys. Doklady*, **1**, 376.

Feucht, D. L., and Woodford, J. B. Jr. (1961), *J. Appl. Phys.*, **32**, 1882.

Fowler, C. M., Caird, R. S., Garn, W. B., and Thomson, D. B. (1962), in Kolm et al., eds., *High Magnetic Fields*. New York: Wiley, 1962, p. 296.

Friedel, J., de Gennes, P. G., and Matricon, J. (1963), *Appl. Phys. Letters*, **2**, 119.

Fröhlich, H. (1950), *Phys. Rev.*, **79**, 845.

Fruin, R. E., and Newhouse, V. L. (1963), *Proc. IEEE*, **51**, 1732.

Fuchs, K. (1938), *Proc. Cambridge Phil. Soc.*, **34**, 100.

Furth, H. P., and Levine, M. A. (1962), *J. Appl. Phys.*, **33**, 747.

Galkin, A. A., and Lazarev, B. G. (1948), *C. R. Acad. Sci. USSR*, **56**, 667.

Garfunkel, M. P., and Serin, B. (1952), *Phys. Rev.*, **85**, 834.

Garwin, R. L. (1957), *IBM J. Res. Develop.*, **1**, 304.

Gauster, W. F., and Parker, C. E. (1962), in Kolm. H. et al., eds., *High Magnetic Fields*. New York: Wiley, 1962, p. 3.

Giaever, I. (1960a), *Phys. Rev. Letters*, **5**, 147.

Giaever, I. (1960b), *Phys. Rev. Letters*, **5**, 464.

Giaever, I., and Megerle, K. (1961), *Phys. Rev.*, **122**, 1101.

Ginsberg, D. M., and Tinkham, M. (1960), *Phys. Rev.*, **118**, 990.

Ginzburg, N. I., and Shalnikov, A. I. (1960), *Soviet Physics JETP*, **10**, 285.

Ginzburg, V. L. (1955), *Nuovo Cimento*, **2**, 1234. (In English).

Ginzburg, V. L. (1958), *Soviet Phys. JETP*, **7**, 78.

Ginzburg, V. L., and Landau, L. D. (1950), *J. Exp. Theor. Phys. USSR*, **20**, 1064; see also Ginzburg, V. L. (1955), *Nuovo Cimento*, **2**, 1234.

Glover, R. E., III, and Sherrill, M. D. (1960), *Phys. Rev. Letters*, **5**, 248.

Glover, R. E., III, and Tinkham, M. (1957), *Phys. Rev.*, **108**, 243.

Goodman, B. B. (1962), *IBM J. Res. Develop.*, **6**, 63.

Gorkov, L. P. (1959), *Soviet Phys. JETP*, **9**, 1364.

Gorkov, L. P. (1960a), *Soviet Phys. JETP*, **10**, 593.

Gorkov, L. P. (1960b), *Soviet Phys. JETP*, **10**, 998.

Gorter, C. J. (1948), Ceremonies Langevin-Perrin, p. 76, Paris.

Gorter, C. J., and Casimir, H. B. G., (1934), *Phys. Z.* **35**, 963; *Z. Techn. Phys.* **15** 539.

Grebenkamper, C. J., and Hagen, J. P. (1952), *Phys. Rev.*, **86**, 673.

Gygax, S. (1958), *Helv. Phys. Acta*, **31**, 287.

Gygax, S. (1961), *Z. Angew. Math. Phys.*, **12**, 289.

De Haas, W. J., and Voogd, J. (1931), *Commun. Phys. Lab. Univ. Leiden*, No. 214c.

Hagedorn, F. B., and Hall, P. M. (1963), *J. Appl. Phys.*, **34**, 128.

Harding, J. T., and Tuffias, R. H. (1960), in Timmerhaus, K. D., ed., *Advances in Cryogenic Engineering*, Vol. 6. New York: Plenum Press, 1961, p. 95.

Haynes, M. K. (1960), in Young, D. R., "Superconducting Circuits," *Progress in Cryogenics*, Vol. I, ed. K. Mendelssohn. London: Heywood, 1959, p. 396.

Heer, C. V., and Daunt, J. G. (1949), *Phys. Rev.*, **76**, 854.

Heer, C. V., Barnes, C. G., and Daunt, J. G. (1954), *Rev. Sci. Inst.*, **25**, 1088.

Hildebrant A. F., Elleman, P. D., Whitmore, F. C., and Simpkins, R. (1962), *J. Appl. Phys.*, **33**, 2375.

Holland, L. (1956), *Vacuum Deposition of Thin Films*. New York: Wiley, 1956.

Hulm, J. K., Fraser, M. J., Riemersma, H., Venturino, A. J., and Wien, R. E. in Kolm, H., et al., eds., *High Magnetic Fields*. New York: Wiley, 1962, p. 332.

Hunak, J. J., Cody, G. D., Aron, P. R., and Hitchcock, H. C. (1962), in Kolm, H. et al., eds., *High Magnetic Fields*. New York: Wiley, 1962, p. 592.

Ittner, W. B., III (1958), *Phys. Rev.*, **111**, 1483.

Ittner, W. B., III (1960), *Proc. Symp. Superconductive Tech. Computing Systems*, Washington, May 1960; ONR symposium report ACR-50, Office of Naval Research, Washington, 1960; partly reprinted in *Solid State Electron*, **1**, No. 4, 1960, p. 239.

Kahan, G. J., Delano, R. B., Jr., Brenneman, A. E., Tsui, R. T. C. (1960), *IBM J. Res. Develop.*, **4**, 184.

Karagounis, A. (1956), *Bull. Inst. Int. Froid Annexe Suppl.* (*Louvain Conf.*), p. 195.

Kaufman, M., and Newhouse, V. L. (1958), *J. Appl. Phys.*, **29**, 487.

Keesom, W. H. (1935), *Physica*, **2**, 35.

Keesom, W. H., and Kok, J. A. (1932), *Commun. Phys. Lab. Univ. Leiden*, No. 221e.

Keesom, W. H., and Van Laer, P. H. (1938), *Physica*, **5**, 193; *Commun. Phys. Lab. Univ. Leiden*, No. 252b.

Keller, J. B., and Zumino, B. (1961), *Phys. Rev. Letters*, **7**, 164.

De Klerk, D. (1956), "Adiabatic Demagnetization," *Handbuch der Physik*, Vol. XV, ed. S. Flügge. Berlin: Springer.

Khukhareva, I. S. (1962), *Soviet Phys. JETP*, **14**, 526.

Kittel, C. (1956), *Introduction to Solid State Physics*, 2nd ed. New York: Wiley.

Kikoin, I. K., and Goobar, S. V. (1940), *J. Phys. USSR*, **3**, 333; see also Broer, L. J. F. (1947), *Physica*, **13**, 473.

Kneip, G. D., Jr., Betterton, J. O., Jr., Easton, D. S., and Scarbrough, J. O. (1962), in Kolm, H., et al., eds., *High Magnetic Fields*. New York: Wiley, 1962, p. 603.

Kolchin, A. M., Mikhailov, Yu., G., Reinov, N. M., Rumyantseva, A. V., Smirnov, A. P., and Totubalin, V. N. (1961), *Soviet Phys. JETP*, **6**, 1083.

Kropshot, R. H., and Arp, V. D. (1961), "Superconducting Magnets," *Cryogenics*, **2**, p. 1.

Kruse, P. W., McGlauchlin, L. D., and McQuistan, R. B. (1962), *Elements of Infrared Technology*. New York: Wiley.

Kunzler, J. E. (1961), *Rev. Mod. Phys.*, **33**, 501.

Kunzler, J. E. (1962), in Kolm, H. et al. eds., *High Magnetic Fields*, New York: Wiley, 1962, p. 574.

Kunzler, J. E., Buehler, E., Hsu, F. S. L., and Wernick, J. E. (1961), *Phys. Rev. Letters*, **6**, 89.

Kuper, C. G. (1951), *Phil. Mag.*, **42**, 961.

Landau, L. D., and Lifschitz, E. M. (1958), *Statistical Physics*. London: Pergamon Press, pp. 434ff.

Laquer, H. L. (1963), *Cryogenics*, **3**, 27.

Laredo, S. J., and Pippard, A. B. (1955), *Proc. Cambridge Phil. Soc.*, **51**, 368.

Lebacqz, J. V., Williams, M. C., Clark, C. W., and Andrews, D. H. (1949), *Proc. IRE*, **37**, 1147.

Lifschitz, E. M. (1950), *J. Exp. Theor. Phys. USSR*, **9**, 834.

Lifschitz, E. M., and Sharvin, Yu. V. (1951), *Dokl. Akad. Nauk. USSR*, **79**, 783.

Livingston, J. D. (1963), *Phys. Rev.*, **129**, 1943.

London, F. (1935), *Proc. Roy. Soc.*, **A152**, 24.

London, F. (1937), *Une conception nouvelle de la supraconductibilité*. Paris: Hermann et Cie.

London, F. (1961), *Superfluids*, Vol. I, 2nd ed., with epilogue by M. J. Buckingham. New York: Dover.

London, F., and London, H. (1935a), *Proc. Royal Soc. (London)*, **A149**, 71.

London, F., and London, H. (1935b), *Physica*, **2**, 341.

London, H. (1936), *Proc. Roy. Soc. (London)*, **A155**, 102.

Lutes, O. S., and Maxwell, E. (1955), *Phys. Rev.*, **97**, 1718.

Lynton, E. A., *Superconductivity* (1962). London: Methuen; New York: Wiley.

Makei, B. V. (1958), *J. Exp. Theor. Phys. USSR*, **34**, 312, (in Russian).

Margenau, H., and Murphy, G. M. (1956), *The Mathematics and Physics of Chemistry*, 2nd ed. New York: Van Nostrand.

Martin, D. H., and Bloor, D. (1961), *Cryogenics*, **1**, 159.

Mason, P. V. (1961), thesis, Cal. Inst. Tech.

Matthias, B. T. (1957), "Superconductivity in the Periodic System," *Progress in Low Temperature Physics*, Vol. II, ed., C. J. Gorter. New York: Interscience.

Matthias, B. T. (1962), *IBM Jour.*, **6**, 250.

Matthias, B. T., Geballe, T. H., and Compton, V. B. (1963), *Rev. Modern Phys.*, **35**, 1.

Matthias, B. T., Suhl, H., and Corenzwit, E. (1959a), *J. Phys. Chem. Solids*, **13**, 156.

Matthias, B. T., Compton, V. B., Suhl, H., and Corenzwit, E. (1959b), *Phys. Rev.*, **115**, 1597.

Maxwell, E. (1950a), *Phys. Rev.*, **78**, 477.

Maxwell, E. (1950b), *Phys. Rev.*, **79**, 173.

Maxwell, E. (1961), in Timmerhaus, K. D., ed., *Advances in Cryogenic Engineering*, Vol. 6. New York: Plenum Press, p. 154.

Maxwell, E., Marcus, P. M., and Slater, J. C. (1949), *Phys. Rev.*, **76**, 1332.

Mayer, H. (1959), *Structure and Properties of Thin Films*, C. A. Neugebauer et al., eds. New York: Wiley, p. 225.

McFee, R. (1962) *Elec. Eng.* **81**, 122.

Meissner. H. (1958), *Phys. Rev.*, **109**, 1479.

Meissner, W., and Ochsenfeld, R. (1933), *Naturwissenschaften*, **21**, 787.

Mendelssohn, K. (1935), *Proc. Roy. Soc. (London)*, **A152**, 34.

Mendelssohn, K., and Olsen, J. L. (1950a), *Proc. Phys. Soc. (London)*, **A63**, 2.

Mendelssohn, K., and Olsen, J. L. (1950b), *Phys. Rev.*, **80**, 859.

Meshkovsky, A. G., and Shalnikov, A. I. (1947a), *J. Phys. USSR*, **11**, 1.

Meshkovsky, A. G., and Shalnikov, A. I. (1947b), *J. Exp. Theor. Phys. USSR*, (Russian), **17**, 851.

Meyerhoff, A. J., Cassidy, C. J., Hebeler, C. B., and Huang, C. C., (1964), in Timmerhaus, K. D., ed., *Advances in Cryogenic Engineering*, Vol. 9, New York: Plenum Press, (to be published).

Meyers, N. H. (1961), *Proc. IEEE*, **49**, 1640.

Miles, J. L., Smith, P. M., and Schonbein, W. (1963), *Proc. IEEE*, **51**, 937.

Miller, P. B. (1959), *Phys. Rev.*, **113**, 1209.

Miller, P. B. (1960), *Phys. Rev.*, **118**, 928.

Misener, A. D. (1936), *Can. J. Res.*, **14**, 25.

Morel, P. (1959), *J. Phys. Chem. Solids*, **10**, 277.

Morel, P., and Anderson, P. W. (1962), *Phys. Rev.*, **125**, 1263.

Moreno, T. (1958), *Microwave Transmission Design Data*. New York: Dover.

Morgan, W. L. (1959), "Bibliography of Digital Magnetic Circuits and Materials," *IRE Trans. Electron. Computers*, **EC-8**, 148.

Morse, R. W. (1959), "Ultrasonic Attenuation in Metals at Low Temperatures," *Progress in Cryogenics*, Vol. 1, ed., K. Mendelssohn. New York: Academic Press, p. 219.

Mott, N. F., and H. Jones (1958), *The Theory of the Properties of Metals and Alloys*. New York: Dover, 1958.

Newhouse, V. L. (1952), *Proc. Phys. Soc. (London)*, **A65**, 325.

Newhouse, V. L. (1954), *Electron. Eng.*, **26**, 192.

Newhouse, V. L. (1961), "Superconducting Circuits for Computing Machines," *Electro-Technol., New York*, **67**, 78.

Newhouse, V. L., and Bremer, J. W. (1959), *J. Appl. Phys.*, **30**, 1458.

Newhouse, V. L., Bremer, J. W., and Edwards, H. H. (1960), *Proc. IRE*, **48**, 1395.

Newhouse, V. L., and Fruin, R. E. (1962), *Electronics*, **35**, 31.

Nicol, J., Shapiro, S., and Smith, P. H. (1960), *Phys. Rev. Letters*, **5**, 461.

Niebuhr, J. (1952), *Z. Physik*, **132**, 468.

Onnes, H. K. (1911a), *Commun. Phys. Lab. Univ. Leiden*, No. 119b.

Onnes, H. K. (1911b), *Commun. Phys. Lab. Univ. Leiden*, No. 120b.

Onnes, H. K. (1911c), *Commun. Phys. Lab. Univ. Leiden*, No. 122b.

Onnes, H. K. (1911d), *Commun. Phys. Lab. Univ. Leiden*, No. 124c.

Onnes, H. K. (1913a), *Commun. Phys. Lab. Univ. Leiden*, Suppl. No. 34.

Onnes, H. K. (1913b), *Commun. Phys. Lab. Univ. Leiden*, No. 133d.
Onnes, H. K. (1914a), *Commun. Phys. Lab. Univ. Leiden*, No. 139f.
Onnes, H. K. (1914b), *Commun. Phys. Lab. Univ. Leiden*, Nos. 140b, c, 141b.
Onsager, L. (1961), *Phys. Rev. Letters*, **7**, 50.
Ovrebo, P. J. et al. (1959), *Proc. I.R.E.*, **47**, 1629.
Peacock, R. V. (1961), *Cryogenics*, **2**, 88.
Peierls, R. (1936), *Proc. Roy. Soc. (London)*, **A155**, 613.
Pines, D. (1958), *Phys. Rev.*, **109**, 280.
Pippard, A. B. (1947a), *Proc. Roy. Soc.*, **A191**, 385.
Pippard, A. B. (1947b), *Proc. Roy. Soc.*, **A191**, 399.
Pippard, A. B. (1950a), *Proc. Roy. Soc.*, **A203**, 210.
Pippard, A. B. (1950b), *Phil. Mag.*, **41**, 243.
Pippard, A. B. (1952), *Phil. Mag.*, **43**, 273.
Pippard, A. B. (1953), *Proc. Roy. Soc. (London)*, **A216**, 547.
Pippard, A. B. (1954), *Advances in Electronics and Electron Physics*, ed. L. Marton. New York: Academic Press, Ch. I.
Pippard, A. B., and Pullan, G. T. (1952), *Proc. Cambridge Phil. Soc.*, **48**, 188.
Quartly, C. J. (1962), *Square Loop Ferrite Circuitry*, Englewood Cliffs: Prentice-Hall.
Quinn, D. J., and Ittner, W. B., III (1962), *Jour. App. Phys.*, **33**, 748.
Ramo, S., and Whinnery, J. R. (1956), *Fields and Waves in Modern Radio*, 2nd ed. New York: Wiley.
Reeber, M. D. (1960), *Phys. Rev.*, **117**, 1476.
Reese, W., and Stegert, W. A. (1962), *Rev. Sci. Instr.*, **33**, 43.
Reynolds, C. A., Serin, B., Wright, W. H., and Nesbitt, L. B. (1950), *Phys. Rev.*, **78**, 487.
Rhoderick, E. H. (1962), *Proc. Roy. Soc.*, **A267**, 231.
Richards, P. L., and Tinkham, M. (1960), *Phys. Rev.*, **119**, 575.
Roberts, B. W. (1964), in *Progress in Cryogenics*, Vol. 4, K. Mendelssohn ed. New York: Academic Press.
Sauer, E. J., and Wurm, J. P. (1962), in Kolm, H., et al., eds., *High Magnetic Fields*. New York: Wiley, p. 589.
Schawlow, A. L. (1956), *Phys. Rev.*, **101**, 573.
Schawlow, A. L. (1958), *Phys. Rev.*, **109**, 1856.
Schawlow. A. L., and Devlin, G. E. (1959), *Phys. Rev.*, **113**, 120.
Schawlow, A. L., Matthias, B. T., Lewis, H. W., and Devlin, G. E. (1954), *Phys. Rev.*, **95**, 1344.
Schmidlin, F. W., Learn, A. K., Crittenden, E. C., Jr., and Cooper, J. N. (1960), *Solid State Electron.*, **1**, 323.
Schmitt, R. W., and Fiske, M. D., U.S. Patent 2,935,694, *Superconducting Circuits*, filed October 31, 1955, issued May 3, 1960.
Schock, K. F. (1961), in Timmerhaus, K. D., ed., *Advances in Cryogenic Engineering*, Vol. 6. New York: Plenum Press, p. 65.
Schubnikow, L. W., and Alekseyevsky, N. E. (1936), *Nature*, **138**, 804.
Schubnikow, L. W., and Chotkewitsch, W. I. (1936), *Phys. Z. Sowjet.*, **10**, 231.
Schubnikow, L. W., Chotkewitsch, W. I., Schepelew, J. D., and Rjabinin, J. N. (1936), *Phys. Z. Sowjet.*, **10**, 165.
Scott, R. B. (1948), *J. Res. Nat. Bur. Std.*, **41**, 581.
Sebastyanov, B. K. (1961), *Soviet Physics JETP*, **13**, 35.
Seeber, R. R., Jr. (1960), *Proc. Eastern Joint Compt. Conference*, p. 179.
Serin, B. (1956), "Superconductivity—Experimental Part," *Handbuch der Physik*, Vol. XV, ed. S. Flügge. Berlin: Springer.

Shalnikov, A. I. (1940b), *J. Phys. USSR*, **2**, 477.

Shalnikov. A. I. (1942), *J. Phys. USSR*, **6**, 53.

Shalnikov, A. I. (1945), *J. Phys. USSR*, **9**, 202.

Shapiro, S. (1963), *Phys. Rev. Letters*, **11**, 80.

Sherril, M. D., and Rose, K. (1964), *Rev. Mod. Phys.*, **36**, No. 1.

Shoenberg, D. (1940), *Proc. Roy. Soc.*, **A175**, 49.

Shoenberg, D. (1952), *Superconductivity*, London: Cambridge University Press. (1960), 2nd. ed. reprinted with additional appendix.

Silsbee, F. B. (1916), *J. Wash. Acad. Sci.*, **6**, 597.

Sim, A. C. (1961), *J. Electron. Control*, **10**, 97.

Simmons, W. A., and Douglass, D. H., Jr. (1962), *Phys. Rev. Letters*, **9**, 153.

Simon, I. (1949), *R.L.E. Tech. Rep.*, No. 126, M.I.T.

Simon, I. (1953), *J. Appl. Phys.*, **24**, 19.

Slade, A. E., and McMahon, H. D. (1956), *Proc. Eastern Joint Computer Conference* p. 115.

Slater, J. C. (1939), *Introduction to Chemical Physics*. New York: McGraw-Hill.

Slater, J. C. (1950), *Microwave Electronics*. New York: Van Nostrand.

Smallman, C. R., Slade, A. E., and Cohen, M. L. (1960), *Proc. I.R.E.*, **48**, 1562.

Smith, R. A., Jones, F. E., and Chasmar, R. P. (1957), *The Detection and Measurement of Infrared Radiation*. New York: Oxford University Press, 1957.

Steiner, K., and Schoeneck, H. (1943), *Phys. Z.*, **44**, 346.

Stromberg, T. F., and Swenson, C. A. (1962), *Phys. Rev. Letters*, **9**, 370.

Swartz, P. S. (1962), *Phys. Rev. Letters*, **9**, 448.

Swartz, P. S., and Rosner, C. H. (1962), *J. Appl. Phys.*, **33**, 2292.

Swihart. J. C. (1961), *J. Appl. Phys.*, **32**, 461.

Swihart, J. C. (1963), *J. Appl. Phys.*, **34**, 851.

Templeton, I. M. (1955a), *J. Sci. Instr.*, **32**, 172.

Templeton, I. M. (1955b), *J. Sci. Instr.*, **32**, 314.

Templeton, I. M. (1960), *Solid State Electr.*, **1**, 258.

Tinkham, M. (1963), *Phys. Rev.*, **129**, 2413.

Tolman, R. C. (1938), *The Principles of Statistical Mechanics*. Oxford University Press.

Toxen, A. M. (1961), *Phys. Rev.*, **123**, 442.

Treuting, R. G., Wernick, J. H., Hsu, F. S. L. (1962), in Kolm, H., et al.. eds., *High Magnetic Fields*. New York: Wiley, p. 597.

Van Beelen, H., Arnold, A. J., de Bruyn Ouboter, R., Beenakker, J. J., Taconis, K. W. (1963), *Phys. Letters*, **4**, 310.

Volger, J., and Admiraal, P. S. (1962), *Phys. Letters*, **2**, 257.

Vroomen, A. R., De, and Baarle, C. Van (1957), *Physica*, **23**, 785.

Whohareva, I., and Shalnikov, A. I. (1954), *Dokl. Akad. Nauk. SSSR*, **99**, 735.

Wilson, A. H. (1953), *Theory of Metals*. London: Cambridge University Press.

Yaqub, M. (1960), *Cryogenics*, **1**, 101.

Yntema, G. B. (1955), *Phys. Rev.*, **98**, 1197.

Young, D. R. (1959), "Superconductive Circuits," *Progress in Cryogenics*, Vol. I, ed. K. Mendelssohn. London: Heywood and Co.

Young, D. R., Swihart, J. C., Tansal, S., Meyers, N. H. (1960), *Proc. Symp. Superconductive Tech. Computing Systems*, Washington, May 1960; ONR symposium report ACR-50, Office of Naval Research, Washington, p. 378.

Young, D. R. (1961), *Brit. J. Appl. Phys.*, **12**, 359.

Zavaritsky, N. V. (1951), *Doklady Akad. Nauk. SSSR*, **78**, 665.

Zemansky, M. W. (1957), *Heat and Thermodynamics*, 4th ed., New York: McGraw.

Index